SILENT SHOCK

Michael Magazanik has worked as a journalist for the *Age*, the *Australian* and ABC-TV, and is now a lawyer with Slater & Gordon. He lives in Melbourne with his partner and three children.

SILENT SHOCK

The men behind the thalidomide scandal and an Australian family's long road to justice

MICHAEL MAGAZANIK

TEXT PUBLISHING
MELBOURNE AUSTRALIA

textpublishing.com.au

The Text Publishing Company
Swann House
22 William Street
Melbourne Victoria 3000
Australia

First published in 2015 by The Text Publishing Company
Typeset in Granjon 12.4/17.36 by J & M Typesetting
Book design by Text
Index by Karen Gillen
Printed in Australia by Griffin Press

National Library of Australia Cataloguing-in-Publication entry
Creator: Magazanik, Michael, author.
Title: Silent shock : the men behind the thalidomide scandal and an Australian family's long road to justice / by Michael Magazanik.
ISBN: 9781922182098 (paperback)
             9781925095098 (ebook)
Subjects: Rowe, Lyn.
             Rowe, Lyn—Family.
             Fetus—Effect of drugs on
             Children with disabilities—Australia—Biography.
             Thalidomide—Side effects—Australia.
             Drugs—Law and legislation—Great Britain.
             Products liability—Drugs—Great Britain.
             Pharmaceutical ethics.
Dewey Number: 362.43092

This book is printed on paper certified against the Forest Stewardship Council® Standards. Griffin Press holds FSC chain-of-custody certification SGS-COC-005088. FSC promotes environmentally responsible, socially beneficial and economically viable management of the world's forests.

This project has been assisted by the Commonwealth Government through the Australia Council, its arts funding and advisory body.

For thalidomide survivors and their families—
and in memory of those who did not survive.

And for Nicole, Asher, Jonah and Zara.

CONTENTS

BRIEF CHRONOLOGY

1946   The Wirtz family establishes a pharmaceutical company called Grünenthal in Stolberg, Germany.

1954   Two Grünenthal scientists create a new chemical compound that will become known as thalidomide. Grünenthal believes thalidomide has promise as a sleeping pill/sedative, and performs animal tests and then trials in humans.

1957   Grünenthal launches its main thalidomide drug, Contergan. It is marketed as completely safe: non-toxic and impossible to overdose on. Within a few years thalidomide will be sold in forty-six countries.

1958   Distillers, under licence from Grünenthal, launches Distaval, the first of its thalidomide drugs, in the UK.

1959–61 Grünenthal is flooded with complaints that thalidomide is causing (often severe) nerve damage in patients taking the drug. Grünenthal continues to promote the drug as safe, fails to place appropriate warnings on the medication and tries to suppress and deflect the rising tide of complaints. At least two German doctors and one pharmacist ask Grünenthal staff whether thalidomide might malform babies. Grünenthal does not investigate.

1960   Distillers starts selling thalidomide in Australia.

1960   December   Scottish doctor Leslie Florence's letter is published in the *British Medical Journal*, the first time thalidomide is publicly connected to nerve damage.

1961   March–May   Dr Frances Kelsey at the FDA, which is considering whether to permit the sale of thalidomide in the US, reads Florence's letter in the *British Medical Journal* and her already sceptical attitude to thalidomide hardens. She demands more information about nerve damage, and then asks whether the drug is safe for the foetus. Kelsey never allows the drug to be sold in the US and is later acclaimed as a hero.

1961   June   Dr William McBride in Sydney, Australia concludes that thalidomide is responsible for the severe malformations and deaths of three babies born to his patients. McBride, who has been trialling the drug for Distillers, tells the company of his suspicion. The drug remains on sale.

1961   June–July   Wendy Rowe in Melbourne, Australia takes thalidomide samples early in pregnancy.

1961   15 November   German obstetrician Widukind Lenz asks Grünenthal to withdraw thalidomide from sale because he believes it is responsible for an epidemic of death and deformity. Lenz has collected fourteen case studies to back his claim. Grünenthal refuses to withdraw the drug and resists until 26 November 1961, when the first report of the disaster appears in the German media. Thalidomide's global death and injury toll later conservatively reckoned to be between ten and fifteen thousand babies. Some estimates put the toll higher still, with many thousands more having miscarried or been stillborn.

1962   2 March   Lyn Rowe is born without limbs in Box Hill, Melbourne.

1968   May   Trial begins of seven Grünenthal executives and senior staff charged with negligent manslaughter and other criminal offences over the thalidomide disaster.

The trial grinds away until, controversially, it is discontinued in December 1970. Grünenthal promises 100 million marks to a fund to compensate surviving children. Courtesy of a German Government law, further legal action against the company in Germany is banned.

1971   June Nine-year-old Peggy McCarrick (and her mother Shirley) are awarded $2.75 million by a Los Angeles jury. This remains the only thalidomide trial to go a jury verdict.

1970s   Thalidomiders in various countries—including Germany, US, UK, Canada, Japan and Australia—receive compensation that, almost invariably, proves vastly inadequate.

1970s   Otto Ambros, convicted and jailed for slavery and mass murder at Auschwitz, serves as chairman of Grünenthal's supervisory board.

2011   11 June Lyn Rowe, now forty-nine and relying on her ageing parents for full-time care, starts a legal action against Grünenthal and Distillers in Melbourne, almost exactly fifty years to the day after her mother took thalidomide.

2012   July Lyn Rowe accepts a multimillion-dollar sum from Distillers to settle her claim. Grünenthal does not contribute to the settlement.

2012   August Grünenthal CEO Harald Stock offers the family-owned company's first ever apology for the thalidomide disaster—and then attributes the fifty-year delay to the company's 'silent shock' at the scale of the suffering thalidomide caused.

MARCH 1962

He was a young man then and it was long, long ago. Yet when he thinks about that day in 1962 it's as if fifty years have vanished and he's back at the Box Hill Hospital on a late-summer morning. 'I'd just delivered a baby when the senior midwife came over and asked me if I could step in and help out with another delivery. The woman's doctor couldn't be found.'

Ron Dickinson pauses; he has not told this story often. It's April 2011 and he's now eighty-five and living a happy retirement, with a satisfying medical career well behind him. Home is a big house perched high on a bluff with commanding views of Australia's wild southern ocean. Today he's seated with his companions in the courtyard of a pretty winery near his home. The doctor's visitor has asked for his memories of that single traumatic day, decades earlier. Dickinson, who has barely touched his lunch, now pushes it aside.

'Well naturally I agreed to deliver the baby,' Dickinson says. The missing doctor was a partner in his busy medical practice, so he felt a sense of obligation. 'And the woman about to give birth was Wendy Rowe. I knew Wendy and her family, liked them. I was happy to help out.'

A thoughtful man with a gentle manner, Dickinson becomes

halting when describing what followed. 'It was an incredibly distressing event and still crystal clear in my memory. At first the delivery proceeded normally. In those days there was no way of telling in advance that anything was wrong, and there was no reason for any suspicion,' Dickinson says. 'Ultrasounds weren't yet available and I knew Wendy had two healthy girls already. So there was absolutely no indication that anything was wrong, or was likely to go wrong.'

But then, quickly, everything changed.

'The baby started to come out. Head first, everything OK. But then I saw that there were no arms. And then no legs. The little girl had only a torso and a head. It was a terrible shock. Shocking and disorienting. I hadn't seen anything like that before.' Dickinson pauses as he dwells on the moment. 'I was utterly devastated, both for the poor little girl but also for Wendy and Ian. They were fine people and I really felt for them.'

Dickinson checked the baby. Surprisingly, she seemed perfectly healthy. But his mind was already on the conversation he knew he had to have with Wendy Rowe. Nothing in his training, or his ten years as a doctor, had prepared him for that moment. Heavens, how on earth do I explain this? he thought. Dickinson decided to be gentle but completely honest.

> After handing the baby to the nurses, I talked to Wendy. I told her that I had some very unfortunate news. I then just simply told her that her baby girl had no arms and no legs. Wendy looked at me for a few moments without saying anything, as if she were processing what I had said. Then she said: 'We'll just have to look after her very well then.'

Dickinson's eyes are full of tears now. 'I've always thought that response was a measure of the woman and her family. They were lovely people.'

That same afternoon Dickinson went to his sister's wedding. It was a difficult occasion for him. He and his wife had three young children, and throughout the wedding celebration his thoughts kept returning to Wendy Rowe and her baby. 'It really cast a pall over things,' he says. 'Very distressing.'

Wendy Rowe was twenty-six years old at the time, and the baby was her third child. She and her husband Ian named her Lynette Suzanne and some of the doctors and nurses urged them to put her in an institution. The baby would not survive for long, they said. Forget about her. Go home and look after your other girls. Try and have another child as soon as possible.

That didn't happen. Instead, Wendy and Ian took Lyn home from hospital and, true to Wendy's word, took care of her. Full-time, round-the-clock care, often exhausting, sometimes backbreaking, always loving. Lyn needed help with everything, and always would. Eating, drinking, toileting, washing, dressing and every single other mundane detail of daily living. Without limbs she could do almost nothing for herself.

All of that lay ahead of Wendy and Ian when they took Lyn home from hospital in mid-March 1962. What they didn't know then was that there was a simple explanation for what had happened to Lyn. She had fallen victim to what would become the most notorious drug in history: thalidomide.

Initially sold as a sleeping pill and sedative, thalidomide was developed in the 1950s by a German pharmaceutical company called Grünenthal. It granted sales licences for thalidomide to other companies, and salesmen sprinkled samples of the deadly drug like confetti in doctors' surgeries around the world. One of those surgeries was in suburban Melbourne, just around the corner from the Rowes' home, where

Wendy Rowe presented herself just a few weeks into her pregnancy with Lyn. Wendy was at her wits' end, anxious and overwhelmed by terrible morning sickness. 'There was nothing "morning" about it,' Wendy remembered. 'I was sick the whole time. Morning, afternoon, evening and night.'

So Wendy's GP, Dr Hugh Indian, a charming former footballer, gave her some pills to try: a new medication called Distaval, one of the many brand names for thalidomide. The pills were reputed to be ultra-effective and outstandingly safe. Wendy took them for about five weeks, but they didn't work. The nausea and vomiting continued until the end of the pregnancy.

By the time Wendy Rowe took those thalidomide pills in mid-1961, the drug was a bestseller. But silently and inexorably it was exacting a terrible toll. When taken by women early in pregnancy, the drug attacked their unborn children: twisting, stunting and shortening limbs, causing deafness and blindness and internal injuries. Thousands of infants had already been born with malformations; many were stillborn or died shortly after birth. But the finger of blame had not yet been publicly pointed at thalidomide. Doctors around the world, Hugh Indian included, were still oblivious and happily handing out the drug to pregnant women.

A few weeks before the birth, Dr Indian examined Wendy and thought he felt two heads. 'He looked really puzzled and kept feeling and poking. He told me that twins were a possibility. Later he told me he must have been feeling the baby's head and the bottom. But with no legs near her bottom he thought he was feeling another head.'

Wendy's recollection of the moments after Lyn's birth is vivid.

> Silence, just silence. During my first two daughters' births there'd been congratulations and comments and chatter

from the doctor and the nurses. This time there was just silence. Everyone seemed shocked. I thought to myself, 'this isn't good'. I knew something had happened, but I had no idea what. Then Dr Dickinson came over and spoke with me.

Wendy hesitates, remembering the news that changed everything.

I'm very glad [Dickinson] was so upfront with me. I know some mothers were just handed their baby in a swaddle and only discovered what had happened when they unwrapped their babies. He told me that he had something very sad to tell me. My baby did not have arms or legs. Well, what do you think about at a moment like that? I actually don't remember if I said anything to him. I just remember thinking, we're going to look after this little girl.

Lyn Rowe was among the most severely damaged of the thousands of thalidomide survivors. For her parents, as for thousands of others, the anticipated joy of welcoming a child into the world turned to grief and shock.

Wendy and Ian struggled on, caring for their daughter for more than five decades, as Lyn passed through infancy and childhood and into her teenage years and then into adulthood and on into middle age. Decades of heartbreak and sacrifice. Decades of scraping for enough money to get by while trying to ensure their other children did not feel neglected.

But what nobody ever imagined was that despite the tragedy of her profound disability, despite a brain injury she suffered as an infant as an indirect result of her missing limbs, and despite her family's desperate financial circumstances, Lyn Rowe would ultimately emerge as a standard bearer for an unrecognised generation of thalidomiders.

In 2011 Lyn faced the two key thalidomide companies in court.

Her legal battle with them would lift the lid on a fifty-year cover-up, exposing the outrageous misconduct that had caused such incalculable grief and suffering.

• • •

I was one of Lyn Rowe's lawyers and from late 2010 until early 2014 I spent almost every working day focused on thalidomide. Over several years, Lyn's small legal team amassed mountains of evidence to back her claim: documents buried in archives on three continents, interviews with elderly former drug-company employees, expert opinions from doctors and scientists, and new research emerging through thalidomide's subsequent incarnation as a cancer drug.

Before becoming a lawyer, I had worked as a newspaper and television journalist. Frequently during the thalidomide litigation, I thought (and told everyone in the office) that Lyn's story, and all that surrounded it, deserved a proper, public telling.

Thalidomide's immediate victims were the damaged babies and their families. That in itself was appalling and heartbreaking, but there was so much more to the thalidomide story: disgraceful corporate behaviour, warnings ignored, World War II medical experiments, massively profitable companies and poverty-stricken victims. And then there was the Rowe family and their struggle over fifty years with the damage caused by the drug.

As the Rowe family revealed their private history to us, their lawyers, so too did thalidomide reveal its secrets. Ultimately our research yielded a wholesale rewriting of the most infamous chapter in pharmaceutical history, as secrets buried for up to fifty years were unearthed.

In July 2012 Lyn triumphed in her legal claim, receiving a

confidential multimillion-dollar settlement, more than enough to provide her with first-class care for the rest of her life. She was also able to send her parents on a long overdue holiday.

Not long afterwards, Grünenthal trotted out its highly paid chief executive to offer an apology to the drug's victims, fifty years after the event. It was, he said, Grünenthal's 'silent shock' at what thalidomide had done that had rendered it unable to apologise for five decades.

An appalled Wendy Rowe appeared at a press conference, tearful but composed, to denounce the 'apology' as an insult to thalidomiders and their parents. 'I suspect he might not know what shock is,' she said. 'Shock is having your precious child born without arms and legs. It's accepting that your child is not going to have the life you wanted for her.'

That moment, as a dignified seventy-six-year-old woman highlighted the shameful behaviour of the German drug company, persuaded me to start writing the thalidomide story I had long been talking about.

Clearly I cannot pretend to impartiality. As a lawyer I was—unequivocally and enthusiastically—on the side of Lyn Rowe and her family and all of the other thalidomiders whose claims we pressed. I was also a participant in many of the current-day events reported in this book, and for that reason this account does not shy away from the first person. Though this book concerns a legal claim, it is not a legal text. A great deal of the minutiae (legal, medical) that obsessed the lawyers in the case, but would bore most everyone else, has been omitted.

What remains is important to telling the Rowe family's story, integral to an account of Lyn Rowe's legal battle fifty years after thalidomide deprived her of arms and legs, and critical to revealing the truth about history's most infamous drug.

Finally, it should be clearly noted that there is an occupational hazard of the participant-as-author account: the inevitable inflation of the author's contribution. That, I concede in advance, is the case here.

CHAPTER 1

Outstandingly Safe

30 October 2010

In a conference room at the Rydges Hotel in south-west Sydney, Peter Gordon takes to the stage to speak to a small group of Australian thalidomide survivors. These are 'official' thalidomiders. All around fifty years old, they are members of a select group of about forty who as children and teenagers received both official recognition and a small sum of compensation.

One of Australia's best-known lawyers, Gordon is about to deliver a radical message. He is convinced that there are many more unrecognised thalidomiders: people who suffered terrible injuries but have either never come forward or have been wrongly and unfairly told that thalidomide was not the cause.

In the audience is Mary Henley-Collopy. It's her birthday. Forty-nine years ago she was born without arms, her fingers emerging from her shoulders, and with tiny legs. One of the most profoundly physically damaged of the official Australian survivors, Henley-Collopy is largely confined to a wheelchair and sometimes uses carers to help her dress, shower and much else. She is, by any standard, profoundly disabled. She also has a razor-sharp brain, a quick wit, a prodigious memory and a ferocious independent streak. Yesterday she travelled to the conference from her home in Temora in country New South Wales, negotiating bus, train and taxi on her own to get to the conference venue.

Henley-Collopy listens closely to Gordon. Her reaction will help rewrite thalidomide history.

> Peter was saying that many people never came forward for compensation during the 1970s, and others came forward but were rejected for trivial reasons. Like they were a month too old or a month too young or the injuries did not look quite right. Like there was a thumb present when the medical experts thought it should be missing.

Gordon finishes by telling his audience that he wants to force the drug companies to pay compensation to the thalidomiders who missed out in the 1970s. Henley-Collopy knows that succeeding in decades-old legal claims will be difficult, to say the least. But she notes Gordon's passion, and as he speaks her thoughts turn to a woman she went to school with forty years ago.

● ● ●

Henley-Collopy was born in Perth in 1961 and immediately given up by her birth parents. Soon afterwards she was sent across the country for medical treatment, and raised by a devoutly religious woman at the Christian Service Centre in Melbourne's eastern suburbs. Later Henley-Collopy was sent to the Yooralla primary school for children with physical or intellectual disabilities.

One of her schoolmates was Lyn Rowe. 'Because Lyn sort of looked like me, she and I were sometimes lumped together,' Henley-Collopy remembered.

> Lyn had no arms or legs and sometimes tottered about at the

school on prosthetic legs. Once I was scooting down a hallway by hanging on to a pram-type thing. I could barely see where I was going and crashed straight into Lyn, who was on her prosthetic legs. She ended up with her head tangled up in the pram. She screamed and wailed and carried on. We can laugh about it now but she was pretty angry with me at the time.

Henley-Collopy never wondered whether Lyn was also a thalidomider. 'When I was a kid I didn't think about that sort of thing.' Once or twice over later years, she heard Wendy Rowe say that a virus during pregnancy had caused Lyn's condition.

But as Henley-Collopy listened to Gordon at the thalidomide conference she began to wonder. 'It was a light-bulb moment. I mean, Lyn was about my age, she had no arms and no legs. I had to wonder: was she a thalidomider? The more I thought about it, the more I realised I had to speak with Peter.'

When Gordon finished, Henley-Collopy joined a queue of people wanting to speak with him.

We had a talk and I told him about Lyn, though I didn't use her name. I said she had no limbs, a great family and that I'd been to school with her. I also told Peter the virus story, which I'd never really thought about until the last few minutes. But now I was thinking about it, and I had a lot of doubts.

Gordon was intrigued. He asked Henley-Collopy to talk with the family.

'It was Melbourne Cup day 2010,' Wendy Rowe later recalled. 'Mary called and said there was a class action going ahead for Australian thalidomide survivors. She told me that she thought Ian and I should contact the lawyers.' Wendy told Henley-Collopy that she had no proof she had taken thalidomide. 'By proof, I meant that I had no prescription, or pills or some sort of medical record. It happened fifty years ago! Mary told me that I should just contact the lawyers for Lyn's sake and see what they said.'

Wendy thought about the phone call for a couple of days and talked about it with Ian and Lyn. None of them had ever been involved in a legal case. The hassle of it all, the disruption, the expense: none of it sounded appealing. The discussions swirled. Wendy was seventy-four years old and Ian was seventy-eight. Both were finding the physical challenge of caring for Lyn increasingly difficult. Wendy had started lifting weights in an effort to maintain enough muscle to physically manoeuvre her immobile daughter. Lyn loved living with her parents, and the thought of going into government care terrified her. But all of them knew that the status quo could not last much longer. Soon Wendy and Ian Rowe were going to be physically incapable of looking after their daughter.

In the end that unavoidable fact prompted Wendy Rowe to call the lawyers.

> For years we'd been worrying about what would happen to Lyn when we were too old to look after her. If there was a slim chance to provide for her future by calling the lawyers, we just had to do it. If we didn't win it would make no difference to our lives. We had very little and we'd still have very little.

Wendy telephoned Gordon Legal and spoke with Peter Gordon's son, Patrick, who was doing his legal apprenticeship with his father, and was at that time one of only two employees. Shortly afterwards, Peter and Patrick Gordon were sitting in the Rowe family's Nunawading living room, drinking tea and listening.

'Lyn was very quiet and didn't speak much,' Peter Gordon remembered.

Ian was cooperative and affable. Wendy did most of the talking for the family. Clearly they had been through a lot. I was listening carefully but I was also doing a legal calculation in my head. Lyn had been exposed at the height of thalidomide availability, there was good evidence Wendy had taken the drug. It was changing everything—this was a bloody good case.

The meeting lasted about an hour. By the time Peter and Patrick Gordon left to drive back to the city, Peter Gordon's mind was made up. 'We knew that this was it. We had to get a result for that family.'

• • •

Ian and Wendy Rowe grew up not far apart in the seaside Melbourne suburb of Brighton, which is today home to some of Melbourne's most expensive real estate and exclusive private schools. In the 1930s, though, Brighton was a far quieter place, with real affluence concentrated in the streets near the beach. Wendy and Ian's family homes were close to Nepean Highway, at the less fashionable end of the suburb.

Ian Rowe was born in 1932, and Wendy Tudor in 1935. Ian's father Bill was a blacksmith and his mother Hilda stayed home to raise the three children. Wendy Tudor was one of six siblings. Her parents placed great emphasis on education, and her father, an electrical engineer, 'just expected that we would all get degrees'. Her four brothers did just that: law, science, architecture and accountancy. 'Liz and I let the side down by getting teaching diplomas. But later on Liz got a master's degree in art history. So in the end, I was the only one who didn't get a degree like Dad wanted.'

Ian and Wendy met at the Male Street Methodist Church. 'It was a fun time,' Ian recalled. 'Dances and socials and so on.'

After finishing school in 1949 Ian started a clerkship at AMP, the life insurance company, where he stayed for almost fifty years. Wendy trained as a kindergarten teacher and then started work in North Melbourne.

The couple married in January 1957, spent their honeymoon touring Tasmania, and moved into their new home in Nunawading the day they returned to Melbourne. While Nunawading in Melbourne's east is middle suburbia these days, back then the roads were unpaved and lined with market gardens. Settling into married life the Rowes began attending the Nunawading Methodist church, where Dr Hugh Indian was a member of the congregation. His surgery was a short walk from their home and, inevitably, Dr Indian became their family doctor. 'He was a good man, a good doctor,' Wendy recalled. When Dr Indian was away or busy the Rowes saw one of the other doctors at the practice, Ron Dickinson or Ron Henry.

Wendy fell pregnant in 1958 and Merrilyn arrived the following April. Two years later Alison was born. 'Life was busy and happy and very normal,' Ian said. When Alison was only about four months old, Wendy began to suspect she was pregnant again. 'I was worried and not very happy. Alison was tiny and Ian and I didn't want to add to the family again so soon,' Wendy remembered. She had been breast-feeding Alison and thought she would not get pregnant.

'Breastfeeding as contraception is a myth but back then I believed it, like a lot of people.' She laughed. 'We didn't know much in those days, nothing like today.'

Ian's mother was surprised by the news of Wendy's pregnancy. 'Hilda was very unimpressed. She thought it was ridiculous I was pregnant again so quickly.' Wendy smiled. 'So did I! But I wasn't going to admit that to my mother-in-law.'

At that time most babies in Australia were delivered by GPs, the move to obstetricians having barely begun. Hugh Indian was Wendy's doctor throughout all four of her pregnancies, and delivered all of her babies except Lyn. Naturally when morning sickness set in, Wendy went to see him. 'I was feeling anxious about being pregnant again and the morning sickness was shocking, much worse than it had been with Merrilyn and Alison. And I had two little children demanding my attention.'

It was late June or early July 1961. Dr Indian told Wendy he had a new medication that would calm her and help with morning sickness. The name Distaval meant nothing to Wendy. 'He said they were very good and the samples were free so I was appreciative. For about five weeks, I took a tablet every morning.'

The Distaval pills contained thalidomide, one of the most powerful and destructive drugs ever let loose unchecked in the market. Scientists would later learn that a single tablet was sufficient to kill or severely malform an unborn child.

When her mother started taking the pills, Lyn was a four- or five-week-old embryo a few millimetres long, about the size of a small grain of rice. At that point the embryo inside Wendy was a tiny collection of rapidly dividing cells, a frenzy of developmental activity.

Curved in shape, and with its visible tail, such embryos look something like a translucent tadpole. The heart is starting to beat rapidly and facial features, including ears and mouth, are starting to form. Many of the organs and structures are beginning to emerge. The tongue, liver, gall bladder, pancreas and lungs, for example, start to develop at around this time. So too do the arms and legs, with hand and foot plates starting a little later.

But like a grenade thrown into a bunker, the thalidomide pills

Wendy took catastrophically damaged the normal growth of the embryo inside her. While many of the developmental processes proceeded unmolested, the thalidomide, ingested and circulating in the embryonic bloodstream, completely halted the development of Lyn's arms and legs.

• • •

The tragic irony, given the drug's terrible dangers, is that the salesmen who promoted thalidomide to doctors around Australia had been instructed to pitch Distaval as an outstandingly safe sleeping pill and, at a lesser dose, as an anti-anxiety medication (a sedative). It was this emphasis on complete and unprecedented safety that allowed thalidomide to prosper in a crowded marketplace.

The full-page ads for Distaval placed by Distillers in the *Medical Journal of Australia*, at the time a key information source for doctors, illustrate the marketing line. A small child is standing on a stool, raiding the family medicine cabinet. The child has opened an unidentified bottle and the reader correctly surmises that an enormous, potentially fatal overdose is about to occur.

Thankfully, though, the advertisement can offer a happier ending. If the unnamed medication is Distaval there will be no tragedy. **This child's life may depend on the safety of 'Distaval'**, the advertisement shouts. *Consider the possible outcome in a case such as this—had the bottle contained a conventional barbiturate,* doctors were urged.

> Year by year, the barbiturates claim a mounting toll of childhood victims. Yet today it is simple enough to prescribe a sedative and hypnotic which is both highly effective... and outstandingly safe. 'Distaval' (*thalidomide*) has been prescribed for over three years in Great Britain, where the

accidental poisonings rate is notoriously high; but there is no case on record in which even gross overdosage with 'Distaval' has had harmful results. Put your mind at rest. Depend on the safety of 'Distaval'.

The advertisement was used in multiple countries around the world, and the safety hyperbole was repeated like a mantra by the sales reps. Years later a Distillers man remembered the simple mnemonic he kept in mind when he met with a doctor or pharmacist. 'SESH— safe, effective sedative and hypnotic. All I did was talk about how dangerous the barbiturates were, how safe Distaval was and away I went. It was that easy. There was a great desire for a safe sleeping pill and our drug filled that gap.'

This pitch was constantly reinforced and sales reps were instructed to follow the script. 'Distaval is a non-toxic, highly effective sedative/hypnotic that can be widely used with complete safety, and with no risk of overdose,' a Distillers manager recalled. 'That was it. Simple.'

This safety claim was the brainchild of the drug's German inventor, the pharmaceutical company Grünenthal, which took it to remarkable heights of invention and dangerous fiction. Distillers unwisely adopted the hyperbolic safety babble after contracting with Grünenthal to market thalidomide in the UK, Australia and a host of other countries.

The safety pitch was, of course, spectacularly misconceived. Thalidomide turned out to be one of the most unsafe general use drugs of all time. Yet for decades Grünenthal and Distillers have claimed that they were just unlucky: that they had no way of knowing their drug was dangerous, and that the whole disaster was a terrible but unavoidable tragedy. They have claimed consistently—for five decades—that they did all the necessary testing, asked all the right questions. Any other drug company in the same circumstances, the story goes, would have suffered the same misfortune.

The 'we did nothing wrong' claim has shaped public opinion. As a result Grünenthal—still a family-owned company—has avoided the sort of odium that might otherwise have stuck to it.

But as Lyn Rowe's legal claim gathered momentum in 2011, material emerged that made a mockery of any notion that Grünenthal and its licensee Distillers had fallen blamelessly into the thalidomide disaster. Documents surfaced demonstrating that, by the time Wendy Rowe started taking the much-hyped drug in mid-1961, the description of thalidomide as outstandingly safe was a barefaced lie. Both Grünenthal and Distillers knew it—although their salesmen in Australia, and often elsewhere, were left in the dark.

Months before Wendy Rowe was given the drug, Grünenthal knew thalidomide was dangerously flawed. It was doing its best to suppress reports that thalidomide had caused serious nerve damage. Privately, Grünenthal was brawling with its own insurer over expected lawsuits by consumers, and the company's internal lawyers were issuing dire warnings about Grünenthal's behaviour in relation to thalidomide.

Worse, long before Wendy Rowe took the drug in Australia, Grünenthal staff in Germany had received reports of birth malformations possibly connected to thalidomide. Yet Grünenthal did not investigate these reports; nor did it halt or slow the thalidomide sales juggernaut.

Skeletons would also emerge from Distillers' closet. Most disturbingly, by the time Wendy Rowe took the thalidomide delivered to her doctor's surgery by a Distillers sales rep, multiple senior Distillers staff in Australia knew that a Sydney obstetrician had reported that the drug might be killing and maiming babies. And again, nothing was done.

So in mid-1961, ignorant of everything the drug companies and their employees knew, Dr Hugh Indian gave Wendy Rowe the pills, and Wendy Rowe, confident in her doctor, gratefully took them.

CHAPTER 2

Don't Look at Her!

A month before he was contacted by Wendy Rowe, Peter Gordon had telephoned me in Perth, where I'd spent several years running the asbestos diseases practice at the law firm Slater & Gordon. Peter Gordon had left Slater & Gordon after almost thirty years and set up his own practice—Gordon Legal. But after becoming interested in thalidomide he had invited his old firm to join him in the class action for thalidomide survivors. Gordon had heard I was moving back to Melbourne. Would I be interested in working on thalidomide with him?

Western Australia has one of the highest rates of asbestos disease in the world, a sad circumstance largely due to two corporations. The CSR-run blue asbestos mine at Wittenoom, which operated for about twenty years in the remote Pilbara region of the state, has claimed many hundreds of lives. Mine workers and their families, including those exposed as babies and toddlers, have steadily fallen victim to deadly diseases. Chief among them is mesothelioma, a rapidly fatal cancer which typically develops thirty to forty years after exposure to asbestos.

The other corporation most responsible for Western Australia's terrible asbestos toll is James Hardie, the former asbestos cement building-products giant which refused to properly heed warning signs about asbestos for decades, and which exposed not just its employees to the deadly fibres, but also generations of tradesmen and home renovators.

Much of my work in Perth involved suing these two corporate giants, along with dozens of other asbestos defendants. After almost four years of wading through thousands of their internal documents, I felt I had a reasonable understanding of the corporate mentality required to behave in reckless or negligent fashion. So when Gordon asked me to work with him on thalidomide, I was interested. Thalidomide was, after all, the most notorious drug disaster in history. And no doubt there was a damning story waiting to emerge, though at the time I knew little of the background. I had also assumed that the litigation was ancient history. But Gordon said many victims had never been compensated, and that we'd be fighting the odds to reopen a fifty-year-old case against two very powerful companies. He did not have to say much more. That sounded very appealing.

In January 2011 my partner Nicole and I returned to Melbourne, and I started on the case that would consume the next three years, of my working life. Immediately I ran hard to catch up, reading as much as possible about thalidomide, the drug companies involved, and the relevant medicine. I learned about the 'unavoidable tragedy' line consistently run by Grünenthal and Distillers. I also discovered that, aside from one 1971 case in the United States, no thalidomide claims had ever been litigated to judgment anywhere in the world.

Gordon had already assembled a small team and in the office we debated the obstacles to succeeding in a thalidomide claim fifty years after the tragedy. Obviously, we would have to show that Wendy took the drug, and that the drug then damaged Lyn. That would be a major task in itself, but nowhere near enough.

We would also have to establish that the drug companies behaved negligently: that, in lay terms, they should have known better. This meant proving they should have realised there was a risk of harming Lyn by supplying her mother with thalidomide. The hard part was that we would have to prove this 'foreseeable risk' of harm, not by the standards of the twenty-first century, but by the standards that applied at the time Wendy Rowe took the drug, mid-1961.

Dozens of other tricky legal issues would beset Lyn's case. For example, we would have to find a way of getting around her statute of limitations problem. Limitations, as lawyers refer to the concept, is the idea that if you are injured by another person you have to make your legal claim within a limited period of time. If you don't act, you lose your rights. Limitations periods can vary. Three years is common, and it's longer if the victim is a child. But fifty years on we knew the drug companies would argue that it was all too late, that Lyn's time to bring a claim had long expired. We would have to persuade a judge that an exception was warranted: that Lyn should be allowed her day in court many years late.

• • •

One of my priorities was to start work on the family's legal statements, their accounts of what had happened fifty years ago and in the years since. This would require a lot of time with each family member. So, to make a start, in February 2011 I arranged to visit the Rowes. It was the first of many occasions I would make the forty-minute train trip to Nunawading and walk ten minutes to the home in a quiet side street.

My first visits were planned as get-to-know-you meetings. I wanted to establish some sort of relationship before taking detailed histories and asking personal questions. First impressions are often completely misleading when meeting injured or ill clients. Frequently they are stressed and anxious, not just about their injury or illness, but also about being cast into an unfamiliar world of lawyers and doctors, usually for the first time in their lives. Sometimes they're angry. They may have been dwelling on the unfairness of it all for months or even years. As a result, first meetings with lawyers can be vexed and halting affairs, and rapport can take some time to develop.

But with the Rowes there was no settling-in period. Wendy, Ian and Lyn were totally direct and forthright, right from that first meeting, perhaps because they had been dealing with their lot for fifty years. No issue or subject matter seemed to bother them, and they had plenty of probing questions of their own—about the legal process and about what they were getting into. And they were resolute. Once Lyn and her parents decided to sue the drug companies, they never wavered throughout all the ups and downs that followed. They were, in fact, dream clients.

During my early visits to their home we sat in their living room. Lyn, of course, sat in her electric wheelchair which she controlled by pressing her head and shoulders against levers. When my note-taking ramped up we usually moved to the kitchen table with tea and biscuits. The front of the house, always neat and presentable, belied the dilapidated state of the rest of the home. It too was tidy—but crumbling. The house had shifted on its stumps so that the floor sloped precipitously, cracks gaped around the skirting boards and the back door was jammed shut. The hallway to the rear of the house was too narrow for Lyn to turn her wheelchair. She had to back up to a place where there was more room. In the bathroom, I trod warily: the floor was cracked and fragile and felt as though I could easily put a foot through it. Clearly, the home was epically unsuitable for someone in a wheelchair. Later, when a building expert assessed the home for a renovation, his strong recommendation was demolition.

Naturally the Rowes were aware of the state of their home, but they had no money for improvements. They had to make do. Looking after Lyn took precedence over everything else. Any extra cash was spent on her needs, and had been since 1962. At one of our early meetings, Wendy reflected on the challenges.

> New mums often find the first few months exhausting. That's what it was like with Lyn, and with all my girls. But with Lyn that never changed. Most babies learn how to walk and to feed themselves, and dress and go to the toilet, and wash themselves. I knew that was never going to happen with Lyn. Fifty years later I still do all of that for her.

Initially, the lives Lyn and her parents had led seemed unknowable to me. How on earth had they coped? How had this family not been overwhelmed by the terrible, unchanging reality of Lyn's missing arms and legs? Could anyone ever come to terms with such a profound physical disability? What toll would it take on parents, knowing that things would never improve for their child, never get better?

Of course I kept these questions strictly to myself. But at that time Nicole and I had a baby boy, Asher, who was only a few months old. One day, suffering from run-of-the-mill sleep deprivation, I asked Wendy in passing when Lyn had first slept through the night. She laughed. 'What do you mean? She's never slept through the night! I get up two or three times a night to move her or to help her use a bedpan. I've been doing that since 1962.'

It was 2011 and Wendy Rowe was closing in on fifty years of interrupted sleep. Without complaint.

Slowly, as I talked with Wendy, Ian and Lyn, their story became more familiar to me, and started to take shape in my notes.

• • •

On the Friday morning of Lyn's birth, after Wendy went into labour, Ian Rowe took her to the Box Hill Hospital and then caught the train into the city. At that time fathers almost never attended their children's birth. On his way from Flinders Street Station to the AMP building on Collins Street, Ian Rowe walked under a ladder. Never a superstitious person, he nevertheless remembers thinking to himself, 'I hope that's not a bad omen.'

In the early afternoon Ian's phone rang. 'I don't remember who it was. It may have been Dr Dickinson. I knew something bad had happened, but whether I was told exactly what had happened I just don't know.' The trauma of the day has left large gaps in his memory.

Ian Rowe raced back to the station and caught a train to Box Hill.

> I remember walking to the hospital and being really anxious. I don't remember much about it. I don't even recall whether I saw Lyn that day. I don't remember who I spoke with or who told me that Lyn did not have legs and arms. I have a faint memory of Wendy being very sedated, and I remember being very concerned about Wendy. But I remember nothing else about the visit.

Ian's memories of that period have vanished. All he remembers is a deep sense of grief and loss. He went straight back to work on Monday three days after the birth. Wendy remembers he visited the hospital every day during the following week, but Ian has no memory of that.

At the time, the doctors told Wendy her daughter would not survive. Lyn would be lying down all the time, they said, and would develop severe chest infections which would lead to her death. One of the nurses said something like, 'Just put her in a home and forget about her, she'll be dead in six months.'

After a week in hospital, Wendy was allowed to leave. She and Ian asked the hospital to look after Lyn for another week, and Wendy's parents volunteered to take care of the older children for a little longer. Then the couple escaped to Victoria's mountains. 'We wanted to talk, just the two of us, about what we were going to do and how we were going to cope,' Wendy recalled.

> So we drove up to the high country, stayed in cheap hotels, slept in the back of the car one night, and just talked and talked. We talked about Lyn and how long she would live, and how the hospital thought we should put her in a home. We talked about our older girls. It was emotional and difficult and we were probably still in shock. But when we got back to Melbourne we collected Lyn and took her home.

It was 1962: there was no counselling, no assistance. Wendy and Ian were a young couple with two young children, and now they had a baby with extremely high needs. 'We were on our own,' was Wendy's summation and the following months were traumatic. 'We were in a desperate state. Struggling to cope with caring for Lyn and our older girls, adjusting to the reality of a terribly handicapped child, trying to accept the fact that there was no cure for Lyn,' Wendy said. 'Nothing was going to bring her limbs back. It was going to be this way, and never change. Forever.'

One of the adjustments was the effect Lyn had on other people. 'Lots of people just didn't know what to say to us,' Wendy said. 'Some people crossed the road to avoid us and other people stared and pointed and whispered. We lost some friendships and it took me a while to become comfortable with going out with Lyn in public.'

This unwanted attention never ceased. 'All of our girls had to deal with other kids pointing and staring at Lyn, people shrinking back in horror or fright, making unkind comments,' Wendy said. At one children's party one of the mothers pointed at Lyn and issued a stern warning to the other children: 'Don't look at her!'

Lyn's sisters struggled with the reaction Lyn drew, but found their own ways of dealing with it, quick with a smart or cutting retort. Wendy remembered a typical reaction from ten-year-old Alison.

> We were all on holidays in New South Wales, in a supermarket, and Alison was pushing Lyn in a wheelchair. A young boy had left his mother and was following Lyn around, pointing and giggling at her. Alison told him to go away several times. When he wouldn't, she told him that her father would come along and chop his arms and legs off, just like he had done to Lyn.

The boy fled.

With the family revolving around Lyn and her needs, Wendy had no illusion about how hard it would be to give her older girls a semblance of normality. 'Merrilyn and Alison were just little girls themselves, yet I knew that Lyn was going to occupy almost all of my time.'

In evenings after the children had gone to bed Wendy always felt an enormous sense of relief, along with complete exhaustion. 'I could pretend for a few minutes that we were a normal family, and that I didn't have a daughter in the bedroom who would need my care and attention for the rest of my life, or for as long as I was able to give it.'

Given the hospital's bleak prediction for Lyn, Wendy was surprised that as the months passed Lyn met all the normal milestones, or at least the ones that weren't out of the question. Obviously she could not crawl or stand or reach for things, but she fed well—she liked food—and ate solids easily. She giggled and smiled and started trying to speak early. She was doing so well she went for her first prosthetic fittings when she was around nine months old. She was a happy baby and, her parents thought, very inquisitive. 'Lyn rolled around and got stuck under pieces of furniture,' Wendy said. 'When her older sisters were playing with Lego, Lyn liked to grab the pieces in her mouth and I'd have to tip her up to get them out.' Wendy hoped that Lyn would be able to develop a satisfying life, full of reading and music and conversation.

But another blow was coming. When Lyn was ten or eleven months old and teething, she developed a fever. Dr Indian visited the home and urged Ian and Wendy to get Lyn to hospital immediately. 'We took her to the Royal Children's Hospital but the fever got worse, and she fell into a coma. She stayed in the coma for a week. The doctors told us that because Lyn was missing all of her limbs, she didn't have the surface area to release heat from her body,' Wendy said. This susceptibility to fever was a common problem for thalidomide babies and many died after lapsing into unconsciousness.

When Lyn emerged from the coma she was noticeably different and the doctors warned she might have suffered brain damage. 'Her development changed, she'd regressed,' Wendy said. 'She had forgotten how to feed and she had to relearn simple things, like sucking on a bottle. She stared a lot and was like a little zombie. After that she picked up new things quite slowly.'

The period after Lyn's coma was as difficult for Wendy as the weeks and months after the birth. 'I was totally devastated. I felt that she had no hope now. She had no limbs and she had brain damage. I saw an incredibly bleak future for her. I had to keep going, but I felt very despondent for a long time.'

CHAPTER 3

Silent Shock

Like every one of the Australian women who took thalidomide, Wendy Rowe ingested a German-made product. The thalidomide in Wendy's tablets was manufactured at the Grünenthal factory in Stolberg and transported as powder to the UK, where it was pressed into tablets by Distillers. The tablets were packaged into bottles and sample packets and shipped to Sydney, then trucked to Melbourne. So despite being at the far end of the world, Wendy and Lyn Rowe were, quite directly, Grünenthal victims. And like every other Grünenthal victim across the globe, Wendy and Lyn Rowe had to wait fifty years for an apology. And when the apology came…well, it was a very mixed blessing.

In August 2012 Grünenthal's chief executive Harald Stock spoke at the unveiling of the statue of an anonymous thalidomide victim in the Stolberg library, just around the corner from the old Grünenthal factory. Stock expressed sincere regret at the harm caused by thalidomide, and apologised for the company's fifty-year silence on the issue. So far, so good. The apology was less than Olympian, but it was something. Stock, though, wasn't finished. 'We ask that you regard our long silence as a sign of the silent shock that your fate has caused us.'

Silent shock? Thalidomiders were predictably outraged: they believed Grünenthal was claiming their suffering as a justification for the decades-long inability to apologise. Presumably Grünenthal had not anticipated that response. But how could anyone have so misread the moment? From a company that had taken fifty years to choose its words, it was an outstandingly poorly judged public relations exercise.

The 'silent shock' explanation for Grünenthal's long failure to apologise was laughable. Grünenthal's drug had been sold in at least forty-six different countries, causing untold suffering. There were about five thousand recognised survivors across the world, and at least that many more who had died or had never been recognised. Some estimates put the global death and injury toll at fifteen thousand or even more, since many thousands died in utero or were never counted. It was these victims and their parents who were entitled to shock, not Grünenthal. One UK activist called the apology an insult. 'We feel that a sincere and genuine apology is one which actually admits wrongdoing. The company has not done that.' Another activist called for compensation rather than weasel words. 'If they are serious about admitting they are at fault and regret what happened, they need to start [financially] helping those of us who were affected.'

When Stock made his speech many of the three thousand or so recognised German thalidomiders were surviving on meagre pensions doled out annually by an underfunded compensation fund. They were among Germany's most disadvantaged citizens. By contrast, Grünenthal's owners and senior executives were members of Germany's wealthy elite: in 2012 Grünenthal declared a pre-tax income of 228 million euros.

• • •

Grünenthal, which translates into English as 'green valley', was established in 1946. It was a spin-off from the Wirtz family's long-established perfume and soap business, Mäurer & Wirtz. The first

Grünenthal factory was in Stolberg, a quaint little town just outside Aachen near the border with Belgium. The post-war era was not an especially auspicious time for some of the luminaries of the German pharmaceutical industry. In 1947, the year after Grünenthal's founding, war-crimes trials started for twenty-four directors and senior employees of IG Farben, a conglomerate of German chemical, dye and pharmaceutical companies.

Created in 1925 by the merger of six German industrial giants, including Bayer, BASF and Hoechst, IG Farben was intimately and heavily involved in the German war effort and complicit in a series of war crimes. It profited massively from its contracts with the military, and boasted active Nazis in its senior ranks. Many of these industrialists, even those convicted of war crimes, went on to shining post-war careers in Germany. Quite incredibly, one of the worst, the convicted mass murderer Otto Ambros, ended up as the chair of Grünenthal's supervisory board.

Ambros was a chemist who rose quickly through IG Farben and during the late 1930s oversaw the production of chemical weapons and nerve agents. In 1940–41, Ambros was involved in IG Farben's search for a site for new synthetic rubber and liquid fuel plants in the territory Germany had conquered to its east. IG Farben settled on a Polish town named Oswiecim. Or, in German, Auschwitz.

Auschwitz was already the site of a concentration camp, and would evolve into one of history's blackest holes: a group of extermination and concentration camps, replete with gas chambers and crematoria, the venue for more than one million murders. Auschwitz's appeal for IG Farben increased when the SS promised to supply labour. Suitably motivated, IG Farben, a prominent financial supporter of the Nazi Party in the pre-war years, started work on its gigantic Auschwitz plants in early 1941. Throughout the war years, IG Farben and its

Auschwitz managers, including Otto Ambros, were locked in a mutually beneficial embrace with the SS. The Nazi war machine deported and murdered the local Jewish population, brought in slave labour and allowed IG Farben to rent a workforce at the flat rate of three marks per day for an unskilled worker, or four marks for a skilled worker. In 1941 Ambros famously wrote to Fritz ter Meer, an IG Farben board member and later also a convicted war criminal: 'Our new friendship with the SS is proving very beneficial.'

IG Farben and the SS soon took their collaboration further, agreeing to the construction of the Monowitz concentration camp on the grounds of the IG Farben complex. Monowitz would house the enslaved workforce and avoid the time wasted in marching the prisoners back and forth from the other Auschwitz camps. Emaciated prisoners died in droves at the IG Farben site, exhaustion, disease and starvation cutting through their ranks. Others were beaten to death or shot by the SS. Yet others were hanged for trying to escape. Regular 'selections' sent the weak to the extermination camp for gassing. Prisoners were told that the only way they were leaving Auschwitz was via the chimney. Senior IG Farben employees bought—at bargain prices—the clothing of people who had been gassed. 'As I am an expert on textiles,' a survivor testified, 'I quite often had to select clothing for the foremen.'

The IG Farben plants ultimately produced almost nothing and were abandoned by the Germans in January 1945 after heavy US bombing and in the face of the advancing Russian army. Thousands more prisoners died as the Germans forced them to march west from Auschwitz through mid-winter. The acclaimed writer Primo Levi was one of the survivors of the Monowitz camp. As a chemist, Levi was transferred from brutal physical labour to a job as a laboratory assistant in the IG Farben plant during the last months of 1944, sparing him the vicious conditions and abuse that claimed so many lives. Ill at the end of the war with scarlet fever, Levi was left behind to die by the retreating Germans, thus avoiding the death march forced on most prisoners. Levi survived and his first and best-known book, *If This Is a Man*, powerfully records his year at Auschwitz.

IG Farben's war record was appalling in every respect. It financed some of Dr Josef Mengele's infamous medical experiments at Auschwitz and an IG Farben subsidiary supplied the SS with the Zyklon B pesticide used in the gas chambers. All of this led to war-crimes prosecutions, and in 1948, after a trial of IG Farben executives, Otto Ambros was sentenced to eight years in prison for mass murder and slavery. He was one of thirteen IG Farben men convicted. Yet by early 1951 Ambros and all of the others had been released from prison, beneficiaries of a grant of clemency. Almost all were welcomed back into the bosom of German business.

Ambros found no shortage of employers. He was chairman of pharmaceutical firm Knoll AG's board during the 1960s and '70s (it was part-owned by Grünenthal) and later the chairman of Grünenthal's supervisory board. He also found lucrative consultancies with US firms.

Ambros was not the only man with a dark history to gain employment at Grünenthal. Dr Heinz Baumkötter was a notorious SS doctor at the Sachsenhausen concentration camp outside Berlin. In addition to overseeing executions and selecting prisoners for the gas chamber, he conducted experiments with injections, explosives and chemicals. One such experiment saw prisoners strapped down and burned with phosphorus so that Baumkötter could test an experimental salve.

Baumkötter was arrested after the war, charged with murder and tried by the Soviets in Berlin in 1947. He was convicted after a short trial, not a surprising outcome given his appalling record and the efficient

Soviet approach to war-crimes justice. Baumkötter was sentenced to life imprisonment but served only eight years before the Soviets returned him to Germany. The exact point at which Grünenthal employed him is unclear, but Baumkötter was certainly working as a salesman in Grünenthal's Münster office in 1960 and 1961. By this time he was facing another round of war-crimes charges—in a German court. In 1962, after a trial in Münster, Baumkötter was convicted of being an accessory to murder and of depraved indifference and sentenced once more to eight years' jail. The time he had already served in the Soviet Union was taken into account and Baumkötter remained a free man. One wonders what his erstwhile colleagues at Grünenthal made of their twice-convicted war-criminal colleague.

There were others too. Dr Ernst-Günther Schenck, another SS doctor, tested an experimental protein sausage intended for German soldiers on concentration camp prisoners, with deadly effects. He was a Russian prisoner of war for almost ten years and later found a job with Grünenthal. Martin Staemmler, an ardent Nazi who wrote widely on the racial superiority of the German people, headed Grünenthal's pathology department from 1960 until shortly before his death in 1974.

So far as is known, the most notorious of Grünenthal's Nazis, Ambros and Baumkötter, had little or nothing to do with thalidomide. Ambros appears to have been at Grünenthal after the disaster, and Baumkötter merely helped to sell the drug. Heinrich Mückter, though, was a different matter.

Born in 1914, Mückter studied medicine and chemistry at university. He joined the army in 1940, and as a captain in the medical corps found his way to occupied Poland as deputy head of the Institute for Virus and Typhus Research in Krakow.

The search for an effective typhus vaccine was an obsession among the Nazi leadership. The typhus work and other vaccine 'research' led to much depraved experimentation and, later, war-crimes charges for thirteen doctors and administrators. Inmates at the Buchenwald concentration camp were the main experimental guinea pigs and the vicious experiments claimed hundreds of lives. Most experiments were carried out in the infamous Block 46 where, in addition to typhus experiments, tests with yellow fever, smallpox, cholera and diphtheria were also conducted. One witness at Nuremberg described the 'dreadful horror' inspired by Block 46. Everyone 'who went to Block 46 as an experimental person did not only have to expect death, and under certain circumstances a very long drawn out and frightful death, but also torture and the complete removal of the last remnants of personal freedom'.

The typhus experiments varied but in general prisoners were infected with a virulent form of the disease. Some were then given a test vaccine and others, a control group, were not. 'There were cases of raving madness, delirium, people would refuse to eat, and a large percentage of them would die. Those who experienced the disease in a milder form, perhaps because their constitutions were stronger or because the vaccine was effective, were forced continuously to observe the death struggles of others,' a witness related. To maintain a ready source of fresh diseased blood for experiments, about five inmates a month were infected with typhus. These 'passage persons', as they were known, died regularly, requiring new passage persons to be infected.

So far as is known Mückter was not at Buchenwald, nor at Auschwitz, which is close to Krakow, and where there were also deadly typhus experiments. Precisely what Mückter did at Krakow is not known and Mückter did not talk about it afterwards, not unusual behaviour for Germans of his generation. The Krakow Institute conducted its own experiments and, certainly, the German military's medical researchers had a reputation for callousness and indifference to the suffering of their human guinea pigs. However Mückter's boss at Krakow, Dr Hermann Eyer, was investigated after the war by the US army and exonerated of war crimes. And curiously, when the Polish authorities charged Mückter at the end of the war, it was only with mistreating prisoners and stealing scientific equipment. In any event, the charges were academic. Mückter had fled to Germany and on 1 July 1946 was employed by Grünenthal.

Mückter quickly found success at his new home, helping his employer win a lucrative contract to produce penicillin. Soon he was Grünenthal's director of research and development, with a generous bonus deal: in addition to his salary, Mückter was promised a percentage of sales, a deal that would make him a very wealthy man, in no small part thanks to thalidomide.

The relevance of Grünenthal's war-criminal connections was the subject of much discussion among Lyn Rowe's legal team. For sure, there was no shortage of men with appalling records in post-war Germany and not all of them were going to disappear into obscurity. On the other hand, there is a clear difference between a run-of-the-mill ex-Nazi or ex-soldier and Otto Ambros, a man convicted of mass murder and slavery, who bore the shame of Auschwitz. Or Heinrich Baumkötter, a doctor convicted of war crimes in both Russian and German courts. What sort of company would allow a convicted mass murderer to hold a senior position? Or any position at all?

Ultimately we felt that while the war-criminal material was only marginally relevant to Lyn's legal claim, it was crucial to understanding the Grünenthal of that era. The fact that Grünenthal would employ an enthusiastic participant in mass murder must say something about the culture of the company at that time, a culture which proved incapable of responding adequately to reports of damage caused by thalidomide.

The details of Heinrich Mückter's sales bonuses are also illuminating. Between 1952 and 1961 Mückter's salary was constant: 14,400 marks per annum. But Mückter was also paid one per cent of the turnover of certain drugs, including thalidomide. In 1957, the year thalidomide sales began, Mückter's bonus was 160,000 marks. By 1959 it had climbed to 200,000 marks and in 1961, the final year of thalidomide sales, Mückter's bonus was 325,000 German marks, a vast sum: about twenty-two times his salary.

The bonus system and Mückter's background seemed to us part of the explanation for Grünenthal's conduct. It almost sounds like a quiz question. Let's say you take a doctor with a forceful personality and a wartime history of medical experiments and then give him a medical laboratory. Dangle generous bonuses in front of him for the drugs he can get to market. Then assume his team invents a drug which is stunningly popular—but has appalling side effects. Assume further that the company which employs him is not, let's say, rigorous about character issues. Throw in a general culture among employees of respect for authority.

What would happen if the company started getting reports that its favourite drug was doing unpleasant things to some of the people taking it? Would our doctor suspend sales and investigate? Or would it be surprising if he dismissed and trivialised complaints, and focused on selling more and more of the drug?

• • •

By comparison with Grünenthal, Distillers resembled a slightly genteel stooge led gullibly into the medical fiasco of the century. Like Grünenthal, Distillers was a recent entrant into the pharmaceutical field. But its roots went back to the 1870s in Scotland, and for decades it had dominated the international trade in Scotch whisky, while profiting from lucrative lines in other beverages.

During World War II, at the UK Government's request, the company diversified into penicillin, churning out the vital antibiotic at a government factory in Speke, Liverpool. After the war the government offered Distillers the factory at a reduced price, so Distillers stayed in the pharmaceutical business via its offshoot, Distillers Biochemicals, which kept producing penicillin while hunting around for further products. Distillers was not especially interested in developing its own drugs; it was more enthusiastic about finding a foreign partner whose drugs it could license for sale in the UK.*

Unfortunately for Distillers its gaze alighted on Grünenthal, which by 1956 had developed a new drug it labelled K17 for internal purposes. The drug was thalidomide, and Distillers was soon clamouring for the British rights. Various Distillers executives made the trek to Germany, practically beseeching Grünenthal to grant them a licence. Eventually, the gentlemen at Distillers would be brought undone by their desperation for a bestselling drug, lack of nous, and willingness to believe Grünenthal's assurances. The hard men at Grünenthal found the well-mannered British executives an easy target. And Distillers would spend many years regretting the folly of ever getting into bed with Grünenthal.

The disaster scarred some of the key figures at Distillers. Pharmacologist George Somers confided to a friend that he felt as though he had driven a bus into a group of schoolchildren when he learned what thalidomide had done to babies. 'I was completely

---

* For clarity: the UK whisky company was Distillers Company Ltd. Its UK pharmaceutical subsidiary was Distillers Company (Biochemicals) Ltd. And the Australian pharmaceutical arm was Distillers Company (Biochemicals) Australia Ltd. The term Distillers is most commonly used in this book, though the parent company was not directly involved in the pharmaceutical business.

shattered, emotionally and professionally.' Walter Kennedy, the company's medical adviser, spent much of his retirement in Scotland trying to compile an exhaustive list of material on teratology, the study of birth malformations.

That is not to say that Distillers is without blame. Nor is it due sympathy. It behaved incompetently while the drug was on the market, explicitly promoting a damaging and untested drug as safe in pregnancy. In the immediate aftermath of the disaster it issued hopelessly inadequate warnings about the millions of pills still in circulation, and it kept selling a limited amount of thalidomide for months after its official withdrawal. It even stooped to the low of encouraging doctors to write to medical journals praising the deadly drug and calling for its return to the marketplace. An enormously profitable company, Distillers also heartlessly dragged its heels for years on compensating its victims. But, relative to Grünenthal's outrageous and colossally negligent behaviour, Distillers appeared a somewhat lesser villain.

• • •

Grünenthal and Distillers headed in separate directions shortly after the disaster. Appalled and shocked, Distillers raced for the exit, selling off its pharmaceutical business almost immediately. But it could not get rid of its legal responsibility for thalidomide. In the 1980s Distillers was taken over by Guinness, and after another merger in 1997 Diageo plc came into existence. Diageo is one of the world's biggest drinks companies, boasting iconic labels including Smirnoff, Johnnie Walker, Baileys and Guinness. The Distillers companies, and their legal liability for thalidomide, travelled through the chain of take-overs and mergers and are today subsidiaries of Diageo, which for all practical purposes assumes legal liability for the drug.

Grünenthal, by contrast, was and remains a pharmaceutical business. It spent about a decade fighting off thalidomide legal threats and is now a successful moderately sized company. It does business all over the world and focuses on pain medication. To this day, Grünenthal remains largely in the hands of its founders, the Wirtz family.

When Lyn Rowe's legal claim was formally issued on 8 July 2011, the writ named as defendants Grünenthal and two Distillers companies: the former parent whisky company and its pharmaceutical subsidiary. Almost exactly fifty-five years after Distillers first started courting Grünenthal, the two companies were still being called to account for their thalidomide conduct, forced yet again to defend the dealings of executives and doctors long dead.

That Grünenthal and Distillers found themselves dragged back into thalidomide litigation in Australia in the twenty-first century was the result of a series of remarkable coincidences.

• • •

Peter Gordon grew up in West Footscray, a blue-collar suburb in Melbourne's inner west. His father worked as a clerk at a nearby airforce base for almost thirty years, before a heart attack left him on a disability pension. Gordon's mother sold bedding at a department store. It was, says Gordon, 'a working-class, churchgoing' childhood. Gordon and his sister Karen went to local Catholic schools and the family attended mass every Sunday at Christ the King Church in Braybrook. When he was thirteen Gordon shocked his parents by announcing he was an atheist. 'It was at about 9.15 one Sunday morning and we were on our way out to mass. I said that consonant with my new status, I wouldn't be going to church anymore. That caused massive trauma. It says something about my sister's diplomacy that about six weeks later she quietly made the same announcement without any consequences whatsoever.'

Gordon was dux of his school and went to Melbourne University to study law. As a self-described 'pathologically shy' teenager, Gordon found it an isolating experience. 'The place was full of confident kids from expensive schools. I had no social skills and no idea at all how to talk to them. I was the nerdiest kid around and I went through law school as a complete loner.' Gordon doubted whether he could find a job in the law after graduating. 'I just assumed that law firms were after people not at all like me.' He sent out about fifty applications, was invited to three interviews, and received one job offer—from Slater & Gordon. It was the only break he needed.

Gordon's workaholic tendencies, combined with a lateral legal mind and a love of bare-knuckle litigation, saw him quickly climb the ladder to partner and then senior partner. Along the way he racked up victories for asbestos victims, women with leaking breast implants, and people who had developed HIV through infected blood transfusions. There were also losses—most notably in tobacco litigation—but even these were high-profile, hard-fought affairs.

By 2009 Gordon had spent several decades engaged in frenetic around-the-clock legal activity. At fifty-one, at the top of his game, he wanted a break. He also had the financial freedom to do something different, to strike out on his own. Just two years earlier Slater & Gordon had floated on the stock market, making instant multi-millionaires out of a handful of the firm's owners.

So in August 2009 Gordon left Slater & Gordon, bringing to an end a twenty-nine-and-a-half-year relationship. He wondered whether he should hang on until the thirty-year mark, 'but then I thought those sort of milestones are just bullshit anyway'. Gordon had plans for some part-time work but also 'to get fit, play golf' and spend more time with his wife Kerri and twin daughters.

A couple of years earlier, Gordon had bought a holiday house on the Mornington Peninsula from an 'official' thalidomider named Tony Specchio who, despite his malformed arms, had established a successful career in the building industry. The two men got on well, and Gordon was impressed by Specchio's grit and drive. Then, not long before Gordon left Slater & Gordon, Specchio got in touch to talk about thalidomide.

He explained that he had been compensated in the 1970s, one of a group of about fifty Australians and New Zealanders accepted as thalidomiders by Distillers. Their compensation was paltry by modern standards and, it would become apparent, in many cases nowhere near enough to ensure proper care and assistance. While Specchio had made a career for himself, many of the thalidomiders were now in difficult circumstances. Their compensation was gone and they were reliant on welfare, coping with ageing bodies, deteriorating health and escalating care needs.

Specchio told Gordon about Ken Youdale, a Sydney businessman and the father of a thalidomider, who was trying to prise top-up compensation out of Diageo, the multibillion-dollar global drinks company that had absorbed the Distillers companies responsible for thalidomide. Youdale, then in his mid-eighties, had sent every known Australian and New Zealand thalidomider a power of attorney that purported to give Youdale authority to negotiate with Diageo on their behalf. Specchio wanted to know whether he should sign.

At first blush Gordon was dubious. Youdale's campaign was unusual to say the least. And what to make of an octogenarian who had not practised as a lawyer for decades running such a quixotic international campaign? But then Gordon telephoned Youdale and as they spoke his doubts started to disappear. 'I told him that it all sounded quite bizarre, but I was impressed by what he was doing and I'd be happy to do anything I could to help.' Youdale was equally impressed. 'Peter was direct and he got straight to the point.'

As many have remarked, they made an unlikely couple. Gordon is rumpled, an aggressive advocate for the underdog. He has a fast, sharp mind, and a broad Australian accent in which an engaging vernacular bumps up against expensive words like *pellucid*, *bifurcate* and *enure*. Youdale, who has lived a long and extraordinary life, is hyper-establishment and impeccably dressed. He speaks in modulated tones, and remained dapper and suave after passing his ninetieth birthday in 2014. As a teenager he was a navigator on bombing raids over Europe. His first flight was the night before the Normandy landing, bombing German gun positions in preparation for the invasion. The day he completed his first tour of thirty-four missions he signed up for a second tour. He felt invincible. 'I didn't think the Jerries would ever get me.' Youdale was awarded a Distinguished Flying Cross. 'King George pinned it on me at Buckingham Palace.' By war's end dozens of his friends and acquaintances had died, leaving him with a deep appreciation of life and a determination to seize hold of it.

In Sydney after the war he studied law, worked briefly as a barrister and then took his competitive drive to the business world. He also proposed to Janet Hayes on their third date, 'hopelessly smitten' by a woman he describes as 'extraordinary'.

In 1961 Janet fell pregnant and, after she complained of morning sickness, Youdale drove her to a local pharmacy. 'The pharmacist gave her some pills he guaranteed would help.' Janet took only two of them. Still, when Niki Youdale was born in May 1962 those thalidomide pills had exacted a heavy toll. 'Niki had a shortened arm and missing thumbs and we didn't even know about the hole in her heart at that stage,' Youdale remembered. 'She was also completely gorgeous.'

Niki Youdale was in and out of hospital for her first year, including Chicago's Mayo Clinic, where her parents took her after being told it offered the best available care. The Mayo doctors discovered Niki's undiagnosed heart condition and told her parents that Niki's continued survival was precarious and that she would eventually require a heart-lung transplant. But Niki's condition stabilised and Ken and Janet Youdale had two more daughters. Niki lived courageously and cheerfully. She found employment as a television and theatre make-up artist and did volunteer work, including as a Lifeline counsellor.

Ken Youdale pursued a successful business career, working for British Tobacco's beverages arm for sixteen years and then running his own management consultancy. During the 1970s and '80s he offered advice on the investment of the compensation Distillers paid Australian thalidomiders, which was held in trust until the children reached the age of twenty-five.

But in 2003 Niki Youdale's life ended in a way no one had expected. With her heart and lungs failing, she was awaiting a transplant when doctors found a tumour in her brain. 'The last time I spoke with Niki they were wheeling her away on a trolley, taking her off for brain surgery,' remembered Youdale. 'Niki said, "Stop a minute," jumped off and ran back to me and told me she loved me. I remember it clearly. "I love you so much," was what she said. Then she ran back, got on the trolley and that was it. She never regained consciousness after surgery.'

Five years later, Youdale was asked to speak at a conference of thalidomide survivors. Preparing for his speech, Youdale did his homework and discovered that UK thalidomide activists had persuaded Diageo to make extra payments to a trust which provides a yearly pension to UK thalidomiders.

Youdale thought Diageo should do the same for Australians, though he knew the company had no legal obligation to do so. After all, the Australian survivors had accepted once-and-for-all compensation in the 1970s. Diageo could correctly argue that the issue was legally dead. But Youdale knew that Diageo was a drinks empire with a clear appreciation of the value of a good corporate reputation. He decided to put his charm, guile and commercial savvy to work persuading Diageo to voluntarily provide extra compensation to recognised Australian thalidomiders.

Shortly afterwards, in late 2008, Youdale flew to London armed with letters of support he had obtained from Australian government ministers. He spent four weeks at the East India Club and met with Diageo executives twice, starting a dialogue that led to two Diageo executives coming to Australia in August 2009.

By this time, Youdale had befriended Peter Gordon. So the two of them—and Lance Fletcher, an influential Australian thalidomider born without ears—met with the Diageo executives over three days at the Blue Hotel on Sydney's spectacular harbour. The talks went well. The Diageo team displayed an appreciation for the suffering of the drug's victims and a willingness to explore what more they could do. That, it must be said, was an unusual and laudable stance. And despite the absence of any legal obligation, and after another lengthy negotiation, Diageo announced in July 2010 what was effectively a fifty-million-dollar voluntary payment. It would provide the official Australian and New Zealand survivors with an annual pension equivalent to that paid to UK survivors.

It is remarkable, then, that this commendable act of corporate goodwill led, at least indirectly, to Diageo getting dragged into exactly the sort of bitter litigation the company wanted to avoid.

In the course of negotiating the compensation deal, Gordon was asked by Diageo and by Youdale if he would have a chat to seven other people who had long claimed to be thalidomiders but had never been recognised as such. Gordon agreed, with the stipulation that if he thought they had been unfairly treated he would say so. The first of the seven Gordon met was Gary Fludder, who still had the empty bottle of thalidomide his mother had been given in 1961. Further, his mother was alive and adamant she had been given thalidomide. Yet Fludder, who was born with severely malformed hands, a truncated left leg that required amputation and a host of other problems, was told as a child that his injuries did not fit a thalidomide pattern and that he was not eligible for compensation.

Disturbed by this and other stories, Gordon embarked on a careful examination of thalidomide medicine, and the curious reasoning that excluded some people from compensation on the basis that their injuries did not fit the so-called thalidomide pattern. At the same time, prompted by publicity given to the fifty-million-dollar deal, calls started coming into Gordon Legal, the new firm Gordon had set up, from people who believed they were the victims of thalidomide. Some stories were flimsy, but many were compelling and cogent.

By October 2010 Gordon had seen enough. He had realised that the 1970s settlement had left many thalidomiders behind. The experts at the time had reached an exclusionary view about what injuries could be caused by thalidomide, a view based on the most obvious and visible injuries rather than the full breadth of damage caused by the drug. Others had been turned away because they lacked evidence that their mothers had taken thalidomide. Many others had never come forward. In late October 2010, Gordon filed a class action for uncompensated Australian survivors of the drug.

So when Gordon spoke at the thalidomide conference in Sydney at the end of 2010, he had been deeply immersed in the issue for a year. He had studied the medicine, researched the history of the not-outstandingly-successful legal actions in Australia and England in the 1960s and '70s, and launched legal proceedings. 'Plain and simple there had been a miscarriage of justice. A lot of deserving people had missed out. And I was appalled that Grünenthal had never paid a cent to a single Australian victim.'

When Peter Gordon is excited and enthused, he is a sight to behold. That day at the thalidomiders' conference he was in full pugnacious flight, brimming with enthusiasm for the fight ahead. However, the trajectory of that fight was changed by Gordon's conversation with Mary Henley-Collopy; and for the better. Once Gordon met Lyn Rowe it quickly became clear that the litigation had to be reconfigured to place her at the front of the queue: to make Lyn the lead plaintiff. There were compelling reasons for this.

First and foremost, Lyn's situation was perilous. She was utterly and completely reliant on her parents for round-the-clock care. Wendy and Ian Rowe were then in their mid- and late seventies. The physically demanding care Lyn required was a growing struggle for her parents. Very soon it would become impossible. None of the Rowe family had any idea what would happen when that day arrived. That looming crisis gave Lyn's claim a real degree of urgency. It had to be resolved before her parents became unable to care for her. If Lyn's claim succeeded, the damages ordered by the Court would eliminate the uncertainty over her future by paying for top-flight care.

Lyn's situation was also a strong argument for an accelerated legal process. This was important. Legal battles with well-resourced companies can become wars of attrition. Defendants often produce a blizzard of applications and legal manoeuvres, which have the effect of miring the litigation in a procedural bog. Time can be the defendant's friend, and the injured party's enemy. We wanted a speedy trial, not an incremental slog towards a receding finish line.

Importantly, Lyn's claim was also relatively strong. In a class action, the lead plaintiff's claim settles some of the disputed issues for the other members of the group. A win by the lead plaintiff makes it easier for the others to prove their claim. But lose the lead plaintiff's claim and the game is effectively over for everyone else. So we needed a strong claim up front. Every thalidomide claim would be hard to win. The big stumbling block was that we were litigating fifty years after the event. But all things considered, we thought Lyn had a real chance of success.

First, it seemed likely that we could gather good evidence that her mother Wendy had taken the drug. Though that sounds easy, it is definitely not. Almost fifty years after the consumption of the drug, memories were certain to have faded, and medical records would very probably have been destroyed. In the case of many of our thalidomide clients, potential witnesses (mothers, fathers, doctors, pharmacists, drug salesmen and so on) had died or could not be found.

Further, in the 1960s patients were often given or prescribed pills and not told what they were. Bottles of pills obtained from a pharmacy were sometimes just labelled 'the medication', with no brand or chemical name on the container.

But proving Lyn's exposure to the drug looked promising. Her parents were alive and well. We had found both the doctor who delivered her and a pharmacist who, in the 1960s, often filled the Rowe family's prescriptions. Various members of Lyn's extended family had valuable memories to share.

Lyn's physical condition was also a factor in proving her exposure to thalidomide. There is much debate over exactly what damage thalidomide can cause. But there is no doubt it can cause what Lyn had: a complete absence of limbs. This was important. If we could show Wendy Rowe took thalidomide, then we could almost certainly prove the thalidomide caused Lyn's injury. If Lyn had suffered from a birth malformation rarely (or never) seen in recognised thalidomide cases, we would have faced a real fight to establish that the drug was even capable of causing that particular malformation.

We also knew the family's personal qualities. Lyn and her parents were open, transparently honest people who had been dealt an awful hand and adapted with grace. Those qualities would be evident during the unavoidably public battle to come, both inside and outside court, and would only benefit Lyn's claim.

Gordon Legal and Slater & Gordon, which agreed to work together, would not charge the Rowes upfront for the millions of dollars of legal work it would require to get the case to trial. It would all be done on a no-win no-fee basis. Only if the case was successful would the Rowes pay legal fees, and any payment they made would be capped. If the case was not successful the two law firms would have to write off the massive investment as a good try for a worthy cause. Looked at commercially, thalidomide litigation was a high-stakes gamble, even for aggressive plaintiff law firms. The litigation didn't make sense without a strong belief in the righteousness of the cause. Fortunately Slater & Gordon's managing director Andrew Grech, a long-time friend of Peter Gordon's, never wavered in his commitment to the case.

By the time we had settled on Lyn Rowe as the lead plaintiff in April 2011, her legal team had been largely assembled. It was a small group and the lawyers had worked together in some combination in the past. Of course, given a surplus of people with forcefully held views, there were occasional disputes and spats. One period of elevated office angst coincided with the Christmas party, leading to a somewhat strained evening. There was, however, little deference to hierarchy in Lyn's team. Everyone—lawyer and non-lawyer—gave valuably and volubly at the regular meetings.

Initially the areas of responsibility among the lawyers were only loosely defined but eventually, by agreement and understanding, we all gravitated to different areas suiting our strengths and inclinations. While everyone frequently veered into everyone else's area, there were few border disputes.

Peter Gordon, Sarah Roache and Brett Spiegel did most of the work on the complex medical issues, including understanding the precise biological mechanisms by which thalidomide is thought to damage embryos. They also dealt with potential competing genetic causes of foetal damage, historic journal articles about what was and was not considered to be a thalidomide injury and the detailed and often lengthy medical records for each of our clients and often their mothers, all of which had to be trawled through, understood and sifted for relevance. The lawyers were assisted by Dr Sally Cockburn, an accomplished Melbourne GP, well known to generations of Melburnians as Dr Feelgood, the dispenser of health and relationship advice on a weekly radio show.

Importantly, the medical team also needed to find and work with experts who would be able to explain to the judge how thalidomide worked and how the thalidomide taken by Wendy Rowe caused the complete absence of Lyn's limbs.

Over the three years of the litigation I had irregular involvement with the medicine. My focus was the Rowe family, retired thalido-mide salesmen, doctors and pharmacists from the era, and Distillers and Grünenthal documents. In all of these areas, I worked with the other lawyers, most frequently Grace Wilson and Patrick Gordon.

The non-lawyers kept the rest of us on track. Peter's wife Kerri O'Toole ran the office efficiently and with a diplomat's skill, and our extraordinary administrative manager Dael Pressnell stayed for the life of the project, with time out after the birth of her daughter.

We guessed Lyn's trial might last three months. It would be exhausting and nerve-racking for everyone—especially for the Rowe family, but also for our other thalidomide clients. Everything rode on Lyn's trial. If Lyn won, she'd be well compensated. And her win would make a good result more likely for the rest of the group. But if Lyn lost, it would probably be all over for everyone. There would be no more thalidomide litigation in Australia.

Yet while our focus was on Lyn, we also had to attend to the people whose claims would follow if Lyn won. By mid-2011 we had been contacted by well over one hundred people. This later swelled to more than four hundred, with each bout of publicity for the case prompting more telephone calls and emails from potential clients. Ultimately, after detailed sifting and checking, we turned everyone away who had no prospect of proving a claim and were left with just over one hundred people who had never been compensated.

There was nothing we could do for this group until Lyn's claim was resolved, but, like all thalidomiders, they were now about fifty years old. Their parents, if alive, were mostly in their late seventies or eighties. These parents would give us the best available evidence of thalidomide consumption and their evidence had to be preserved. We couldn't just put those claims on the shelf until Lyn's was resolved. The mothers and fathers and other relatives with a story to tell might well have passed away by then. So a decision was made: Grace Wilson and Patrick Gordon would also work on these claims. This was a mammoth job, and a major (but vital) diversion from Lyn's claim. So in addition to the Lyn-specific litigation, sworn affidavits were taken from hundreds of people: the clients whose claims would follow and their mothers, fathers, aunts, uncles and so on. All of this safeguarded us against the likelihood that some of the witnesses would not be around to give their evidence when the time came.

• • •

One of our obvious priorities was to learn whatever we could about Distillers and Grünenthal, the tragedy their drug caused and the litigation that followed in the 1960s and '70s, absorbing every available lesson along the way. Considering it's the most notorious drug disaster in history, thalidomide has generated a surprisingly slim general literature. There are a number of moving personal memoirs by survivors, but in terms of understanding the political, legal and medical history of the drug, only a few useful accounts exist.

One was a result of the campaign for thalidomide victims run by the *Sunday Times* in London during the late 1960s and '70s. After much legal wrangling, a book written by the paper's investigative team—*Suffer the Children*—was published in 1979. The chief author was the distinguished journalist Phillip Knightley who, despite his advancing years, was exceptionally supportive. He spoke with me on the telephone, met with me at his home in London and lent me documents from his personal collection.

More recently Professor Trent Stephens and Rock Brynner (a writer and the son of the actor and anti-smoking activist Yul Brynner) wrote *Dark Remedy*, a history of thalidomide that gave prominence to the ongoing scientific quest to understand the precise mechanism by which thalidomide wreaks its damage. When we contacted Stephens he was generous and helpful with his time and expertise. Even better, he was so good at explaining complex science in plain English that we engaged him as an expert, repeatedly flying him to Australia from his home in Pocatello, Idaho.

But these books were secondary documents. Obviously we needed source material. Happily we were able to locate various stores of original documents in Europe and elsewhere.

In 1962, in the wake of the withdrawal of the drug, and the news that thousands of babies had been maimed or killed by thalidomide, the public prosecutor's office in Aachen, Germany began an investigation into Grünenthal's handling of thalidomide. The five-year probe which followed resulted in the March 1967 indictment of nine Grünenthal executives on charges of negligent manslaughter and assault-related offences.

The prosecutors prepared for the trial with German thoroughness. They produced an indictment of more than 550 pages, plus a massive footnote volume. These volumes referenced thousands of other documents collected by the prosecutor, some of them through police raids on Grünenthal. The documents included embarrassing admissions by Grünenthal's own legal department and correspondence between Grünenthal and its thalidomide licence partners.

As we'll see, the criminal trial of the Grünenthal executives was ultimately a crushing failure for the prosecution. But fortunately for us, after the trial collapsed in 1971 the prosecution deposited all of its material, including about one hundred boxes of documents, into a government archive. Many of these documents never saw the light of day in court: the trial was terminated before the prosecution was able to lead much of its best evidence.

For forty years these documents had gathered dust. Examining them would be a critical step in revealing Grünenthal's culpability for thalidomide's damage, and dispelling some of the myths about the drug.

Another important store of documents was held by the *Sunday Times* in London. In 1967, the paper was approached by Montague Phillips, a pharmacologist who was advising the lawyers representing the UK thalidomide children. Phillips had an offer for the paper.

In civil litigation there is a procedure called discovery, in which each side turns over its relevant documents to the other. Starting in 1964, Distillers had given thousands of its internal documents to the children's lawyers. Those lawyers, acting slowly and in a fashion that would eventually attract great criticism, had in 1966 given copies of them to their scientific adviser, Phillips. The lawyers wanted Phillips to interpret the documents and advise them on Distillers' failures and possible negligence.

Phillips was horrified by Distillers' internal documents, appalled at what he saw as the company's scientific shoddiness and its blind acceptance of Grünenthal's assurances. But he was also growing disenchanted with the glacial pace of the litigation. So, setting aside his obligations as an expert witness (one of which is to keep confidential material confidential), Phillips marched off to the *Sunday Times* and, after some discussion, offered to sell his documents.

In 1968 the newspaper paid Phillips £8000. The documents were copied and returned to Phillips and the paper's investigative team set to work.

Not long afterwards, another mother lode of thalidomide documents was dropped on the *Sunday Times* by Henning Sjöström, the lawyer representing Swedish thalidomide victims. Sjöström had got hold of some of Grünenthal's internal documents and, in a very unusual move for a lawyer, his agent was offering them to various newspapers in London. The *Sunday Times* bought them for £2500.

The *Sunday Times* and Distillers would later fight a long court battle over the material Phillips sold. But the fight was worth it—the documents gave the paper an incredible insight into the bumbling way in which Distillers had first embraced Grünenthal, and then exported the thalidomide disaster to Australia and other chunks of what was still the British Empire.

We knew that if the *Sunday Times* still held any of those internal Grünenthal or Distillers documents, they would be a vital resource for Lyn Rowe's claim. They would help us articulate (in formal court documents) what the drug companies had done, how they had ignored warning signs and failed to act prudently. Later in the litigation, under the discovery process, we would be entitled to see the drug companies' own collection of documents. But a preview, via the *Sunday Times*, would be very helpful.

After some negotiation, the *Sunday Times* generously agreed to give us access to its archives, though it could not guarantee how much had been retained. When we finally inspected the archive, we found that most of Sjöström's Grünenthal documents had disappeared, but a valuable portion (a fraction really) of the Distillers material was still there.

Eventually we would also access a cache of material generated by the Swedish thalidomide litigation, and thousands of pages of thalidomide material held by the Food and Drug Administration in the United States. All of this information helped us build Lyn Rowe's legal claim.

CHAPTER 4

A Horrible Preparation

In May 2011 I boarded an early morning flight from London. I was headed to Düsseldorf to have a firsthand look at the documents deposited forty years earlier by the team that had tried (and failed) to convict senior Grünenthal executives involved in the thalidomide disaster. The large English gent wedged into the budget flight seat beside me felt compelled to warn me about the culinary treats awaiting me. 'Worse than the crap we eat. Cabbage, spicy sausage and pickled pig's trotter,' was his ungenerous summation of German food.

It was not my first visit to Germany. Coincidentally, as a toddler I had spent a year in Uerdingen, a town just outside Düsseldorf. My father had been sent to Germany by his American employer to supervise the start-up of a Bayer chemical plant. My brother Simon was born at the maternity hospital in Düsseldorf where not many years earlier thalidomide babies were being born. I was eighteen months old when Simon was born and some of my first words were in German, thanks to the neighbours with whom we had become close friends. I had visited Germany as an adult and had studied German at university so I had some basic language skills. But I knew, of course, that my German would be far from adequate for the documents at the archive. So help was at hand. We had arranged for a number of German-speaking consultants to meet me in Düsseldorf.

Nina Stähle had been recommended to us after doing the archival research in Germany and the UK for the Australian inquiry into the fate of the HMAS *Sydney*, the Australian cruiser sunk by a German raider off the coast of Western Australia during World War II. Stähle, who spoke French and flawless English in addition to her native German, did an enormous amount of important work for us. She brought to bear not just her language skills but also a detailed appreciation of our case theory and a precise, forensic approach to the prosecutor's material. The other consultants, who prefer not to be named, also played important roles in unravelling the Grünenthal story.

The archive—Landesarchiv Nordrhein-Westfalen—was located in a quiet residential street. Close by was a synagogue, in front of which two bored policemen appeared to be permanently stationed. The archive was welcoming but strict. No pens, only archive-approved pencils. No cameras. Complete silence. Among Stähle's talents was negotiating German bureaucracy, so the first volumes of thalidomide material we had requested were waiting for us. The files emerged in irregular-shaped folders, yellowed with age but perfectly and precisely catalogued. And as a bonus for me and my rudimentary German, there was a great deal of material in English—letters between Grünenthal and its UK, US and Canadian licensees, journal articles and witness statements.

In a few critical respects the German prosecution team had a tougher job in the 1960s than we were facing five decades later. The German prosecutor had tried to secure convictions against the Grünenthal executives for negligent manslaughter and other serious criminal charges. That meant he had to prove his case according to the criminal standard, usually expressed as *beyond all reasonable doubt*. By contrast we had to establish Grünenthal's responsibility for Lyn Rowe's injuries only on *the balance of probabilities,* the civil law standard. That was a much lower bar for us to get over. In plain terms, the difference is between 'all but certain' and 'more likely than not'.

Also, the German prosecution team was trying to prove the guilt of individuals. Only that person's own knowledge, actions and omissions could be held against him. It was a restriction that did not apply to us because we were focused on the company as a whole. So the behaviour and negligence of any number of Grünenthal executives and staff could help us establish the overall negligence of the company.

To succeed in proving Grünenthal's (or Distillers') negligence, we did not have to prove that Grünenthal actually knew there was a risk to the foetus in giving thalidomide to pregnant women. That would be a bonus. It would be enough to show that a reasonable, careful pharmaceutical company, by the standards of the time, *should* have foreseen a risk of harm—even if Grünenthal did not.

So we were looking for warning signs in the Düsseldorf archive. Were there any flashing lights that should have alerted Grünenthal to the potential danger of thalidomide? Were they ignored? Had Grünenthal properly tested the drug? Had Grünenthal responded appropriately to reports of side effects? The answers would emerge during long sessions with the prosecutor's documents.

• • •

There is no doubt that the thalidomide experience scarred Grünenthal. The massive death and injury toll has left a shadow over the company and Grünenthal spent years and vast sums defending the criminal charges against its executives. Even today, fifty years on, Grünenthal is bitterly accused by thalidomide groups of hopelessly negligent behaviour in the 1950s and '60s, followed by a failure to front up to its obligations to victims. These charges are hotly denied by Grünenthal.

To understand the competing views we have to go back to the events that led up to the launch of the drug in 1957. Grünenthal was established immediately after World War II and focused on the booming antibiotics market. In 1954, with the company looking to expand into synthetic drugs, Dr Heinrich Mückter (the former army doctor who did typhus experiments in occupied Poland) set two of his staff, Wilhelm Kunz, a chemist, and Dr Herbert Keller, a pharmacologist, to work developing new antibiotics. The story goes that, as part of this hunt, Kunz heated a commercially available chemical and created a new compound. Its name would be N-Phthalyl glutamic acid imide: more commonly, thalidomide. Keller is said to have thought that the compound appeared to be a 'structural analogue' of the barbiturates, which then dominated the sedative and hypnotic (sleeping pill) market. This apparent similarity persuaded the Grünenthal men to check whether the drug would have a barbiturate-like sleep inducing or sedative effect. Rats were the chosen test subject.

Around this time Grünenthal was developing something of a name for making inflated efficacy and safety claims for its products—including a tuberculosis drug and a variant on penicillin. But the criticism it had attracted appears not to have led to a more cautious approach. Instead Grünenthal charged headlong into a much bigger and vastly more damaging controversy. To test thalidomide Grünenthal used a 'jiggle cage', which in a convoluted fashion tried to measure the amount of movement (or jiggle) in drugged and un-drugged rats. The tests led to a published paper claiming that thalidomide had a pronounced sedative effect on the rats.

This finding has always been somewhat mysterious. Widukind Lenz, the German paediatrician who forced the withdrawal of thalidomide in late 1961, described the jiggle-cage paper as possessing 'so little scientific value' that it should not have been accepted for publication. 'The authors claim to have shown a sleep-inducing effect, though no sleep was observed,' Lenz noted. Other pharmaceutical companies were later unable to replicate thalidomide's claimed sedative effect in animals and wondered what the Grünenthal men had done.

This question mark over the early testing has contributed to some speculation that perhaps the first test subjects were humans, in whom thalidomide certainly does have a sedative effect. Allied with this speculation is a theory that the early testing was done by Nazi doctors during World War II, and that thalidomide later made its way to Grünenthal via one of these doctors. We never saw any persuasive evidence for this theory, which has been given some media coverage in part through the efforts of Martin Johnson, the former director of the UK Thalidomide Trust. Johnson holds firm to this view and has some adherents, but Lyn Rowe's lawyers were not among them. In any event, the questions over the Grünenthal tests are never likely to be resolved as Grünenthal long ago destroyed a large part of its early research.

In the wake of its testing, Grünenthal decided its drug held promise as a rival to the barbiturates as a sedative/sleeping pill. And even better, Grünenthal had the perfect sales pitch for its drug: complete safety. By feeding increasing amounts of a drug to test animals, researchers can establish its lethal dose or, more precisely, its LD50—the dose at which the drug kills fifty per cent of the test animals. The Grünenthal testers found that no matter how much of the drug they forced into test animals it was almost impossible to kill them. Thalidomide thus has a startlingly high LD50, which sparked a very compelling (though horribly wrong) super-safe sales pitch. In a marketplace crowded with barbiturates which carried serious overdose risks and had contributed to an epidemic of accidental deaths and suicides, an 'ultra-safe' sleeping pill held great appeal.

But safely stuffing large amounts of a drug into an animal—or even a human—in one-off experiments proves little. Any medically trained person (then and now) knows that all sorts of side effects can emerge from the long-term use of a drug, even in low doses. This was not a consideration that appeared to cause Grünenthal and Distillers much concern. So keen were they on the safety claims that they later used reports of failed suicide attempts with thalidomide to further ramp up the sales pitch.

Next for Grünenthal after the animal tests were human trials. This has led some critics to observe that it took less than twelve months for Grünenthal to move from invention (or synthesis) of thalidomide to tests in humans, with relatively little animal testing in between. Further criticism arises because the clinical trials on which Grünenthal embarked frequently amounted to small-scale use by doctors, many of them friendly to Grünenthal.

One bizarre—or, to modern eyes, brutally primitive—study took place in Bonn. Dr Konrad Lang treated forty children, many of them brain damaged, over extended periods with extremely high doses of thalidomide: up to twenty times the recommended dose for an adult. None of the children's parents had been informed of the trial. Lang had never before performed pre-market testing on a drug, and he later conceded that his experiments with thalidomide did not amount to a proper trial. No doubt many of the children were effectively sedated by these massive doses. In addition, one child with a congenital heart defect died, a three-month-old baby suffered heart failure and died, and another child temporarily lost her sight. Dr Lang decided that the deaths and other side effects had not been caused by the drug and reported to Grünenthal that thalidomide was a rapid-acting sedative 'particularly suited for children'.

Many reports to Grünenthal from its 'testers' were glowing. Doctors reported a pronounced sedative and hypnotic effect and no hangover. Amid the good news, though, questions emerged. One doctor reported he had dropped the drug because of 'absolute intolerability'. Among the side effects he noted was slight paraesthesia, a tingling or burning sensation often caused by nerve damage. Responding to this report, Grünenthal's Heinrich Mückter conceded in a letter on 3 April 1956 that thalidomide seemed 'a very strong sedative' which if used in high doses over a long period could cause 'disturbance in the nervous system'. Mückter was right about that. Thalidomide would soon damage the nervous systems of many thousands of Germans, in addition to killing and malforming thousands of babies.

Throughout its testing and into the sales period, there were significant gaps in Grünenthal's understanding of thalidomide. Why the drug caused sedation and sleep was simply not known. Grünenthal did not know the details of where in the body thalidomide acted, or how it was broken down and absorbed. Even Keller, one of the inventors, thought that the trials had 'not been very impressive' and the testers had not been 'particularly enthusiastic'. But the uncertainties did not get in the way. Dubious testimonials and commercial ambition would suffice as the drug's launching pad.

Rushing a drug to market had very recently been shown to be a poor idea. In 1953 a French company had started selling a treatment for boils called Stalinon, after grossly inadequate testing. A tin-based compound, Stalinon proved horribly toxic in humans. It caused more than one hundred deaths, most commonly from cardiac or respiratory failure, and many serious injuries. Some survivors suffered after-effects for years. In December 1957 a French court awarded the victims 643 million francs and the pharmacist responsible received a two-year jail sentence. In 1958 an examination of the 'worst disaster ever caused by a drug' found that had Stalinon been properly tested in animals, its toxicity would have been evident and it would never have been trialled in humans. Grünenthal, clearly, was paying insufficient heed to the cautions underlined by the Stalinon events.

In October 1957 Contergan, Grünenthal's main thalidomide product, was launched with a huge splash. Advertisements and pamphlets promoted the drug as completely non-toxic and totally safe. The market was swamped with promotional material. During 1958 alone, Grünenthal placed fifty advertisements for thalidomide in medical journals and sent more than 200,000 letters to doctors, plus further mail-outs to 50,000 doctors and pharmacists. Sales started slowly but Contergan would soon become the success story Grünenthal had been hoping for: by early 1960 it was the best-selling sleeping pill in Germany.

Grünenthal, of course, received some negative reports about the new medication, including dizziness, vomiting and agitation. Some complaints were strident. 'Once and never again,' one Swiss doctor declared. 'This was a horrible preparation.'

But eventually one particular side effect of thalidomide began to stand out. Peripheral neuritis is a condition in which the peripheral nerves are damaged. It usually starts in the hands and feet, and causes numbing, tingling, itching or burning. Peripheral neuritis (also often referred to in various thalidomide documents as polyneuritis or neuropathy) can vary in seriousness and persistence, but at its most extreme it is an agonising torment. Thalidomide, it became clear, could cause a horrible brand of peripheral neuritis. There was no effective treatment and much of the damage persisted for long periods. Sometimes it was permanent.

It was this nerve-damage side effect, not the capacity of the drug to harm foetuses, which came to light first and it did so in great numbers. Grünenthal later estimated the number of nerve-damage victims in Germany at four thousand—a gross underestimate but still a terrible toll. Others have put the figure many times higher.

Many doctors argued that the nerve damage alone justified the removal of thalidomide from sale. The injuries were serious and the drug was, after all, only a sedative or sleeping pill: there was no shortage of alternatives available. Yet Grünenthal's response to the nerve-damage reports, detailed later, was to suppress, spy, deny, lie and mislead.

But a revelation far worse than nerve damage lay ahead. Thalidomide was wreaking havoc on unborn babies in Germany, Spain, Brazil, Syria, Australia, New Zealand, Canada, Japan, Sweden, Ireland, the United Kingdom, Norway, Italy and many other countries across the world.

CHAPTER 5

Maybe the Idiots Are Happy

By the time Grünenthal launched thalidomide in 1957 there had been at least one unintended test on a pregnant woman. Some of Grünenthal's staff had sampled the drug, and the first known victim was born on Christmas Day 1956 to the wife of an employee. This was nine months before the drug went on sale. The baby girl was born without ears, usually a rare malformation, but one commonly caused by thalidomide. Predictably, given their easy access to the drug and belief in the company's safety propaganda, Grünenthal families suffered disproportionately. At least six and possibly many more babies born to Grünenthal families were damaged by the drug. But this spate of malformations was apparently never noticed, or looked for, or remarked upon by anyone at Grünenthal.

It later emerged that Grünenthal had not bothered to test thalidomide on pregnant animals before putting it on the market, nor at any time when it was on the market. To this day Grünenthal insists that such testing was neither required nor of any real utility at that time. (This claim, which does not bear scrutiny, is dealt with in chapter 11.)

Grünenthal has also long argued that nothing about thalidomide warranted concern about its effect on the foetus. But this claim was undermined by one of the first documents we found in the Düsseldorf trial archive: a senior Grünenthal doctor had been sufficiently concerned, even before thalidomide went on sale, to ask for its effect in pregnancy to be checked.

On 5 July 1957, three months before thalidomide's launch, a Grünenthal doctor who later faced criminal charges over thalidomide wrote to Professor Harald Siebke, the professor of gynaecology at the University Women's Clinic in Bonn. The clinic had previously investigated the safety of various medications in pregnancy, and Grünenthal wanted Siebke to test thalidomide. 'Even though I work in the industry,' the Grünenthal executive wrote,

> I personally believe that sleep disturbances in pregnant women should first be treated with domestic remedies, cold leg compresses, but if this therapy fails to work the issue of an effective and non-hazardous sedative is left unresolved... What I would like to ask you, dear Professor, is whether it would be possible that as part of your studies on sleep medications used by pregnant women, you could also examine [thalidomide] at some point.

Siebke never responded and Grünenthal dropped the issue. The meaning of the letter was much debated in the lead-up to the German criminal trial of Grünenthal executives. But even on the narrowest possible reading, the letter establishes this: before thalidomide went on sale a senior Grünenthal man knew that pregnant women suffering insomnia should only be medicated as a last resort, and then only with an 'effective and non-hazardous sedative'.

With an unresolved question hanging over the safety of thalidomide in pregnancy, Grünenthal might have hesitated in pushing the drug in that market. It might also have rethought its failure to test in animal pregnancy. But pregnant women were a glittering sales opportunity. Dr Augustin Blasiu had used thalidomide in his Munich obstetric and gynaecological practice at Grünenthal's request, and so Grünenthal encouraged him to write an article. On 2 May 1958, 'Experiences with Contergan in Gynaecology' was published in a German medical journal. It concluded that thalidomide was an effective sedative for breastfeeding mothers. So far, so good. But Blasiu had made certain not to give thalidomide to a single pregnant woman. 'It is my fundamental outlook never to give mothers-to-be sleep drugs or sedatives,' he later told German authorities. 'It is an old fact of experience in medicine that, fundamentally, mothers-to-be are not to be given barbiturates, opiates, sedatives or hypnotics because these substances can affect foetuses.'

Sadly, Blasiu's caution did not register with Grünenthal. On 1 August 1958 it sent extracts of Blasiu's report plus a covering letter to 40,245 German doctors, encouraging the false inference that Blasiu had used thalidomide in pregnancy and it had been 'harmless to mother and baby':

> Dear Doctor, during pregnancy and lactation, the female organism is subject to particular stresses. Sleeplessness, inner unrest and tiredness are recurring complaints. It is therefore often necessary to prescribe a sedative and hypnotic which is harmless to mother and baby.

Blasiu himself was appalled when the prosecution team showed him the Grünenthal letter in 1964. 'From the contents one would have to assume that I had [used]…Contergan during pregnancy and breastfeeding, because it harms neither the mother nor the child. As already mentioned, this is not the case…I regard this letter of the company to the medical profession as unfair, misleading and irresponsible.'

In 1959, the year after the Blasiu article appeared, Grünenthal was presented with a golden opportunity to stop the mounting tragedy in its tracks. Dr K lived in a small town on the Rhine only about an hour's drive from Grünenthal HQ in Stolberg. He had started prescribing thalidomide in 1957. In August 1958 Dr K told a Grünenthal sales rep that thalidomide was causing difficulties with walking in some patients. Perhaps it was this negative experience with the drug that led to his suspicions when his son was born in March 1959 with damaged ears and eye problems. His wife had been taking Contergan during early pregnancy. 'There were no [genetic] injuries on either side of the family. This prompted me to think that Contergan might be responsible for the deformities. I discussed these thoughts at length with my wife.'

Dr K also discussed his suspicion about thalidomide in 'great detail' with a friend of his, a doctor who worked as a sales rep for Grünenthal. This Grünenthal doctor, Dr K said, 'always explained [to me] that he just could not imagine thalidomide causing these type of injuries'. Adding to Dr K's concerns was that two more of his patients who had taken Contergan gave birth during 1959 to malformed babies. The Grünenthal doctor was also interviewed by the prosecutor. He said he had not passed Dr K's concerns to his superiors at the company because he did not regard the birth damage connection 'as being so probable that I should have reported [it]'.

Had Grünenthal and its staff been more concerned or vigilant an investigation would have been straightforward. Dr K could have been questioned and his three cases examined in detail. Grünenthal's doctors could have visited maternity hospitals and asked whether there had been any spike in malformations. Obstetricians could have been consulted. Animal tests could have been conducted. None of that was done. Instead, Grünenthal carried on promoting the drug as useful and safe in pregnancy and the number of victims quickly grew.

In early 1959 Dr S fell pregnant with her second child. She asked a doctor working for Grünenthal whether she could take Contergan during pregnancy. 'I asked this because I had been suspicious of any medication during pregnancy, in particular during early pregnancy.' The Grünenthal doctor answered with the standard pitch about thalidomide being completely harmless. In January 1960 Dr S's child was born with malformations of the nose, lips, ears, hands and feet.

Dr S was just one of many doctors reassured by Grünenthal's soothing promises about thalidomide and pregnancy. Another doctor's wife had a baby with shortened arms after her husband was told by Grünenthal that the medication would be perfectly safe if taken during pregnancy. Later the woman pressed for a divorce, accusing her doctor husband of having been too gullible.

In Munich, Mrs H fell pregnant in October 1960 and her husband, a GP, asked a Grünenthal sales rep if he could safely give his wife Contergan. The response was boilerplate. 'Contergan [is] totally non-dangerous and frequently prescribed especially during pregnancies.' In July 1961, Mrs H gave birth to a severely malformed baby. Her GP husband believed Contergan was to blame. When he spoke with the prosecutor in 1963 he said he thought he had made his suspicions clear to a Grünenthal sales rep after the July 1961 birth but could not recall the rep's name.

In the eyes of many, Grünenthal's assurances about the safety of thalidomide in pregnancy make a mockery of its insistence that it acted properly by the standards of the time. It had never tested the drug in pregnancy or checked on babies whose mothers had used the drug. Yet it proclaimed the drug completely safe for the unborn child.

This, though, is only a small part of Grünenthal's failure. During the very period it was promoting the drug to pregnant women as incapable of causing harm, it was dealing with a growing surge of nerve-damage reports. The first reports of possible nerve damage turned up in trials as early as 1956. In 1958 and 1959 there were further reports of mild nerve damage, but in late 1959 the trickle of reports started to rapidly gather pace.

Grünenthal would learn its wonder drug was causing severe itching and burning plus associated side effects such as unsteadiness while walking. Some victims were so tormented they considered suicide. Whatever testing Grünenthal had done pre-sale, it must have been clear to the company now that it had not turned up all of the drug's side effects. Thalidomide was obviously not as safe as Grünenthal claimed—in fact it could be downright dangerous. And the drug had always been something of a mystery: how it worked was not clear and how it caused nerve damage was not understood either. Yet the escalating nerve-damage reports had little or no impact on the way thalidomide was pushed by Grünenthal.

Grünenthal's shocking behaviour in relation to nerve damage was all set down in black and white. In Düsseldorf we found a mountain of documents compiled for the criminal trial of the Grünenthal executives which had to be studied to be believed. The material, which reads like fiction, shows Grünenthal lying, hiring private detectives to keep tabs on thalidomide critics, deceiving its business partners, misleading doctors, staring down increasingly hysterical warnings from its own lawyers, and refusing to the bitter end to issue adequate safety warnings with its drug.

It's a mark of how appalling the behaviour was that Grünenthal, never inclined to self-flagellation over thalidomide, admits that the criminal court in 1971 found 'misconduct' in Grünenthal's handling of the nerve-damage issue. But misconduct is only part of the story. Even though the criminal prosecution of the Grünenthal men was dropped after the trial had run for more than two years, the judges issued a decision stating that had the trial continued to a formal verdict it was unlikely that the Grünenthal defendants would have been acquitted. Further, 'the overall behaviour [Grünenthal] presented towards the outside world did not meet the standard required of a diligent and conscientious drug manufacturer'. In fact, Grünenthal's behaviour did not come close to the expected standard. The deviation was 'considerable', the judges remarked.

• • •

In April 1961, the head of Grünenthal's Hamburg sales office, Arthur Tachezy, made a sales visit to a hospital with a psychiatric wing. By this time, Tachezy knew that thalidomide was causing widespread nerve damage. And, as Tachezy expected, there were multiple complaints about thalidomide on the general medical wards. But surprisingly, there was no reported nerve damage on the psychiatric wing, despite the patients consuming 'huge' quantities of thalidomide. Tachezy seemed to find this apparent failure to report nerve damage amusing. In a letter to his bosses at Grünenthal HQ, he speculated that the psychiatric patients were too disturbed to realise they were being damaged by thalidomide. 'Maybe,' he concluded, 'the idiots are happy when there's tingling!'

Tachezy was not the only employee blinded by zealotry. Another sales rep in Cologne, Dr Göden, reported to his bosses in February 1961 that when the subject of thalidomide and nerve damage arose at a neurological clinic his main aim had been to 'cause confusion'. Dr Göden was quite the character. In December 1960 he had suggested that Grünenthal consider combining thalidomide with other ingredients to make it possible to blame nerve damage on the other components. 'However, beware if this commendable intention should backfire at any stage!'

Later, the legal team prosecuting the Grünenthal executives did its best to add up the individual cases of nerve damage known to have been reported to Grünenthal. By the end of February 1961 Grünenthal had received more than four hundred reports, from at least 120 doctors or pharmacists, among them many professors and specialists. The numbers continued to soar. By the end of 1961, on the prosecution's count, Grünenthal had received around 2500 reports of nerve damage and complaints from about nine hundred doctors and pharmacists.

Neurologist Ralf Voss, who would become a persistent critic of the company, reported a nerve-damage case to Grünenthal in October 1959. Voss decided the next month that thalidomide had a toxic effect on nerves, and in April 1960 gave a lecture at a medical conference concerning the dangers of the drug. Obviously the issue was serious. Grünenthal HQ sent a memo to its sales representatives on 17 May 1960 noting the 'severity of side effects' and admitting ignorance about how thalidomide caused nerve damage.

But even while it was starting to privately acknowledge the scale of the problem, Grünenthal was perfectly happy to deceive its licence partners. In July 1960 it started negotiations to supply German firm Kali-Chemie with thalidomide for use in a non-competing product, a cough medicine. The two firms reached an agreement in January 1961. Throughout the six-month negotiation, Grünenthal kept Kali-Chemie in the dark about nerve damage, despite the reports flooding into Grünenthal HQ. Once the deal was done, Kali-Chemie put its own thalidomide product on the market, only to hastily withdraw it when thalidomide's responsibility for birth damage came to light in November 1961. In February 1962, when some of the details of Grünenthal's behaviour started to emerge publicly, a Kali-Chemie executive wrote a furious letter to Grünenthal threatening legal action. It was incomprehensible, he fumed, that Kali-Chemie had not been told about nerve damage during the contract negotiations two years earlier.

Grünenthal considered the accusation and admitted in an internal memorandum that it had deceived its business partner. That deception, Grünenthal confessed privately, 'now exposes us to the accusation of fraudulent intent'. Fraudulent intent was not all. Grünenthal had seen itself as at war for its key thalidomide drug Contergan. 'We will fight for C to the last, with all measures,' one Grünenthal man said.

Grünenthal was also doing its best to block negative publicity. In October 1960 two Grünenthal men paid a visit to a neurologist, Dr Horst Frenkel. They tried to persuade him to withdraw a manuscript detailing thalidomide nerve damage which he had submitted to the medical journal *Die Medizinische Welt*. Frenkel refused, telling Grünenthal he had seen more than twenty nerve-damage cases in his clinic. Grünenthal then went to work on the magazine's editor, trying to prevent or delay publication and criticising Frenkel's work as unscientific. 'The friendly connection with [the editor] contributed to the delay in treatment of the manuscript,' Grünenthal bragged internally.

But the bad news kept pouring in. In November 1960 a Grünenthal report noted side effects on a 'massive scale' and the Frankfurt sales office begged for more information, reporting that 'we are completely helpless and do not have a clue as to what is actually happening'. From Hamburg came a report that Contergan had been labelled 'devil's stuff' by several doctors.

The reported nerve damage was bad enough. But Grünenthal must have known that it was dealing with only the tip—or at best a chunk—of the iceberg. Not all doctors reported the side effects they observed and many doctors saw nerve-damage patients without connecting it to thalidomide. Grünenthal's Düsseldorf sales office admitted as much in a December 1960 memo. 'Do we actually really know how many side effects have been caused by Contergan?' the author asked. 'We do have to ask how many patients there are who have as yet not been identified as damaged.'

Then in late 1960, with the nerve-damage issue boiling away, Grünenthal was again told of a possible link between thalidomide and birth damage. Friedrich Koch, who lived in a small town in north-west Germany, had been a pharmacist for more than thirty years. He had always been careful about selling drugs to pregnant women because, as he put it, the female body was particularly sensitive during pregnancy. But because Contergan was billed as completely harmless he was happy to provide it to customers repeatedly and without prescription.

In October 1960 one customer who had been taking Contergan gave birth to a baby with internal malformations. 'Her husband had taken it into his head that [the malformations] might be connected to Contergan,' Koch later told the German prosecutor. Koch thought the connection was possible. After all, he reasoned, drugs were capable of affecting the foetus and thalidomide was a new medication with a new chemical composition.

So, on 24 November 1960, Koch wrote to Grünenthal. He described the damage to the baby and asked Grünenthal if Contergan, taken regularly in pregnancy, might harm the foetus. Grünenthal wasted no time in responding.

'Dear Mr Pharmacist,' the Grünenthal letter dated 2 December 1960 read:

> Based on all observations and findings on hand to date, in particular from gynaecological departments, we can negate any causal connection [between Contergan and birth injuries]. To date, not a single indication exists at all to suggest that

a human or animal—irrespective of age—could suffer any form of liver damage through Contergan. We therefore feel safe in assuming that the liver damage diagnosed shortly after the birth of the baby you are referring to is not to be connected with the mother's Contergan use.

One of the many startling things about this letter is the ease and speed with which Grünenthal dismissed Koch's concerns. Grünenthal had done no tests on pregnant animals, and had not investigated the effect of the drug on a foetus in human pregnancy. It did not ask Koch further questions, and did not seek to visit the family or examine the mother's medical records or, apparently, consult experts. It did not approach maternity hospitals and ask if there had been any increase in the rate of birth malformations, even malformations similar to those reported by Koch. Instead Grünenthal simply told Koch that thalidomide could not have damaged the baby. End of story.

Koch was reassured by Grünenthal's response, but was distressed a year later when the drug's shocking effect became public. Perhaps, he thought, Grünenthal had never investigated the possible effect of Contergan on the foetus. 'This would mean that my letter would have been written in vain,' he sadly complained.

Indeed, Koch's letter *had* been written in vain. Another warning had been missed. It seemed to us, in Lyn Rowe's team, another piece of remarkable Grünenthal negligence. Of course it was not difficult to imagine what Grünenthal would say. It was one isolated report, and not even from a doctor, the argument would run. Was Grünenthal supposed to jump to attention in response to every inquiry, no matter how far-fetched or medically dubious?

And the response would be this: it's hard to imagine a more serious potential side effect than maiming a foetus. Such a report—by an experienced pharmacist—demanded to be taken seriously. Especially by a company that had never checked the effect of its drug on the foetus, knew the foetus was vulnerable to chemical insult, and knew (and intended) that its drug was widely used by pregnant women. And then there is the context. Koch's letter was not a single storm cloud in an otherwise perfectly blue sky. The drug was doing serious damage to the nerves of some of the people taking it. Grünenthal did not properly understand how the drug worked or why some users were damaged and others were not. How then could Grünenthal be so sure it could not damage unborn people? Wasn't it possible that it might attack nerves in a foetus, or cause damage in other unknown ways?

In London, Distillers had also been receiving reports of nerve damage—but only a relative handful. Unlike Grünenthal, Distillers quickly accepted this was a toxic manifestation of the drug and it claims to have added a warning about nerve damage to its packaging in about August 1960. Distillers did not know of the flood of German reports. Nor did Grünenthal's US licensee, Richardson-Merrell. Grünenthal was keeping its business partners in the dark.

Grünenthal finally told Distillers about nerve damage on 4 November 1960, but in a deceptive fashion. It advised that 'in rare cases' there had been 'nerve responses' to thalidomide that quickly cleared up when the drug was withdrawn. Distillers accepted this at face value and wrote back, volunteering that it knew of only seven nerve-damage cases.

At this time, though, another thalidomide issue was causing Distillers greater concern than nerve damage. Distillers had been planning to follow Grünenthal's lead and introduce a liquid version of the drug. In Germany 'Contergan Saft' (Contergan juice) had become enormously popular for use on children, so much so that it was sometimes referred to as cinema juice (Kinosaft), a reference to parents sedating children while they went to the movies.

In preparation for the introduction of a liquid version, Distillers' pharmacologist George Somers had been doing animal tests with thalidomide dissolved in a sugar solution. What he found disturbed him: the liquid version was far more toxic than the tablet version and could kill mice. Somers began to worry that it might be capable of killing children too. 'We are of the opinion that there is a very real danger of deaths occurring following overdosage,' he wrote in one internal report.

Somers became opposed to Distillers marketing the mixture. A lengthy internal debate ensued; Grünenthal was drawn into the argument and its scientists disputed Somers' findings. Grünenthal was in no doubt: Somers' results were putting the entire 'extreme safety' marketing pitch for thalidomide at risk. In February 1961 Somers went to Germany for two days of discussions. Grünenthal produced the results of tests in which the liquid had not been fatal to mice and told Somers about 'a substantial number' of German children who had consumed an entire bottle of the thalidomide liquid but recovered uneventfully. This seemed to reassure Somers. He accepted that his worrying results had been caused by a 'difference in sensitivity between the English and German mice'.

Grünenthal's determination to stick to its claims of complete safety should have triggered concern or suspicion at Distillers. Had Distillers been even half-alert it would also have suspected that Grünenthal was withholding information about the extent of the nerve-damage problem. Grünenthal simply could not be trusted to tell the truth about thalidomide.

CHAPTER 6

A Very Real Fear

On any reasonable interpretation, 1961 was a truly disgraceful year for Grünenthal. In the face of an avalanche of warning signs, it fought furiously on multiple fronts to defend thalidomide. The fight was so excessive and so appalling that it later landed some of the company's most senior executives and scientists in court on criminal charges, including negligent manslaughter.

The year began with Grünenthal dreaming of vast riches through US sales of thalidomide. Just twelve months later that dream had vanished, the drug permanently etched in history as the cause of an unprecedented epidemic of infant death and injury. In November 1961 Grünenthal grudgingly withdrew the drug from sale—a move forced on the company by German paediatrician Widukind Lenz, who had finally connected the rocketing number of seriously malformed German babies to Grünenthal's super-safe sleeping pill. But, as the documents in Düsseldorf and elsewhere illuminate, the drug should have been withdrawn long before Lenz arrived on the scene.

In January 1961 two Grünenthal executives travelled to East Berlin to try to arrange for the sale of thalidomide products in the communist east. Crossing from east to west was still relatively easy—the Berlin Wall would not go up until later that year—but the trip was a failure. The East German health authorities refused point blank to allow the sale of thalidomide: it was not a vital drug, and the reports of nerve damage demonstrated it was not as harmless as claimed. And there was another factor: the East Germans believed that the chemical structure of the thalidomide compound 'might [cause] unexpected effects when taken long-term'.

The East Germans were very wise. Across the border the drug was exacting a heavy toll. In April 1961 Grünenthal learned that one thalidomide victim had finished up in a psychiatric hospital after being tormented by severe nerve damage. Grünenthal was also nursing a belief that rival drug companies were collecting nerve-injury cases and using them to damage thalidomide sales. A private detective named Ernst Jahnke was hired and told to investigate thalidomide critics. The detective enthusiastically got to work, using a pretext to check visitor books at rival pharmaceutical manufacturer Bayer. Bingo! He reported to Grünenthal that a number of Contergan critics, including the neurologist Voss, had visited Bayer. The detective began planning checks at Merck, Ciba and Schering. In March 1961, Jahnke told Grünenthal he was eighty-five per cent certain that Bayer was behind the campaign against Contergan. It is hard not to see this nonsensical conspiracy theory as a farce. Later, even Grünenthal's private eye reported that doctor anger, not commercial envy, was driving the campaign against thalidomide.

During this whole period, the fact that Contergan was freely available over the counter was a boon for sales. Grünenthal regularly—in private—discussed means of preventing a prescription requirement being forced on the drug. And it was not until the German spring of 1961, amid increasing complaints about the unrestricted sale and damaging side effects, that Grünenthal began desultory efforts to have Contergan put on prescription.

The company moved slowly and grudgingly towards regulation, knowing that sales could only suffer. As one observer later put it, Grünenthal wanted to appear 'conscientious without losing its profitable market share'.

Meanwhile, Grünenthal's public relations efforts continued. A February 1961 company report stated that efforts to 'delay and [make] changes to negative publications about Contergan have continued very intensively'. In March 1961 Grünenthal learned that an influential physician in Bonn had banned the use of Contergan at his clinic. 'The situation is serious, as the Contergan ban will certainly spread,' the internal Grünenthal report concluded.

As the nerve-damage toll grew, so too did the queries over thalidomide and pregnancy. In the United States in February 1961, a scientist at one of Grünenthal's licence partners, the US firm Richardson-Merrell, had what would turn out to be a grimly ironic idea: maybe thalidomide could stop women miscarrying their babies. The scientist wrote that thalidomide's sedative effect might calm women who became 'emotional about their pregnancies' and miscarried as a consequence. These 'habitual aborters' could be another lucrative market for the drug. If that were the case, the scientist continued, the drug had to be further evaluated and 'studies in pregnant rats, etc need all to be considered'.

Marketing thalidomide to pregnant women wanting to preserve their babies was in hindsight not the greatest idea of the century, but the call for studies in pregnant rats was sensible. A memo was sent to Grünenthal with a query: 'Do you have any kind of experiences with Contergan in women who have suffered repeated premature pregnancy losses?'

Grünenthal considered the matter. It knew that pregnant women were being given thalidomide. It knew it had not done 'studies in pregnant rats, etc' or any other checks in pregnancy. On 23 March 1961, Grünenthal responded that it had no information on Contergan and pregnancy or whether the drug reached the foetus. 'Animal experiments on the question of the transfer of Contergan to the foetus are perhaps very useful, although, based on everything we know from animal experiments to date, we do not wish to assume that there is any impact on the foetus.'

Here was the Grünenthal team forced to confront the issue of what thalidomide might do to a foetus. Grünenthal's conclusion? *We don't know and we are not making any assumptions.*

Not everyone was as uninterested. In March 1961 Professor Fritz Kemper of Münster University asked Grünenthal for some thalidomide for animal experiments. By October 1961 Kemper had concluded that thalidomide interfered in the sexual function of chicks by blocking their absorption of folic acid. He thought that if thalidomide had that effect in humans it might explain the nerve damage, as one known cause of nerve damage was drugs that inhibited vitamin absorption. Kemper discussed his work with Grünenthal and then began work on the effect of thalidomide on the foetus, using chick eggs for his experiments. Kemper found malformed chick embryos, though this finding was made after the drug had been withdrawn from sale in November 1961. Grünenthal, defending the criminal prosecution, dismissed Kemper's chick malformations as irrelevant. Many safe drugs, it asserted, given in similar massive doses would also have caused malformations.

Yet Kemper's work is important because that exact train of inquiry was open to Grünenthal at any time. As the archive documents demonstrated, its staff—like Kemper—had independently suspected that thalidomide might have a vitamin-blocking effect, and vitamin deficiencies were a known cause of birth defects.

• • •

Some basic medical concepts appeared foreign to Grünenthal, including the fact that thalidomide would certainly pass the placenta and reach the foetus. As other scientists at the time knew, molecules with a molecular weight of less than 1000 were believed to pass the placental barrier and reach the foetus. Thalidomide has a molecular weight of 258, meaning, as one scientist later testified, that it was 'obvious' thalidomide would reach the foetus. But when a gynae-cologist questioned Grünenthal about this in July 1961, the response was that there 'is no indication that Contergan crosses the [placental] barrier to the foetus'. (In preparation for the later criminal trial the Grünenthal men changed tack and claimed they had always known thalidomide would reach the foetus, and that any earlier statement to the contrary was a misunderstanding.) On 14 July 1961 Heinrich Mückter, belatedly and only briefly, appeared to see the thalidomide debacle for what it was. 'If I were a physician, I could not now prescribe Contergan,' he told colleagues.

In the same month, July 1961, far away in Australia Wendy Rowe had begun taking the thalidomide tablets that would render her unborn daughter limbless.

Consider Grünenthal's position at this point: the torrent of severe nerve injuries, the questions about malformations and pregnancy, the protests by doctors, the company's professed ignorance about what effect the drug might have on a foetus, the lack of pregnancy testing. Why on earth was the drug still on the market?

And what might Wendy Rowe have thought if she'd known of the sobering news sent to Grünenthal bosses by Arthur Tachezy (the sales rep who had mocked psychiatric patients as idiots)? In May 1961 Tachezy told his superiors that even Grünenthal employees were now refusing to use thalidomide drugs. '[A] very real fear of side effects has set in which has even led to a rejection of the product when it comes to use within [staff] families.'

Obviously Wendy Rowe would have been concerned had she known about this, and even more so had she known the full story of the escalating German thalidomide debacle. Many others might have been concerned too, including Wendy's doctor—any doctor—health authorities and Grünenthal's licence partners. The problem was that only Grünenthal was in full possession of the facts, and it was not budging. In fact Grünenthal was doing its best to keep the true story under wraps. Worse, thalidomide was still being promoted around the world as an exceptionally safe medication.

• • •

In late June 1961, at almost exactly the same moment Wendy Rowe was taking her thalidomide pills, Inge Eisenberg took her baby boy to a doctor in Cologne, Germany. Joachim was sleeping badly and was becoming agitated. The doctor recommended Contergan Saft, the liquid version of thalidomide intended especially for children. And take some yourself, the doctor told Inge, it will help you sleep.

Inge Eisenberg took just one teaspoon. It made her feel numb and sick, and her husband Hans poured the rest of the bottle down the toilet. Eisenberg did not know she was newly pregnant with her second child but that solitary teaspoon of Contergan Saft was enough to severely damage the embryo inside her. Eight months later, in February 1962, Monika Eisenberg was born. Her left arm was short and her left hand had four fingers and no thumb. Her right hand had five fingers but no thumb. Both hips were profoundly damaged, making it impossible for Monika to crawl or walk as a baby. Her shoulders and back were also malformed.

In late 2012 I spent a day with Monika Eisenberg in Aachen, home to Grünenthal's global headquarters. Eisenberg, known to her friends and family as Moni, lived in Belgium just across the border from Aachen, and was deeply engaged in thalidomide activism. She met her husband Rainer when he volunteered to help at a hunger strike by thalidomide survivors. Eisenberg's brother Joachim married another of Germany's several thousand survivors of the drug. When Moni and Rainer offered to give me a tour of Grünenthal's local history, I accepted gratefully.

On the outskirts of Aachen, we found Grünenthal's bright, shining corporate offices and production facilities. These replaced Grünenthal's headquarters during the thalidomide era, a decaying gothic complex nearby. Visiting the modern factory, we found bright pink banners bearing the English words 'Made in Grünenthal—Successful in the World'. Eisenberg, whose warmth and easygoing manner can give way to outrage and disgust when Grünenthal enters the conversation, suggested I photograph her in front of the banner. 'After all, I'm made by Grünenthal, or at least parts of me are. And I hope I've been successful in the world.'

Moni and Rainer also drove me to Stolberg, just east of Aachen, where we walked around the attractive but economically depressed town. The old Grünenthal factory, spectacularly grim and foreboding, looks like a deserted movie set. Not far away, the Wirtz family's imposing stone compound, where some members of the founding Grünenthal family still live, warrants its own tourism plaque installed by the local authority. When we visited there was no security in sight, but Eisenberg has often been asked to move on when showing other guests around.

Close by is the Stolberg library, where a statue of a thalidomide survivor stands in the foyer. It was at the unveiling of the statue in 2012 that Grünenthal chief executive Harald Stock offered his 'apology'. Eisenberg was in Greece and was surprised and pleased when she heard about the apology. But then she found the text of Stock's comments on the internet. 'It was pure bullshit. Grünenthal was sorry for being quiet, for being in shock. Grünenthal didn't express any remorse or apologise properly,' Eisenberg said. 'Anyway I don't want an apology. What I really want is revenge. Grünenthal damaged my body, damaged my family, damaged thousands of others and killed thousands of babies. We survivors live with pain. Pain in our bodies and pain in our souls.'

Like many mothers of thalidomiders, Inge Eisenberg was traumatised and shocked by her daughter's birth. 'The birth is usually a special moment of bonding,' Moni Eisenberg said. 'Mother Nature does everything to create a strong connection. But my mother and many other mothers could not feel it. My mother was in complete shock. She was functional but numb and it took her a few months until she could even talk about the situation.'

Because there were so many thalidomide children in Germany, all close to the same age, special facilities were established and Moni Eisenberg was able to receive medical attention and therapy during the school day. Later she trained as a teacher and then also as a family therapist and social worker. Years of treatment and therapy allow her to walk well, although not without pain. When I visited she was commuting weekly between her home in Belgium and her job as a social worker in Cologne.

In about 1972, when she was ten years old, Eisenberg began receiving an annual payment from the compensation fund established by the German Government and Grünenthal. 'It was a pittance. Almost useless.' In 2013, the German Government put more money into the fund, substantially raising the pensions. 'It's better now but still not enough,' Eisenberg said.

Grünenthal didn't contribute a single euro to the new pensions. Instead Grünenthal has set up its own fund which they say is for one-off special needs. So if you need an electric toothbrush because your arms don't work you can go to Grünenthal and fill in forms and beg—that's what I call it, begging—and if you're successful they'll give you an electric toothbrush.

Eisenberg's scorn is complete. 'Grünenthal is rich and so is the Wirtz family. They should put more money into pensions for the people their precious drug maimed. Not toothbrushes.'

Eisenberg has spent some time at the Düsseldorf archive looking at Grünenthal's internal documents and is appalled at what she read. 'It did not have to happen to me or many others. All the nerve damage was bad enough. But then there were people telling Grünenthal about the damage to babies.'

A few years ago Eisenberg made contact with the son of Heinrich Mückter, the Grünenthal doctor who was paid a percentage of thalidomide sales and was charged with criminal offences over his thalidomide conduct. Mückter's son, Harald, was a highly regarded toxicologist at a leading German research institute. 'We met three or four times, and kept in contact via email afterwards,' Eisenberg said. The meetings were emotionally charged for both of them, and Eisenberg and Mückter agreed to keep the content of their discussions private. 'But it was a good experience for me. I have always felt anger at Heinrich Mückter [who died in 1987] because as much as anyone he was responsible for the way I was born. But his son Harald Mückter is a very nice man, extraordinarily nice, very decent. It was a good experience for me, to meet him and find him so supportive.'

These days, when Eisenberg hears about the death of a German thalidomider she takes flowers to Grünenthal's front gate. 'The security guards recognise me, and at first the flowers were removed straight away. But the last time a security man gave me water for the flowers.' Eisenberg makes these flower trips in part to 'shame Grünenthal at their home, in public', she says.

> They have to know we are still here and the public has to know that too. People are scared of Grünenthal, especially journalists, and that's why there's not much said in Germany about Grünenthal's treatment of us or the way they handled the drug. When I was a child I was scared too. But now I'm just furious. If Grünenthal can get away with how they have acted in the case of Contergan then there are really no boundaries between right and wrong.

● ● ●

Grünenthal's determination to protect its drug in 1961 meant that something or someone extraordinary was going to have to intervene. And that intervention, by the extraordinary German doctor Widukind Lenz, was still five months away when Wendy Rowe and Inge Eisenberg were unwittingly exposing their babies to Grünenthal's poison. In the months afterwards, as Grünenthal proceeded on its grim and determined way, several thousand German babies and many others around the world joined the death and malformation toll.

On 5 July 1961 the nerve-damage situation was dire enough for Grünenthal's internal lawyers to produce a long memo agonising over its insurance coverage. It predicted the insurer would blame Grünenthal for the whole problem, and try to limit any insurance payout.

For the members of Lyn Rowe's legal team, seeing this internal legal advice was remarkable. As lawyers you never get to see the other side's legal advice. Plaintiff lawyers often wonder what the defendant's lawyers are saying in private to their client. We speculate but we never know. Yet in the Düsseldorf archive there was a pile of 1960s memos by Grünenthal's legal department written before and after thalidomide was withdrawn from sale. This was as unexpected as it was hard to believe. It felt like eavesdropping to read the translated documents and learn what Grünenthal's lawyers had said in private.

In short, the lawyers were extremely critical of their own company. In July 1961, with the drug still a bestseller, Grünenthal's legal department warned that Grünenthal may not have done sufficient animal testing with thalidomide, and that a caution about nerve damage should have been put on the medication from May 1960. Calling thalidomide 'safely effective' and 'non-toxic' had been ill-advised, the lawyers said, and so too was implying that nerve damage would clear up when thalidomide use ceased. The legal department was perfectly clear about Grünenthal's prospects when faced with a claim by a nerve-damage victim. 'Under these circumstances it does not seem justifiable to conduct a trial in this matter.' The cases should be settled, the lawyers advised. And so they were: that month the first payment was made to a nerve-damage victim, and by the end of September another twelve cases had been settled.

Grünenthal's legal department was now ringing the alarm bell loud and clear and repeatedly. Another memo in August 1961 described the thalidomide situation as 'dangerous and uncomfortable'. Unbelievably, in the midst of all this internal handwringing, Grünenthal had still not ensured that all doctors had been told that nerve damage even existed. 'Up to now doctors abroad have not been informed about the side effects of Contergan in any form,' an internal memo on 10 August 1961 admitted. 'Various European countries still have brochures with the wording "completely atoxic". Immediate change necessary.' Grünenthal's ceaseless thalidomide promotion was increasingly angering the medical profession. 'The only thing that makes sense is: Get rid of Contergan!' one doctor who was suffering from nerve damage wrote to Grünenthal in September 1961.

By the next month, October 1961, Grünenthal was facing almost one hundred legal claims over nerve damage, and its lawyers were warning that a legal misstep 'would indeed unleash an avalanche coming at us'. Yet, despite the alarm at Grünenthal, the drug was still being widely prescribed across Germany and was also freely available over the counter in seven German states. And the mountain of damning reports and acute legal danger did not slow the fiction pouring out of company HQ. On 17 November 1961, Grünenthal wrote to a doctor advising that it was 'unlikely' that his patient's nerve damage had been caused by Contergan. 'We have never heard of any such complaints before.' When one of the prosecutors read this document years later, he was so shocked he scribbled 'unbelievable!' in the margin.

One wonders how the management of a modern pharmaceutical company would react in a similar situation: a flood of serious injuries, lawsuits, highly critical journal publications, a revolt in the medical profession and increasingly damning indictments from the company's own lawyers. With panic, anxiety and terror presumably. Not so for Grünenthal's hard men. By now they were seasoned veterans of the thalidomide campaign and unshaken in their determination to keep the product on the market.

• • •

The United States was spared a major thalidomide catastrophe, as we'll see in chapter 8, because an astute and courageous FDA doctor, Frances Kelsey, read about nerve-damage reports in a medical journal in early 1961 and became suspicious about the drug. One of her concerns was that thalidomide could conceivably harm a vulnerable and growing foetus. Kelsey was operating on the basis of sketchy reports. In contrast, Grünenthal was at the coalface: it knew of literally hundreds of reports of serious nerve damage, and its staff had heard about birth damage potentially connected to the drug. Yet Grünenthal was deeply reluctant to take the Kelsey question seriously: what might this toxic drug do to a foetus?

Grünenthal had repeated opportunities to front up to the foetus issue. Another one came and went in July 1961 when Grünenthal received three critical questions about thalidomide from a Finnish doctor. The first: if thalidomide is given to pregnant patients, does it cross the placenta? The handwritten Grünenthal response was: *Not known*. The second question: can thalidomide have a damaging effect on the child in the event that it crosses to the child via the placenta? Grünenthal's response: *Improbable*. And the third question: in which part of the body is thalidomide broken down? *Probably by the liver*.

The questions and answers expose Grünenthal's ignorance. It did not know if the drug reached the foetus and could not say categorically that the drug did not damage the foetus. 'Improbable' was the best it could do. Grünenthal had no idea how its drug—Germany's best-selling sleeping pill—behaved inside a pregnant woman.

The Finnish inquiry seemed to kick off some soul-searching at Grünenthal. At a meeting of scientific staff the possibility of tests to see whether thalidomide passed the placenta and reached the foetus was discussed. One senior Grünenthal employee later told the prosecutor that during the middle of 1961 there was concern at the company that thalidomide might be causing injuries more severe than nerve damage: animal tests were discussed as a way to 'determine the possibility of damage to the foetus'.

Finally, on 13 September 1961, Grünenthal reached out to an

external expert for help. It wrote to Dr Ernst-Albrecht Josten, who in 1956 had written a journal article on the effect of medications on the foetus.

> Dear Dr Josten, we have learned by chance through one of our employees that you used to be particularly involved in the issues of effects of medication on the foetus and the newborn respectively. We therefore take the liberty today of inquiring whether you still have the ability to perform such tests or, if this should not be the case, who in your opinion within the Federal Republic would be particularly capable of carrying out such tests?

Nothing came of the inquiry and Grünenthal did not pursue it. Much later Josten could not recall what his response had been. Certainly there were no tests, and the drug continued to be promoted as safe.

It was now the eleventh hour for Grünenthal and thalidomide. A handful of German doctors, working largely in isolation and in ignorance of most of the disturbing information Grünenthal had about thalidomide, were closing in on the drug as the cause of the rising death and injury toll. While those doctors worked feverishly, Grünenthal continued to ignore red flags. On 3 October 1961 Grünenthal received a letter from the National Drug Company in the United States noting that the FDA had inquired 'whether Contergan is transferred to the foetus. I presume they want to incorporate a special warning for pregnancy'.

What Grünenthal made of the FDA query is not known, but there's an intriguing claim that the company privately prepared its own pregnancy warning stickers. In 1969 Dr Günter von Waldeyer-Hartz, a chemist who was disturbed at the progress of the trial of Grünenthal executives, wrote to the German Government stating that in October 1961 he had visited Grünenthal and had been shown a packet of Contergan with an attached sticker bearing the words NOT FOR PREGNANT WOMEN. Von Waldeyer-Hartz's letter found its way to the chief prosecutor but the evidence was not presented at trial.

While there remains a serious question mark over Grünenthal's pregnancy stickers, there is none over a query it received from Dr Hermann Brandt in Lübeck, northern Germany. 'In March 1961 I was called out to attend to a malformed child. It was the first time that I ever saw such a child. It had severe malformations of the upper extremities,' Brandt later told the prosecution team. On 15 September 1961 the father telephoned Brandt, told him that he knew of a number of malformed babies born in the area and that Contergan was widely prescribed. The father told Brandt he believed thalidomide was causing malformations.

Brandt told the father he would discuss it with Grünenthal, and a few weeks later he told a Grünenthal sales rep about the case and the suspicions about thalidomide. '[The sales rep] promised me that he would discuss this set of questions with his company and notify me, should anything be known about it.'

Years afterwards the German lawyers prosecuting Grünenthal were intrigued by Brandt's story. They kept digging, conducting further interviews to find out what happened to Brandt's report. What they learned was that the first Grünenthal sales rep passed Brandt's report to his local Grünenthal superior. That man thought the link between thalidomide and malformations was impossible. But he too, it appeared, passed the report up the Grünenthal chain, telling Grünenthal's 'manager of scientific field services' about the warning.

But nobody from Grünenthal contacted Brandt or the family. 'I did not hear anything more in regard to this matter until I happened to read about Lenz's suspicion in the newspaper at the end of November 1961,' Brandt later recalled.

Dwell for a moment on this episode. Certainly it was late in the piece—Grünenthal would soon be forced to withdraw the drug. But Grünenthal's response is telling: three Grünenthal employees knew of Brandt's report, yet nothing happened. No inquiry. No follow-up contact with Brandt. No contact with the family. No attempt to check for other cases of malformations in the area. Silence.

• • •

To a citizen of the twenty-first century it seems remarkable that the German medical community took so long to notice an epidemic that damaged and ended so many lives. Thalidomide had been causing shocking malformations in Germany for more than three years before the rising toll was even identified and the hunt for a cause begun. On one hand, the time lag is explicable. This was the late 1950s and early 1960s. Doctors shared their experience through printed papers and conferences. They communicated by letter and telephone. Specialists could be completely unaware of events in a nearby city for weeks at a time. And the thalidomide victims were spread across Germany. Doctors who had seen only one or two cases might justifiably write them off as random occurrences, unaware of the total numbers.

On the other hand, even given the time and context, there was a distinct lack of curiosity and engagement within the German medical profession. It took so long, and the tragedy had to reach such a boiling point, for the malformations to be noticed that one wonders what was going on. These were not trivial malformations: they were rare, once-in-a-lifetime events for most doctors and there were a lot of them. Enough for many lifetimes. Yet it took years until a handful of curious and energetic doctors realised this was an epidemic and started hunting for the cause.

The first mention of what turned out to be a thalidomide baby in a German medical publication came in December 1959, when Dr Arnulf Weidenbach of Munich published a short article in a magazine for obstetricians and gynaecologists about a baby with shortened arms and legs, a very rare condition known as phocomelia (from the Greek for 'seal limb'). In his article Weidenbach speculated about possible causes but acknowledged that the case was a mystery. Years later Weidenbach said he had received many requests for copies of his article, but could not recall any doctor telling him of a similar case.

By that time in Germany there had in all likelihood been about two hundred children born with thalidomide malformations, including many cases of phocomelia. At least one hundred recognised thalidomide babies born prior to this time survived into their teenage years, and studies have suggested that about fifty per cent of all thalidomide babies died at (or shortly after) birth or during infancy. So the one hundred long-term survivors would have been about matched by an equal number who did not survive. Yet not a single one of these cases was reported to Weidenbach, and no alarm was raised.

The next milestone came in October 1960 when two German doctors, Wilhelm Kosenow and Rudolf Pfeiffer, set up a display about two malformed babies at a national paediatric conference in Kassel. The babies were phocomelic, and one had a blocked small intestine, injuries that would later be recognised as typical of thalidomide. Kosenow and Pfeiffer did not give a speech, but merely presented an exhibit that attending doctors were welcome to inspect.

By this time there had been more than six hundred thalidomide babies born in Germany and many of the attendees would have seen one or more, yet apparently none mentioned that they too had seen something similar. The exhibit attracted little comment.

But the disaster was now rapidly gathering pace. In March 1960 Contergan had become Germany's most popular sleeping medication, and by the middle of the year it accounted for almost half of Grünenthal's revenue: 'Everything is done to keep this apple of our eye secure,' one company report stated. In January 1961 sales peaked at 1.6 million marks for the month.

As more and more pregnant German women took the drug, the number of damaged babies escalated. By the end of 1960 more than one thousand thalidomide babies had been born, and about half of them survived. The toll had started slowly but by late 1960 it was reaching full speed. Yet still this massive outbreak of death and injury had not been identified.

Dr Hans-Rudolf Wiedemann, a paediatrician who headed the children's hospital in Krefeld, near Düsseldorf, started seeing a surge of unusually malformed infants in late 1960. He questioned the parents, made inquiries of colleagues in nearby towns and decided that something recently introduced into daily life was responsible. In September 1961 Wiedemann published an article dealing with thirteen cases in *Die Medizinische Welt*, but noted that he was aware of a total of twenty-seven such cases in the area of his clinic. He suggested similar malformations might be spread across Germany and that the nationwide toll could approach a hundred, a 'frightening' figure he deemed an epidemic. In fact, probably more than 2500 thalidomide children had been born by the time he published. Wiedemann had drastically underestimated the magnitude, but he had—finally and thankfully—publicly identified the epidemic. Wiedemann was not the only doctor on thalidomide's trail. Others in Scotland, Australia, Japan and Sweden were investigating, but Germany was the epicentre of the tragedy and Wiedemann was among a number of German doctors who came agonisingly close to solving the mystery.

Through painstaking investigation Wiedemann was able to eliminate a number of possible causes including botched abortions, infections and some medications. But he had not yet solved the puzzle when a change of jobs and a move to another city diverted his attention.

Heinz Weicker, a Bonn paediatrician, saw his first thalidomide baby in January 1961. When he started seeing further cases he realised from the birth dates that the wave of malformations had begun in late 1958 or early 1959. Weicker wanted to know if similar births were occurring elsewhere and wrote to colleagues in fifty large clinics in Europe, the United States and elsewhere. Almost all of the clinics wrote back advising they had seen no increase in such malformations, advice that later turned out to have been wrong in many cases. Weicker worked feverishly, seven days a week, on his investigation, visiting dozens of afflicted families and questioning them extensively. He briefly considered thalidomide as the cause because about twenty per cent of his mothers had mentioned taking it. But thanks to his correspondence he believed that there had been no cases in the US, where he mistakenly thought thalidomide was very popular. In fact, thalidomide had not been approved for sale in the US. But Weicker's thalidomide suspicions were weakened as a result. By late 1961 thalidomide was only eighth on his list of suspected causes, a list topped by three similar detergents. (Wiedemann—and later Lenz—also suspected detergents, which had only recently come into widespread use in Germany.) Other products Weicker had ahead of thalidomide on his list included an anti-nauseant medication and a widely used hormonal pregnancy test. Later, when the truth about thalidomide emerged, Weicker went back to his group of mothers and learned, on more detailed questioning, that almost all recalled taking it.

Another investigator, Dr Hans Wegerle in Marburg, came within a hair's breadth of establishing the link. Wegerle first suspected Contergan in October 1961 for a number of reasons: its chemical composition; it appeared in some of his case histories; and the malformation epidemic had started about the time thalidomide sales began. Like Weicker, Wegerle corresponded with colleagues overseas and concluded that Germany was 'obviously preponderantly affected'. He had considered but discarded other possible causes including radiation fallout from bomb tests, abortifacients, vitamin deficiencies, disease, fertilisers and pest control agents. He had collected eleven Contergan-positive cases but was warned by colleagues to strengthen his evidence. Wegerle therefore was busy making further investigations when he was beaten to the punch by Widukind Lenz. Generously, Lenz later credited Wegerle with suspecting thalidomide before he did.

• • •

In 1961 Widukind Lenz was the forty-two-year-old head of the children's clinic at Hamburg University. He had qualified as a doctor in 1943 and then worked at military hospitals, including in occupied France. Lenz was captured and taken to Britain, where he was held until his post-war return to Germany.

Lenz's first unknowing brush with thalidomide damage came in early 1961, when he was consulted about a baby with unusual malformations. Lenz thought the probable cause was a gene mutation. In June 1961, after being consulted about two further cases, Lenz again suggested gene mutations.

Then, on 22 June 1961, came a visit that changed Lenz's life. Two months earlier, Karl Schulte-Hillen's wife Linde had given birth to a son with shortened arms and missing fingers. 'What's with your husband? Has he got no arms?' one of the midwives asked Linde Schulte-Hillen shortly after Jan's birth. Six weeks earlier, Schulte-Hillen's sister had given birth to a baby with almost identical malformations. Schulte-Hillen, a lawyer who represented the thalidomide children's interests during the trial of Grünenthal executives, was so distressed by these events that he wandered around Hamburg in disbelief. 'For days I didn't see people's faces or bodies,' he later said. 'All I saw were their hands.'

When Schulte-Hillen asked a senior doctor at the hospital for an explanation he was told: 'There's no special reason, we see one or two cases a year.' Given his sister also had an afflicted baby, Schulte-Hillen initially believed there must have been a genetic problem in his family. Then he learned there were several more malformed children in his home town of Menden. One had been born the day before his son, in the same hospital, with very similar malformations. He became convinced a geographical issue was at play and soon afterwards a friend suggested he contact Widukind Lenz. 'He has no car, only an old military coat,' the friend said. 'And he rides an old bicycle, a woman's bicycle, but he's the man for you.' Schulte-Hillen met with Lenz, who was sceptical about his visitor's geographic theory and equally sceptical that there could be as many similar cases as Schulte-Hillen claimed. But he promised to make some inquiries. Soon afterwards Lenz telephoned a Menden obstetrician, and was shocked to be told there had been many babies born with limb malformations in Menden, Beckum and Münster, three towns not far from each other in north-west Germany.

Soon Lenz was in touch with other doctors and found many other cases. By August 1961 Lenz firmly believed that 'one single common cause must be responsible'. At a meeting with Schulte-Hillen, Lenz remarked that the search needed a detective rather than a doctor. He wondered whether a new lipstick or face cream was responsible, and also questioned Schulte-Hillen about the family's use of detergents.

Lenz had previously studied the rate of various birth malformations in Hamburg. Using those figures, he calculated that the new malformations were about two hundred times as frequent as they had been: there had been one case of phocomelia in Hamburg in the twenty-eight years up to 1958, and eight cases in just the last year. He realised a massive epidemic was underway.

Lenz's investigations continued and by 8 November 1961 he was focused on 'a single new factor…a noxious agent which has never previously been prevalent to a similar extent'. Lenz considered a food additive possible; he doubted the culprit was a drug because he had not been able to find one consistently taken by the mothers of the damaged babies. Only once had Lenz's attention been directed to thalidomide at this point: by a mother who had taken thalidomide throughout her pregnancy and developed nerve damage. She told Lenz she thought her baby's malformations had been caused by the drug.

Then on 11 November 1961 the mother of a baby girl without arms told Lenz she had taken Contergan during early pregnancy, and so had a friend with a similarly injured child. The following day the father of another malformed baby told Lenz he blamed Contergan for his baby's injuries because he knew it caused nerve damage. Lenz was closing in. That day, 12 November 1961, he wrote to a colleague saying that he had a 'hot lead' in his hunt for the cause of the malformations.

In a flurry of activity over the next few days Lenz visited affected families to check drug histories, asked his colleagues at the university clinic to help him with his research and called on other German doctors to check their files. By 15 November 1961, Lenz had gathered fourteen cases in which there was evidence that the mother of a typically malformed infant had taken thalidomide. This, he later wrote, warranted 'practical steps' even though it fell short of proof.

So on that day, 15 November 1961, Lenz telephoned Heinrich Mückter at Grünenthal, outlined his evidence and asked for the drug to be withdrawn from sale. Mückter would not agree but said he would send someone to talk with Lenz. Lenz thought this an inadequate response. To increase the pressure, he put his concerns in a letter which he sent to Grünenthal by registered express mail. His letter concluded by warning that it would be irresponsible to 'wait for the strict scientific proof. I consider it necessary to withdraw the drug immediately from the market until its innocuousness as a teratogenic agent in man is proved with certainty'.

The next day, Thursday 16 November 1961, Grünenthal arranged to meet with Lenz the following Monday to discuss his concerns. But in the meantime Lenz attended a paediatric meeting on the Saturday. Concerned about the delayed Grünenthal response, he shared his information with the shocked attendees.

On Monday 20 November 1961, Lenz met with the Grünenthal executives, a meeting that was quickly shifted (by Lenz) to the health authorities' offices. Lenz later said he thought

> the Grünenthal representatives showed no interest in the facts, or the arguments that pointed towards thalidomide being the root cause of the deformities. Quite the reverse. They showed a lively interest in every detail which showed up the quality of my research in an unfavourable light.

Lenz also said he was threatened with legal action. Grünenthal concluded the meeting by refusing to withdraw thalidomide from sale.

Bizarrely, even now, Grünenthal was focused on selling more thalidomide. The German prosecutor later found that on the same day it was meeting with Lenz, Grünenthal sent out 66,957 copies of a pamphlet addressed to doctors in which Contergan was described as a 'safe medicine'.

Later that week, Friday 24 November 1961, there was another meeting between Lenz, Grünenthal and ministry officials. Grünenthal was again aggressive, threatening a legal action for compensation if the drug was banned. As the meeting wore on the company eventually offered to attach a sticker to the medication warning against use in pregnancy. The ministry officials refused to accept this and told Grünenthal to withdraw the drug voluntarily or it would be banned.

The following day, Saturday 25 November 1961, Grünenthal's top executives gathered in Stolberg where Mückter shocked his colleagues by producing a letter from Distillers in London. The letter reported six malformed (and subsequently deceased) babies, noted that thalidomide was suspected as a possible cause and asked whether Grünenthal had any similar reports.

Incredibly, that still was not enough for Mückter to agree to withdraw the drug. While most present were now resigned to thalidomide's demise, the best they could get from Mückter was an agreement that doctors be informed of Lenz's views. Mückter insisted that the drug remain on sale. (Grünenthal says the decision to withdraw the drug was taken at that meeting, a disputed view of history.)

But the next morning, a prominent article in the newspaper *Welt am Sonntag* (*World on Sunday*) sealed thalidomide's fate. Though it did not name the drug, the article cited Lenz's fears that a popular sleeping pill was malforming babies, reported that the company involved had not withdrawn the drug and called on the authorities to intervene. Later that day Grünenthal finally capitulated: thalidomide was withdrawn, and in follow-up press releases Grünenthal blamed the media frenzy for the withdrawal rather than the grave suspicion about the drug being deadly.

It had taken sustained pressure from Lenz and the health authorities, and the start of a media campaign, to force Grünenthal to withdraw thalidomide. Grünenthal had fought to the end and the company's bitterness about Lenz was palpable. One senior Grünenthal man later recalled the response of senior staff when told of Lenz's charge. 'I still remember that several gentlemen from the research department—I can no longer recall individual names—made ironic remarks about Dr Lenz—son of a top Nazi, nothing sensible could be expected from somebody with the first name "Widukind", or similar remarks of this ilk.'

This obsession with Lenz's father was not a one-off. Dr Fritz Lenz had been a high-profile advocate of eugenics, or scientific racism, who firmly believed in the superiority of the Aryan race. Grünenthal seemed to think the fact that Lenz had a notorious father might be helpful. In January 1962 a memo circulated at Grünenthal attaching an article about Fritz Lenz and asking: 'Is this the father of the Hamburg paediatrician Dr Lenz? What do we know about the "racial hygiene" this man advocated and what he did during the NS-time?' NS is short for *Nationalsozialistische*, usually abbreviated in English to Nazi. A curious tack for Grünenthal to take.

CHAPTER 7

It Could Have Happened to the Queen

It was December 2011 and Lyn Rowe was about to get a demonstration of Grünenthal's determination. Two weeks before Christmas, Grünenthal sent its legal team down to the Supreme Court building in Melbourne. Their mission was to persuade Justice David Beach to effectively throw Lyn's claim against Grünenthal out of the Australian court system before it had even begun. Germany, according to Grünenthal, was the natural place for the claim to be heard. It was where Grünenthal's witnesses were and also the location of up to 1.8 million pages of relevant documents, almost all of them in German. Additionally, Grünenthal argued, Rowe's claim was oppressive and vexatious and an 'abuse of process'. For all of those reasons, and others, Grünenthal wanted a permanent 'stay', or freezing of Lyn's claim, in Australia.

Naturally Lyn's lawyers resisted the application. If Grünenthal was successful it would mean the end of Lyn's claim against that company. She simply could not litigate in Germany. So we filed material detailing Lyn's personal circumstances, her total dependence on her elderly parents, the family's precarious financial position, the difficulty for the Rowes in travelling to Germany, and even the family's complete unfamiliarity with the German language. Obviously, we argued, the trial belonged in Melbourne, the city where Lyn lived, where her mother had taken the Grünenthal-made drug, where she was born with serious malformations, where her medical experts were, and where her lawyers practised.

Clearly if there was a choice to be made about which party should have to litigate in a foreign jurisdiction it had to be Grünenthal. It was a wealthy corporation with thousands of employees and access to the best defence lawyers anywhere in the world. Lyn Rowe was severely injured and penniless.

Grünenthal's move seemed a desperate long shot to many of us on Lyn Rowe's legal team. But it was evidence of the take-no-prisoners approach we had expected. Grünenthal's Melbourne law firm, Clayton Utz, had been in these sorts of fights before, having represented corporations in tobacco, asbestos and pharmaceutical claims. So while we all considered Grünenthal's gambit had little chance of success, it was not taken lightly.

Justice Beach gave all sides a patient hearing and then a week later produced a strongly worded judgment. Grünenthal's attempt to have Lyn Rowe's claim removed to Germany was scotched because 'it cannot be said that Victoria is a clearly inappropriate forum,' Justice Beach observed. 'Grünenthal's application for a stay must be dismissed.'

In court there were a few minutes of conversation after the decision, including talk about a further court date the following week. Lyn Rowe had absorbed her legal win without visible emotion but, as she listened to the ensuing conversation, she assumed she would have to return to court the next week. She started crying silently. Lyn can be stoic and emotional in quick succession. At that moment she thought that to attend court she would have to cancel an appointment to pick up a long-awaited new wheelchair. She was devastated. Lyn had been looking forward to the new wheelchair for months. As she wept, Grace Wilson, one of the legal team, wiped away her tears with a tissue and whispered that she was not needed in court and could keep the wheelchair appointment. Later more than one journalist reported—understandably but incorrectly—that Lyn had wept tears of relief at the decision to keep her trial in Melbourne. After leaving court, Ian Rowe, who had become an effective spokesman for Lyn, made a brief statement.

> Now that we have the umpire's decision that the trial should be here in Melbourne, I'd like to call on Diageo and Grünenthal to let Lyn have her day in court. Please don't cause any more delay, just for delay's sake. Time is not on our side. Wendy and I are getting older now, I'm almost eighty. And we really need to know that Lynette will be provided for when we can no longer do it ourselves. Every delay that Diageo and Grünenthal throw up makes it more difficult to get any security. Lyn is a brave woman—despite everything she never complains. And all she wants is the chance for a court to hear her claim. So that's what I'm asking Grünenthal and Diageo to do—let Lyn have her day in court. Let's get all the information on the table, and let's get a decision.

In the days that followed Justice Beach set out a hectic schedule for pre-trial steps. This was intended to expedite the trial process and focus attention on the matters that really were in dispute. Most of our office spent the holiday period t-shirt clad, bashing away at computers—but we were relieved that Grünenthal's attempt to sink our ship had been so categorically dismissed.

By that time there had already been a flurry of legal documents passing between the parties. In July 2011 we sent Grünenthal and Distillers Lyn's statement of claim, the first serious salvo by the plaintiff in most legal cases. Drawing on almost eighteen months of work, it set out the history of the development of thalidomide, the licence granted by Grünenthal to Distillers to sell the drug in Australia, the warning signs that had been ignored and what we described as the negligent fashion in which the unsafe and improperly tested drug was promoted in Australia as safe and suitable for pregnancy. The statement of claim also detailed the ways in which the drug companies could have protected Lyn Rowe, and it sought damages to compensate Lyn for her losses. Finally, it also asked for additional damages—punitive or exemplary damages—to underline the gravity of the defendants' failures.

Both Grünenthal and Distillers responded with requests for 'further and better particulars'—lawyer-speak for more detail. Our responses ran to almost two hundred pages, providing sources for many of our allegations, citing dozens of medical journal articles, and referencing many documents from the criminal trial collection in Düsseldorf and the *Sunday Times* cache in London.

Grünenthal and Distillers also filed defences in which most of Lyn's allegations were denied or not admitted. But as well as asserting that its testing had been adequate by the standards of the time, Grünenthal made some admissions. It admitted that it had received reports about thalidomide's side effects from doctors, licensees, researchers, distributors and hospitals; that in various countries it had promoted thalidomide as safe and non-toxic and that some doctors had criticised it at the time for doing so; that it had received inquiries from doctors about whether thalidomide crossed the placenta and affected the foetus; and that it did no reproductive testing of thalidomide and had conducted no investigation into the effect of thalidomide on the foetus. Grünenthal also admitted that by the start of 1961 members of the German medical profession were concerned about the increase in birth malformations in that country.

These admissions were surprising and welcome, but we had a clear appreciation of the challenge ahead. Winning Lyn's claim required us to succeed on every single element of the claim. Fail on any element and her claim was over. Lyn had to prove that her mother Wendy did in fact take thalidomide and that it caused Lyn's absence of arms and legs; that Distillers and Grünenthal should have foreseen that thalidomide might damage her; that they behaved negligently by the standards of the time in exposing her to that risk; that the two companies had a duty to protect her in distant Australia; and that there was something they could have done to avoid the risk (such as withdraw the drug or put warnings on it). And then there was perhaps the biggest hurdle of all. Lyn's time to bring her claim under the law had very probably run out—she had to persuade the judge that it was in the interests of justice to grant her permission to bring her claim after so many years.

If Lyn did win she would be awarded a lot of money. Journalists often asked how much Lyn wanted and the answer was always the same: we don't know, but a lot. At that point we had not specified precisely what figure Lyn was seeking. We knew, and so did Grünenthal and Distillers, that it would be a very large sum: in the millions of dollars. If she succeeded, she was entitled to several categories of damages.

The first was for 'pain and suffering'—properly known as general damages. The maximum payable in this category had been capped by law at just under $500,000. We felt certain that if Lyn succeeded at trial, her fifty years without limbs would entitle her to the maximum award.

Lyn was also entitled to lost earnings—past and future. This calculation would be unavoidably speculative. Lyn was not an injured worker with a career history and a predictable course of future employment. Lyn had never had the chance to have a career, and her moderate brain damage (the indirect result of thalidomide, and which particularly damaged her ability to concentrate) further complicated the picture. Lyn told us she would have wanted to be a nurse or doctor in other circumstances. But whatever hypothetical past and future employment a judge imagined for Lyn, her lost earnings over an entire working life would amount to a very large sum.

That left the biggest damages category of all: the cost of providing Lyn with proper and secure care. This had two components. First was care in the future, until her death; and second was reimbursement for past care. This second category in effect amounted to valuing Wendy's unpaid care over fifty years. Providing proper care for a limbless woman is an expensive business. Because Lyn could do almost nothing for herself she needed a carer present at all times. We would seek the cost of professional care on a full-time, twenty-four-hours-a-day basis for the rest of Lyn's life. On top of that would be things like wheel-chairs, hoists and technological aids such as voice recognition software to make her life easier. The bill for all of this would be very high.

• • •

During the months after Grünenthal tried—and failed—to force Lyn to litigate in Germany, we continued to take statements from various members of Lyn's family.

One of them was Bronwen Shannon, Lyn's cousin on Wendy's side. In 1976, when she was nineteen years old, Bronwen moved from Canberra to Melbourne to study, and got to know the Rowes. Bronwen vividly remembers the first time she fully appreciated the depth and complexity of Lyn's disability. She had visited Lyn, who was in the Royal Children's Hospital recovering from having a rod inserted into her back to correct her spine curvature and was feeling suicidal. 'She was in pain, scared and vulnerable,' Bronwen said. Lyn hated being in hospital, hated being away from her family, and was looking at six months on her back and then another six months in a brace. Lyn told Bronwen that if she were able, she would have gone to the top of the hospital building and wheeled herself off the edge. 'Having led a fairly sheltered existence, this was really traumatic,' Bronwen recalled.

The visit was topped off when a doctor brought a group of medical students into the room. Without a word of introduction, Bronwen said, the doctor 'pulled back the bedclothes to show the students Lyn's body, poked and prodded her and generally ignored Lyn as a human. He talked to the students about Lyn as though she were a medical specimen on display. He never even spoke to her'. Bronwen was horrified and too overwhelmed to say anything. She visited Lyn in hospital just that one time. 'I was too immature to handle it then, but I'd love to go back in time and set that doctor straight. Still, the visit gave me an insight into how much humiliation and embarrassment Lyn has had to suffer.'

Later Bronwen lived with the Rowes for a few months while looking for a job, and helped out with Lyn's care despite Wendy's initial reluctance. 'She didn't want Lyn to be a burden to anyone,' Bronwen said. 'Luckily Lyn was eager for me to help and I learned how to help her with the toilet, dressing, going to bed and so on. It was all done physically in those days. The Rowes got a hoist later, but at that time we just physically lifted Lyn in and out of bed or her chair or the car.'

Lyn still gives her cousin a hard time about one incident during that period, when Bronwen was distracted after undoing Lyn's seatbelt. Lyn leaned forward in her wheelchair, toppled, and fell face first onto the floor. She broke her nose, which she has done many times, but she especially loves that story and reminds Bronwen of it regularly.

Bronwen Shannon had grown up in Canberra believing that Lyn was a thalidomider, so when she mentioned it to Wendy, the response surprised her. 'She said there was no proof about thalidomide. Wendy explained that her doctor had said it was just one of those things that happen and probably the result of a virus.'

The virus explanation was something that Wendy and Lyn had told many people over the years, and it was a central issue that Lyn's lawyers had to deal with: Lyn had not in the past identified as a thalidomider. Obviously we had to get to the bottom of it. Our case was all about Lyn being a thalidomide survivor, not a virus survivor.

We had to understand the basis for the virus story, in order to dispense with it as a possible cause of Lyn's malformations. We also had to gather all the available evidence that Dr Indian had in fact given Wendy thalidomide. We knew that Wendy's medical records from the period had been destroyed, and that the empty pill containers had long since disappeared. There would be no hard physical proof that Wendy had been given the pills. There was no test we could give Lyn that would prove scientifically and with certainty that thalidomide was the cause of her limblessness. We would have to build the evidence of thalidomide consumption incrementally, piecing it together as best we could, largely from witness evidence. However, we did not need absolute proof, just a probability that Wendy had taken the drug and that it had caused Lyn's injuries.

To make our case we had to go back to the start, and Wendy Rowe held many of the answers. When Lyn was born in March 1962, Wendy had never heard of thalidomide. Just three months earlier, in late November 1961, the drug had been connected to birth damage and withdrawn from sale. However when we went to the newspaper archives, we found that the story had made barely a splash at the time. Most coverage was confined to the medical press, and initially it was thought there had been very few Australian victims. Distillers, in fact, had done its absolute best to discourage local coverage. If such a disaster happened today there would be blanket media attention with extensive coverage of the victims and dire warnings issued. The drug would be ruthlessly hunted down. But in late 1961 and early 1962, when thalidomide's danger was first revealed, the story sank. It was not until more than six months later, in the middle of 1962, that newspapers started paying close attention.

So it's not particularly surprising that in the immediate aftermath of Lyn's birth in March 1962, none of the doctors mentioned thalidomide to Wendy. Maybe they also didn't know about the drug. Or maybe they didn't want to distress Wendy any further. Dr Indian told her it was all just bad luck. 'It could have happened to the Queen, it's a chance in a million,' is what Wendy remembered him saying shortly after Lyn's birth.

But when Lyn was a few months old, Wendy's father Ted Tudor sent her a newspaper clipping about thalidomide, and told her that Lyn looked like a victim of the drug. Tudor followed up with further clippings and a handwritten note, which Wendy was able to find fifty years later, with contact details for the Society for the Aid of Thalidomide Children in England. (Ted Tudor's concern for his granddaughter ran deep. He was convinced that technology would ultimately make Lyn's life much easier and spent much of his spare time designing aids for her, including the rotating spoon device Lyn eats from to this day.)

Alerted by her father, Wendy Rowe raised the thalidomide question with Dr Indian at his surgery. Wendy and I spent a lot of time talking about this discussion as it seemed a critical event. Of course there was always something exceedingly optimistic about my questions: the conversation had happened more than fifty years earlier. Many of us have trouble recalling detail after just a few months or even weeks. But despite the passage of time, Wendy's memories were remarkably clear. Wendy knew Dr Indian had given her Distaval, and by then she knew it was the brand name for thalidomide. But Dr Indian 'seemed defensive and uncomfortable with my question. He said it was impossible that pills could cause the sort of injuries that Lyn had, and that Lyn's injuries must have been caused by a virus'.

It seems a strange response. Nobody was blaming doctors for the disaster; certainly Dr Indian was blameless. Perhaps he had heard only of thalidomide causing the more common shortened arms and legs; maybe he thought the complete absence of limbs was not something thalidomide could have done. Perhaps he felt such guilt or regret that he could not face the truth. Perhaps he thought that it would be better for Wendy to think the tragedy had been an act of God—something, as he'd already remarked, that could equally have happened to the Queen.

Wendy's own response to Indian might also be thought odd at this distant remove. She did not argue or confront Indian with what she knew about thalidomide. She more or less accepted his explanation without comment. Sitting at her kitchen table in 2011, reflecting on events, Wendy explained the context.

> I wasn't assertive or confident in those days. I was twenty-six years old and struggling to cope with the shock of what had happened, with the demands that Lyn's arrival had created, with the needs of the other two children in the wake of Lyn's arrival and with Ian's fragile mental state. I knew Dr Indian must be feeling bad about what happened, no matter what the cause. I didn't want to be impolite and I liked and respected

him. He had delivered my first two daughters. Also, he was a doctor. If he said it was a virus then he was probably right.

And then there is this: would it really have mattered to Wendy what had caused her daughter's malformations? Decades on, we lawyers wanted Wendy to have fought back and forced some kind of confession from Indian. But how realistic was that? 'It wasn't something I spent time thinking about. There was no cure for Lyn, nothing was going to bring her limbs back,' Wendy said. 'We weren't thinking about legal action, it's not something we knew anything about.'

Others were suspicious. In 1962 the Victorian health authorities wondered whether Lyn was the victim of thalidomide and investigated Wendy's medical records. They discovered that Indian had kept no record of any medication Wendy had taken during the pregnancy. This finding was relayed to Wendy, convincing her that further investigation was pointless.

It would be another twenty years before Wendy Rowe had a second conversation with Dr Indian about the cause of Lyn's malformations. And as time passed she felt less and less certain about what had happened. Indian had been so certain about the virus and there was no proof about thalidomide anyway. Wendy tried to think about it as little as possible. She tried to cut conversations about the issue short. When people asked whether Lyn was a thalidomide baby, she always said, 'No, the doctor said it was a virus.'

In the early 1980s, Wendy heard about some court cases concerning birth malformations said to have been caused by Debendox, the morning-sickness drug Dr Indian had prescribed after the Distaval did not work. She decided to investigate whether she might be able to bring a Debendox claim for Lyn. So Wendy visited the pharmacist where she had filled the prescriptions more than twenty years earlier and obtained a note confirming she had indeed taken Debendox. Then she went to see Dr Indian.

> I asked him whether he was aware of the claims about Debendox and whether he thought that Debendox might have caused Lyn's injuries. Dr Indian told me I was wasting my time. He told me Debendox was perfectly safe and that he had given it to his own daughters during their pregnancies and that their babies had been fine. He said I would be wasting my time if I thought I could get any compensation for Lyn as a result of taking Debendox.

Dr Indian's advice about Debendox was sound. Despite the flurry of (largely unsuccessful) legal action in the 1980s, and the subsequent withdrawal from sale of Debendox (marketed as Bendectin in the US), the drug is not considered to be dangerous to the unborn child. In fact in 2013 the US FDA approved its reintroduction. But Wendy Rowe's Debendox query was an opportunity for Dr Indian to correct his advice of twenty years earlier, and tell Wendy that if she was thinking about legal action, she should be focused on thalidomide. Again, we could only speculate why he did not. Dr Indian was, by everyone's account, a careful and compassionate doctor. He passed away long before the legal action began and was never able to give us his side of the story.

Nonetheless our evidence that Wendy Rowe had taken thalidomide was coming together. We had her detailed, consistent evidence that Dr Indian had given her Distaval samples. We also had a cogent explanation for why she had used the virus story for so many years. We had medical evidence that the likelihood of a virus alone causing complete absence of limbs was close to zero.

But Wendy's evidence needed support. There was no doubt that her recollection of thalidomide would be disputed and challenged at trial. How can you remember what you took fifty years earlier? she'd be asked. We needed backup. Further information, no matter how scant, would help. So we took a detailed statement from Dr Indian's former medical partner, Dr Dickinson, the doctor who delivered Lyn Rowe. He confirmed that there had been Distaval samples at the surgery at the relevant time. Dickinson recalled that sales reps from Distillers and other pharmaceutical companies visited the surgery frequently and often left free samples which he and the other doctors kept in their desk drawers and gave to patients when appropriate. Dr Dickinson recalled that Distaval was a popular drug at the time: 'Safe and non-toxic and an improvement on the barbiturates.'

Then Wendy put me in touch with her sister-in-law Margaret Tudor in the hope more than the expectation that she might have helpful memories. Margaret, seventy-nine years old when I met her in 2011, had married Wendy's oldest brother Ted, a lawyer, and the couple and their four children had settled in Canberra. My first few telephone conversations with Margaret were so encouraging that we flew her down from Canberra so we could talk in person.

The minor cost of the flight paid off in spades. Margaret remembered a trip to Melbourne in mid-1961—she was able to pinpoint the timing almost exactly by reference to her own children's birthdays—when Wendy Rowe had just fallen pregnant with Lyn. Margaret remembered that Wendy 'was not entirely delighted to be pregnant' and at a family lunch the conversation turned to Wendy's morning sickness.

> She said that the doctor had given her a new medication which he said would help. I was interested in such things because I had wanted to be a nurse before training as a teacher. I was also a mother and by that time had four children...I asked Wendy what the name of the medication was. She said it

was called Distaval. I hadn't heard of Distaval before. But because of the context and my interest in these things—and most importantly because of what happened afterwards—the name Distaval stuck in my memory.

This was an important piece of the jigsaw: corroboration that Wendy had been given Distaval. We were also assisted by Wendy's youngest sister, Liz Trennery, who was eighteen years old and staying in Canada with their brother Graham in 1962 when Lyn was born. She vividly recalled receiving the news about Lyn's condition.

> Graham came into my room obviously upset and read me a letter. Our father had written to us with the news that Lynette had been born without arms or legs. He wrote that Wendy had been given thalidomide pills during her pregnancy. I remember all of this very clearly. This was shocking news. I could only imagine the shock and sorrow that Wendy and Ian and their daughters and my whole family were feeling in Melbourne.

Later, while pregnant with her two children in the 1970s, Liz Trennery refused all medication despite suffering severe migraines.

Margaret and Liz, both impressive and confident women, had armed us with significant supporting evidence that Wendy had taken thalidomide. Taken as a whole, the evidence was looking highly persuasive.

We had one further lead to pursue. We consulted a leading Melbourne geneticist, Ravi Savarirayan, who suggested testing Lyn for a couple of genetic conditions that have caused limblessness in an incredibly tiny number of people. We needed to be sure Lyn did not have either condition. None of us believed she did, but we held our breath anyway until, reassuringly, the test results came back negative.

We now felt confident of proving—on the balance of probabilities, and to the satisfaction of a judge—that Wendy Rowe had indeed consumed thalidomide. But that was just one hurdle. Many others loomed, including getting to grips with Distillers' track record with the drug.

• • •

The small town of Turriff in northern Scotland is an unlikely setting for a piece of thalidomide history. Turriff boasts a population of only about five thousand and is probably best known for its annual agricultural show. But it was in Turriff in 1960 that a thirty-three-year-old Scottish GP wrote to the *British Medical Journal* suggesting that thalidomide might be the cause of nerve damage in four of his patients. In doing so, Dr Leslie Florence became the first doctor to publish on the connection between thalidomide and nerve damage.

Florence's letter was brief—just three paragraphs. It was headed, memorably: 'Is Thalidomide to Blame?' He recorded the symptoms of nerve damage in his patients (tingling and coldness in the feet and hands and occasional unsteadiness), noted the common consumption of Distaval and the slow recovery after the drug was withdrawn, and wondered whether other doctors had a similar experience with the drug, which by then had been on sale for almost three years in the UK. 'It would appear that these symptoms could possibly be a toxic effect of thalidomide,' he concluded. A flood of correspondence followed— other doctors had indeed had the same negative experience and thanks to Florence were now connecting it with thalidomide. And, as if to seal Florence's place in history, a few months later in Washington DC the FDA's Dr Frances Kelsey read Florence's letter and wondered what thalidomide might do to the foetus—a concern which helped block the sale of thalidomide in the US and saved many lives.

So Florence's letter became one of the pivotal moments in the thalidomide story—but the man himself receded into the shadows. One published account even referred to Leslie Florence as a woman named Florence Leslie. In 2011, when I read the famous letter, I wondered whether Florence was still alive. Out of curiosity rather than any conviction it might help Lyn Rowe's case, I did some internet searches. Before long I had found a retired doctor of that name living in Paraparaumu on the North Island of New Zealand. Within a few seconds of telephoning I knew I had the right number. A thick Scottish accent had given the game away.

Florence proved a fascinating man, keen to talk at length about thalidomide, and somewhat aggrieved he had not been accorded a more exalted place in history. He felt the FDA's Kelsey had piggy-backed on his work to achieve global fame: 'I didn't even get a thank you from her,' he complained more than once. When I gently suggested that Kelsey and he had both made important contributions, he slapped me down good-naturedly. 'What would you know, you're a lawyer. The important thing is, I was first.' While voluble about his rightful status, he was also a little suspicious and slightly concerned that if he helped us, Distillers might somehow exact revenge.

I told him Distillers was now part of a hugely successful multinational company (Diageo) and there was little chance thugs would be sent across the world to threaten a retired octogenarian. But Florence's doubts were hard to assuage, including those he held about me. On one occasion, I was telephoned by a Paraparaumu policewoman whom Florence had asked to check that I was not some imposter with an elaborate ruse to scam him. The next day I telephoned Florence to apologise if I had worried him with my questions. 'Don't worry laddie,' he interrupted. 'Can't be too careful, that's all.'

When, soon afterwards, I suggested I visit so we could speak in person, he was enthusiastic, even inviting me to stay with him. (I declined for fear of further police checks.)

So in February 2012 I visited Florence's townhouse in the seaside New Zealand town. He was well prepared, with his vast collection of thalidomide documents arrayed on his dining table. I quickly received a detailed tour of the (insufficient) praise and credit he had won for his letter. That was followed by the now-familiar litany of complaints: a book that was to feature him was never published because of the author's premature death; other doctors including Widukind Lenz had hogged the limelight for publicly connecting thalidomide with malformations; and, most galling of all, the FDA's Frances Kelsey would not have shot to global fame for blocking thalidomide sales in the US but for his letter which had got her thinking along the right track. And yet there was Kelsey, a feted hero still receiving accolades in the United States, and here he was, an obscure retired GP living on a pension in suburban New Zealand.

If this all sounds bitter, it was only marginally so. Most of Florence's complaining was done with good grace, and he was charming company. While he continually inquired about his hourly rate (and joked that all Scots were obsessed by money), he never actually asked to be paid and was relishing the thought of belated recognition late in life, if only as a by-product of giving evidence at Lyn's trial.

Florence's account was important for the contemporary perspective it gave us on Distillers and its unhappy thalidomide history. As we've seen, Distillers was a drinks company that branched into pharmaceuticals during World War II. In June 1956, Distillers' German-speaking medical adviser, Dr Walter Kennedy, visited Grünenthal, then a minor German drug firm. Kennedy examined a number of drugs but the one that interested him most was still in development—thalidomide. He was assured it was spectacularly effective and non-toxic and, on return to England, Kennedy gushed about it to his superiors. Completely smitten, he experimented with thalidomide on his own asthma and declared it 'undoubtedly of help'.

Distillers management jumped to attention and so began a serious courting of Grünenthal. At this stage thalidomide had never been sold anywhere, Distillers knew little about the drug, Grünenthal's animal work was lacking, and the so-called clinical trials in Germany were more testimonial than science. Nonetheless by late 1956 a draft licence agreement was on the table and the final version was signed in July 1957. The stringent terms of the contract illustrated Distillers' desperation: it had just nine months to get the drug to market, and it would have to buy raw thalidomide from Grünenthal until it was selling enough of the drug for its German partner to trust it with the recipe.

To get the ball rolling, Distillers obtained a supply of pills from Grünenthal and sent them out to friendly doctors in the UK. Thus, in September 1957, seven months before launch date, Distillers' Dr Kennedy advised Grünenthal he had 'spread' the drug among a 'large number' of doctors. This scattergun approach would reduce the clinical value of the work and not satisfy 'medical purists', Dr Kennedy admitted, but such 'pilot scale trials' were easier to arrange and they 'arouse interest' in the drug. Distillers was thinking of publicity and marketing more than valid science. Clearly in a rush, Distillers had been lulled by Grünenthal's glowing assurances and appeared to believe that the safety of the drug had already been established. Its pharmacologist George Somers later admitted Distillers had erred in relying on Grünenthal's unsatisfactory animal tests. 'I did not have the time to carry out my own long-term research on [thalidomide] before it was launched here. It was early days in the establishment of [Distillers] as a drugs company, I had little assistance, and I was working on three other drugs at the time in very cramped conditions.'

So Distillers limited itself to some routine animal testing, and did not consider checking for a possible effect in pregnancy. Distillers later defended this omission as 'the accepted pattern' in the UK. This was sleight of hand. A number of sensible drug companies in the UK and overseas did perform reproductive checks at that time (as is detailed in chapter 11).

Subsequent events suggest that if Distillers scientists had done the tests they would have turned up warning signs: within weeks of withdrawing the drug from sale in late 1961, Distillers found reduced litter sizes in rats dosed with thalidomide and, soon after, malformations in rabbits.

Nor did the company check the effect of the drug in the sensitive early period of human pregnancy by following up on the babies of pregnant women who had taken it—not during the testing period and not while thalidomide was on sale.

In April 1958, with all the fanfare it could muster, Distillers launched Distaval and Distaval Forte, the first drugs in the thalidomide range, and by far the best sellers. Advertising declared the drug a major advance and salesmen were dispatched far and wide, armed with the familiar 'super-safe, super-effective' sales pitch. 'The whole of our promotion is based on the extreme safety of Distaval,' a Distillers executive later stated.

A few months after the launch one Distillers salesman found his way to remote Turriff in Scotland, where the young Dr Leslie Florence was the senior GP. At the very time Distillers had been looking for new drugs, Florence had been looking for a new job. Having studied medicine at the University of Aberdeen (where he won two university prizes), he had worked in a succession of medical jobs until in 1954 he saw an advertisement for a GP vacancy in Turriff. Florence beat eighty other applicants and he and his wife Dora moved to the town, where Florence and a junior doctor attended to about seven thousand people in Turriff and the surrounding area.

From an early age Florence had suffered with severe eczema, and the associated itchiness often led to very disturbed sleep. He frequently experimented with sleeping medications, and found they left him groggy if he had to wake to make house calls during the night. So Florence was very interested when the Distillers salesman who came to his surgery in 1958 told him about a sensational new sleeping pill, Distaval. The salesman gave him some samples. 'Some weeks afterwards I decided to try it myself. I also gave a lower dose to my three-year-old son, who also suffered from eczema.'

Florence was impressed. 'It allowed both of us to get a much improved sleep. I found I was wide awake and alert immediately on waking, and could drive safely.' Soon Florence was trying the medication on his older patients who were having trouble sleeping.

On 17 February 1959 Florence wrote to Distillers, complimenting Distaval and asking for further samples. He also requested a list of thalidomide's side effects. A week later he received a reply from Dr Denis Burley, Distillers' medical director. Burley admitted his knowledge of 'the absorption and metabolism of Distaval is very scanty' but that 'it is impossible to give a toxic overdose'. At home in New Zealand in 2011, Florence still had these letters, which he regarded as treasures.

Burley's glowing testimonial to Florence about thalidomide was emblematic of Distillers' delight with its new drug. A year on from the launch, sales were steadily improving and there were plans to add further thalidomide medications to the range. Eventually Distillers would sell about 100 million thalidomide tablets. The only slight early annoyance for Distillers was that reports of nerve damage following the use of thalidomide started to trickle in. One such report—indeed the most influential report—was from Leslie Florence.

Florence had spent much of 1959 liberally dispensing Distaval to family and patients, reassured by the Distillers claim that it was impossible to give a toxic overdose. But then, towards the end of 1959, he and three of his patients developed symptoms of peripheral neuritis.

> First it was tingling in my feet and then in my hands, an occasional lack of steadiness on my feet, and cramping at night.
>
> I thought it curious that all four of us should develop the same symptoms at about the same time. I studied the records and realised that we had all been taking Distaval for an extended period. I wondered whether the symptoms might be linked to Distaval. I knew that Distaval was a relatively new drug and I considered it possible that this was a side effect of the drug that had not yet been publicised.

So in February 1960, Florence contacted Distillers again to ask whether it could confirm the nerve-damage side effect. He remembered the response. 'No such symptoms had been reported as a result of Distaval use, thalidomide was non-toxic,' Florence summarised. 'Distillers suggested that I re-examine my patients and consider other possibilities.'

That advice caused Florence to doubt his thesis and he continued to use thalidomide. But later that year the symptoms worsened, and Florence stopped using the drug to see if the symptoms improved. Florence also drove thirty-five miles to the University of Aberdeen to consult with Professor Alastair Macgregor, a highly regarded professor of therapeutics. 'I showed him my case files and my letters to and from Distillers.' Macgregor backed Florence's theory.

Further reinforcing Florence's suspicion was the fact that his symptoms, and those of his patients, were slowly lessening now that the drug had been withdrawn. With Professor Macgregor's encouragement, he decided to write his famous letter to the *British Medical Journal*, and it was published on 31 December 1960. In the very next edition of the journal, 14 January 1961, Distillers' Dr Denis Burley responded to Florence, admitting that 'isolated' reports of nerve damage had been sent to him since early 1960, and that nerve damage could indeed be caused by thalidomide.

Burley's admission irritated Florence. He felt the company should have told him earlier, especially as he had carried on using thalidomide during 1960 after being told by Distillers that it was safe. The eminent Professor Macgregor agreed. On 30 January 1961 he wrote to Florence generously congratulating him on his letter. 'I think it is quite disgraceful that after you had raised the matter with the Distillers Company that they did not inform you officially of the fact that they had reports suggesting peripheral neuritis.'

Macgregor and Florence were not the only parties aggravated by Distillers. In late January 1961, a Grünenthal delegation arrived at Distillers' offices in London. The Grünenthal men specifically complained that Burley's nerve-damage admission (prompted by Florence) had appeared in the pages of the *British Medical Journal* without any attempt to discuss the matter first with Grünenthal. This was 'definitely not in our interest' because of the 'worldwide importance of thalidomide', is how a German note recorded the discussion. 'Furthermore we pointed out the possible implications for the registration in the US.'

Grünenthal's concern was clear. It expected US Food and Drug Administration approval for sale in the US at any moment. US sales would send a flood of profits towards Grünenthal. So far, its US licence partner, Merrell, did not know about nerve damage and neither did the FDA. Grünenthal was worried that letting the cat out of the bag might delay FDA approval—a concern which proved well placed. The Florence–Burley exchange alerted both the FDA and Merrell to the nerve-damage issue and Merrell started asking questions of Grünenthal. This sent the German company into full propaganda mode. Grünenthal told the Americans, inaccurately, that nerve damage was rare, only followed long-term thalidomide use, appeared in predisposed people, and usually disappeared rapidly when the medication was withdrawn. It suggested that there had only been about fifty reported nerve-damage cases in total, though the German prosecutor later counted more than four hundred nerve-damage cases reported to Grünenthal by the end of February 1961. By this time some German doctors had rejected the drug completely.

• • •

While Leslie Florence's substantive involvement in the thalidomide affair ended in early 1961, he suffered from nerve damage for years, an ongoing reminder that he should never have believed Distillers' guarantee of non-toxicity. In 1966 he migrated with his wife and children to New Zealand, practising for decades as a GP in a suburb of the capital, Wellington.

Occasionally over the years references to Florence's 1960 letter appeared in the medical literature, cheering him no end. In 1982, the *British Medical Journal* ran an article headed 'Florence'. The author, Dr E. Saphier, described reading Florence's letter on New Year's Day 1961. 'I too had had a similar patient [with nerve damage]. The letter clicked. I felt sure he was right. I never used thalidomide again. I told other people. They in turn told others. I remember a psychiatrist friend telling me how several of them had stopped using the drug.' Dr Saphier noted that in the wake of the drug's withdrawal, Florence seemed to have been forgotten. 'In all the name calling that ensued I do not remember [Florence's] name being mentioned, and so far as I am aware, no tribute was ever paid him. Yet he must have saved a lot of suffering.'

Leslie Florence's health deteriorated in 2013 and in 2014 he entered a nursing home suffering dementia. Had there been a trial, rather than a settlement, he would have been an important witness. And had his health been better I have no doubt his most trenchant—and good-humoured—complaint about this book would have been the absence of several more chapters devoted to him.

• • •

Throughout 1961, Distillers had to deal with ongoing reports of thalidomide nerve damage and a debate about the condition in the pages of the UK medical journals. It was not the torrent of cases that Grünenthal was receiving (and concealing), but a steady stream nonetheless. Distillers' own count was 417 cases by December 1961, a fraction of the real damage, but still a substantial figure.

Yet despite the nerve-damage toll, Distillers continued to advertise the drug as safe, drawing bitter complaints from doctors. In October 1961, Distillers' safety assurances cranked up another notch. 'It is with absolute safety that "Distaval" can be administered to pregnant or breastfeeding women without any adverse effects on the mother or the child,' read one brochure. There was no basis for this broad assurance. Distillers had not tested the drug in early pregnancy, nor followed up pregnant women who had been given the drug.

Another safety-focused Distaval advertisement in the *British Medical Journal* on 4 November 1961 attracted yet more doctor criticism. By this time thalidomide sales had slumped because of the nerve-damage controversy and the company was under pressure to withdraw the drug. But like Grünenthal, though without the ruthless determination, Distillers was holding firm.

However events in Australia and Germany had overtaken the nerve-damage debate. On 17 November 1961, Woody Woodhouse, a Distillers employee in Sydney, Australia, wrote a letter to his colleagues in London detailing a visit to a local obstetrician, William McBride. McBride had told Woodhouse of malformations in six babies whose mothers had taken thalidomide. Woodhouse's letter was received by Distillers in London on 21 November 1961, just six days after Widukind Lenz, the German paediatrician, had first telephoned Grünenthal with his conviction that thalidomide was maiming and killing babies.

The next day, 22 November 1961, Distillers wrote to Grünenthal. 'We have had a rather disturbing report, from a Consultant Obstetrician, of deformities in children which could be associated with the taking of thalidomide by the mothers early in pregnancy, for morning sickness.' The report described the malformations, and the deaths of all six children.

> There is no history of infection and the administration of Distaval seemed to be the only common factor in these cases. I should be grateful if you could let me know whether you have heard of any similar reports. We believe that the cause of the abnormalities in these cases was much more likely to be due to undetected virus infection, but nevertheless we feel that the report must be investigated as fully as possible.

Five days later, on Monday 27 November 1961, Grünenthal responded with a telephone call alerting Distillers to the German malformation cases and its decision to withdraw the drug. Distillers quickly followed suit. Grünenthal also alerted its US licensee, Merrell, which had been trying for more than a year, increasingly desperately, to obtain approval from the US Food and Drug Administration (FDA) to sell the drug in the United States. It had a huge stockpile of the medication ready to go, and a massive sales force already schooled in the myriad wonders of thalidomide. Merrell believed thalidomide would make it a fortune. The only obstacle was a persistently stubborn FDA doctor who simply would not accept that thalidomide was fit for sale.

CHAPTER 8

Saving America

Dr Joseph Murray was impatient and frustrated. Fed up. As director of scientific relations for the drug company Merrell, it was Murray's job to push and prod the FDA regulators into approving thalidomide for sale in the United States. But for more than six months Murray had fumed as Frances Oldham Kelsey, a novice FDA medical officer, raised a never-ending list of complaints and concerns about the safety of his pet German drug.

This was not the sort of treatment drug companies expected from the business-friendly FDA. But Kelsey was not the usual sort of FDA officer. For a start she was a woman, and a qualified pharmacologist as well as a medical doctor. Although she had recently arrived at the FDA, she was forty-six years old: experienced, confident and apparently immune to the pressure Merrell had been applying to her.

Kelsey was nursing her own good reasons to be irritated with Merrell and its chief lobbyist, Joseph Murray. Months earlier she had received the 31 December 1960 edition of the *British Medical Journal*. To her surprise she found Leslie Florence's letter suggesting that thalidomide had caused nerve damage in four of his patients. This was a serious side effect and Kelsey was peeved Merrell had never mentioned it. She felt she had been misled.

It was now 11 May 1961 and Kelsey and Murray were meeting yet again: Kelsey annoyed and suspicious of the glowing claims for thalidomide; and Murray, angry that Merrell's chosen date for the drug's launch had come and gone, held up by a lone nitpicking FDA staffer.

Kelsey was accompanied by two other FDA officers at the meeting, but that didn't daunt Murray. He again pressed the FDA to 'expedite clearance' of thalidomide and tried to explain away Merrell's silence about nerve damage. Kelsey refused to be charmed or railroaded. She told Murray the FDA was unconvinced about thalidomide's safety and gave him a list of issues on which more information was required. Most of the list was familiar to Murray: nerve damage, the need for long-term animal experiments, overdose information. But on Kelsey's list was a new issue. What information was there, Kelsey demanded, to establish that thalidomide was safe for the foetus when used in pregnancy?

Later, when it emerged that thalidomide was responsible for the death and malformation of thousands of babies, Kelsey's query assumed legendary status. But why did Kelsey raise the pregnancy question? What did she know that others did not? Was she, as many drug-company backers claimed, simply lucky? Or was there something about the drug that tipped her off? Some have even claimed that it was all an urban myth and that Kelsey never expressed concern about the foetus.

But Kelsey certainly did—for the first time at that meeting in May 1961 (more than six weeks before Wendy Rowe started taking thalidomide), and then repeatedly in the months that followed. Kelsey's questions about thalidomide—including the concern that it might harm a foetus—blocked Merrell's plan to make the drug a bestseller in the United States. Merrell was still struggling to satisfy Kelsey more than six months later in November 1961, when news about the malformations in Germany and Australia emerged, forcing Merrell to shelve its US thalidomide plans permanently.

Kelsey's role in the saga soon became public and she vaulted to national prominence, feted by President Kennedy at the White House and celebrated as the woman who saved the United States from the scourge of thalidomide. She also very probably saved Merrell from lawsuit-driven bankruptcy. 'If it hadn't been for her, we'd be out of business,' a Merrell lawyer noted. As it was, Merrell had irresponsibly spread millions of thalidomide sample pills across the US, causing at least ten recognised cases of birth damage (plus others never located and yet others who died at birth or shortly afterwards). But it could have been unimaginably worse.

Kelsey was and remains a hero to many—not least to the members of Lyn Rowe's legal team. We asserted repeatedly in court documents that a careful and responsible pharmaceutical company would and should have worried that thalidomide might harm a foetus and done something about it: warned consumers, stopped or limited sale of the drug, surveyed pregnant women who had taken the drug, checked with doctors. Clearly, in our view, Kelsey took this assertion out of the realm of the hypothetical and made it real. Fact: a qualified, careful doctor at the FDA had questioned the effect of thalidomide on the foetus before its malforming effect had become known.

But how did Kelsey do it? The explanation for what led Kelsey to that moment in May 1961 is one of the keys to understanding exactly why so much of the thalidomide disaster was avoidable.

● ● ●

Frances Oldham (she added Kelsey after her marriage) was born in 1914 on Vancouver Island, Canada, into a family that encouraged women into higher education. Kelsey's mother had two sisters: one a doctor, the other a lawyer.

After high school, Kelsey studied at Montreal's McGill University, gaining a science degree and then a master's degree in pharmacology in 1935. She then applied for a job at the University of Chicago's pharmacology department. The acceptance letter from Professor Eugene Geiling started, 'Dear Mr Oldham'. Kelsey agonised over whether to write back admitting to her gender, and offering Geiling the chance to reconsider. Undecided, she consulted her academic supervisor. 'Don't be ridiculous,' he responded. 'Accept the job, sign your name, put Miss in brackets afterwards, and go!'

Perhaps Kelsey was lucky: she later found Geiling very fair, but old-fashioned and conservative. 'He did not really hold too much with women as scientists.' And Geiling never revealed whether or not his offer would have held had he known Frances Oldham was a woman. In Chicago, Kelsey was awarded a PhD in 1938—her investigations concerned the posterior pituitary gland of the armadillo—and then did postdoctoral work and taught.

By this time, thanks to the most notorious drug disaster of that era, Kelsey had already learned something about the potential risks of new drugs. Sulfanilamide was developed in Germany in the early 1930s. The drug revolutionised the treatment of infection, though it was later partly superseded by penicillin. One US drug outfit in Tennessee, S. E. Massengill Company, decided in 1937 to mix sulfanilamide into a liquid solution to make it more easily ingested, especially by children. The company's chief scientist, Harold Watkins, created 'Elixir Sulfanilamide' by combining sulfanilamide with a flavouring and the solvent diethylene glycol, also known as DEG. Diethylene glycol was chemically related to anti-freeze and, unknown to Watkins, very toxic.

At that time there was little government regulation of the drug industry, an open-slather approach that led to a marketplace full of quack remedies. It also meant that 'Elixir Sulfanilamide' was untested in animals or humans when it was shipped out of the Massengill factory. A slew of deaths quickly followed—more than one hundred in total. Many of the dead were children, victims of kidney failure. The drug was hastily withdrawn and the FDA turned to Frances Kelsey's boss Professor Geiling at the University of Chicago for assistance in analysing the elixir. Geiling set up toxicity experiments in dogs, rabbits, rats and monkeys and enlisted his graduate students to help. The animals were given the different elements of the elixir and the effects were monitored. 'My particular task was to watch the rats,' Kelsey recalled. 'In no time at all it was perfectly apparent that it was the diethylene glycol that was at fault…the rats soon died [of kidney failure] just as the kids did.'

The company owner, Dr Samuel Massengill, expressed sympathy but denied all responsibility for the deaths in a manner eerily similar to Grünenthal's twenty-five years later. 'My chemists and I deeply regret the fatal results, but there was no error in the manufacture of the product. We have been supplying a legitimate professional demand and not once could have foreseen the unlooked-for results. I do not feel that there was any responsibility on our part.' Watkins, the chemist who created the elixir, felt far worse than his employer: he reportedly took his own life.

Kelsey's involvement in the sulfanilamide affair was the first in a remarkable series of events and circumstances which later made her among the most qualified and able people in the world to pick up the warning signs about thalidomide. The next critical experience— which gave Kelsey an insight into the vulnerability of foetuses—came when she and Dr Fremont Ellis Kelsey, a pharmacologist and fellow faculty member in Chicago she married in 1943, worked on a wartime hunt for a new antimalarial drug.

In 1942 Japanese forces invaded and occupied the Dutch East Indies (Indonesia), then home to the cinchona plantations that were the source of the majority of the world's quinine (a product extracted from cinchona bark). Quinine was the key antimalarial drug, and the Japanese occupation cut off much of the United States' supply. This was potentially disastrous at a time when a massive supply of the drug was needed for troops in malaria-affected war zones.

Part of the US Government's response was to coordinate a research effort to find replacement drugs. The University of Chicago (and both Frances and Ellis Kelsey) played a role by running tests on some of the potential antimalarial compounds synthesised elsewhere. Rats, dogs, chicken, ducks and monkeys were infected with malaria and then treated with the test compounds. A limited supply of quinine was used to treat infected animals for comparison purposes.

Recounting this experience decades later, Kelsey recalled with amusement a veterinarian in Texas who had sent in a proposed malaria cure. He had tested it on his secretary and was planning to try it on his cattle. 'When we read this, we said it shows the relative value placed on women and cattle in Texas.'

In addition to the hunt for new malarial drugs, the Chicago researchers were able to do some research on the side. Rabbits were known to break down quinine very quickly. Frances and Ellis Kelsey decided to see whether pregnant rabbits and rabbit embryos also possessed this ability. The result was interesting. The pregnant rabbit had a reduced ability to metabolise quinine, and the rabbit embryo no ability at all. That meant quinine in rabbit embryos was not removed from the (foetal) body and built up to toxic levels. This firsthand experience taught Kelsey, as she put it, that 'the embryo or the young may handle a drug differently from the mother'. She also knew that a drug that did not harm the mother could severely harm a foetus.

The doctors Kelsey and their co-workers authored several published articles on their quinine work in the 1940s.

At the end of the war Kelsey decided to study for a medical degree; she graduated in 1950, having given birth to daughters in 1947 and 1949. Kelsey was conscious of her health during pregnancy. She was, in any event, a non-smoker and drank very little. She was also 'very cautious about using drugs during my own pregnancies'. After medical school Kelsey took a job with the *Journal of the American Medical Association* assessing articles submitted by doctors about new drugs. Kelsey observed that the science in the articles was frequently poor, and that certain authors' names kept recurring. It was clear that some doctors had a sideline in talking up new drugs for the drug companies. 'We would jot down, oh it's Dr So-and-so again,' Kelsey said.

In 1952 the Kelsey family moved to Vermillion, a small town in South Dakota, where Ellis Kelsey taught pharmacology and Frances Kelsey worked as a researcher, teacher and locum GP. By 1960 the couple wanted to move to a big city and both obtained job offers in Washington: Ellis Kelsey at the National Institutes of Health and Frances Kelsey at the FDA.

The FDA employed Kelsey as a medical officer. Her job was to assess NDAs, or new drug applications, submitted by drug companies seeking FDA sale approval. A team of three assessed each NDA: working alongside the medical officer, who was responsible for corresponding with the drug companies, were a chemist and a pharmacologist. Kelsey was in fact an exceptionally well qualified medical officer, with her PhD in pharmacology as well as her medical degree.

Kelsey spent her first few weeks familiarising herself with the FDA and its operations. Then, in early September 1960, she was assigned two NDAs at about the same time. One was for a rectal enema, Kelsey later remembered. The other was an apparently straightforward application for a sleeping pill. 'I was the newest person there and pretty green, so my supervisors decided, "Well, this is a very easy one. There will be no problems with sleeping pills."' The drug was Kevadon, Merrell's chosen brand name for its German drug, thalidomide.

● ● ●

If not for a false start the thalidomide NDA might have landed at the FDA several years before Kelsey arrived. In 1956 another US drug company, Smith Kline & French (SKF), did a deal with Grünenthal to test and potentially market the drug. SKF did extensive animal and human testing with the drug—and, in the process, caused one known malformed birth. Careful monitoring and follow-up might have connected the baby to the test drug and raised concern. But, sadly, the testing was so poorly scrutinised that SKF said it did not become aware of the case until years later. In any event, by January 1958 SKF had gone completely cold on thalidomide. Its animal testing did not identify a significant sedative effect and, worryingly (and unlike Grünenthal), SKF was able to kill cats and stop dogs breathing using large doses of thalidomide. SKF concluded that thalidomide's apparent harmlessness was not an inherent property, but rather a result of the drug being poorly absorbed.

SKF also found little clinical potential, in part because it believed the drug was not strong enough to remedy even moderate insomnia. In a carefully worded January 1958 letter, SKF told Grünenthal it was not interested in the drug. Grünenthal was not fazed. Almost immediately it did a deal with another US firm, Wm. S. Merrell, which, to its lasting regret, would prove far more enthusiastic than SKF.

Merrell was an old Cincinnati firm, established in 1828, which during the thalidomide era was a division of Richardson-Merrell.

Merrell believed thalidomide to be a winner, and was desperate to get it to market. It reached an agreement with Grünenthal in 1958 and was hoping to get FDA approval the following year. In 1959 it estimated the total sedative market in the US was worth $20 million and, Merrell noted, thalidomide would have to be aggressively promoted as 'highly effective' yet 'safe and comfortable'. Fortunately Frances Kelsey would reach her own view about the drug's safety.

The FDA Kelsey joined in 1960 was in something of a crisis. A senior employee, Dr Barbara Moulton, had resigned in February 1960 and turned whistleblower. In June that year Moulton appeared in the caucus room of the Old Senate Office Building and gave incendiary evidence to a senate subcommittee. Moulton charged the FDA with 'failing utterly' to protect the public from unsafe drugs, and branded certain officials corrupt, stupid or misinformed. Fraternisation, she said, was rife between FDA officers and industry, and urgent action was needed to protect young FDA officers from 'brainwashing' by drug lobbyists. Even if a medical officer was able to resist industry pressure, he or she might still be overruled by an FDA superior anxious to appease the drug company. On one occasion, Moulton told the committee, her boss at the FDA had insisted she ease off on a drug company. 'I will not have my policy of friendliness with industry interfered with,' he told her.

Moulton called for urgent reform. FDA officials who had placed the 'welfare of the [drug] industry above that of the consumer' should be sacked. The FDA, Moulton said, should be given the power to judge a drug's efficacy, not just its safety, because judging safety in the absence of efficacy was absurd. 'No drug is safe if it fails to cure a serious disease for which a cure is available. No drug is too dangerous to use if it will cure a fatal disease for which no other cure is available.'

Moulton was right: existing drug laws were archaic. The 1937 sulfanilamide affair and the heavy death toll had led to important law reform in the guise of the Food, Drug, and Cosmetic Act of 1938—but it was far from adequate. Under the 1938 law—still in force when Moulton gave her evidence—drug manufacturers were obliged to supply the FDA with information on a drug's chemistry, animal test results, and the outcome of (human) clinical trials. If the FDA judged the drug safe then the drug could be marketed. While a major step forward, there were big gaps. Under the 1938 law drug companies could conduct as many clinical trials as they pleased, without FDA approval or involvement and before even basic safety tests in animals. And they could also pick and choose their clinical investigators, with no regard to expertise or independence. This meant much of the drug company clinical trial work was deeply unscientific: one senior FDA officer described it as 'all baloney' and 'essentially a bunch of testimonials'.

Another critical failing was that the question of whether or not a drug was actually effective was not within the FDA's remit. This led to the continued criticism that an enterprising company could have bottled water and marketed it as a medicine. In fact some did—one cancer treatment was found on analysis to be almost pure distilled water.

The slack state of the law meant that to sell thalidomide, Merrell just had to persuade the FDA that it was safe. Effectiveness only entered the equation via the back door. FDA officers might be willing to tolerate more side effects (or a bit less safety) if a proposed new drug was critical or lifesaving. Conversely, if a drug was not critical an FDA officer might insist on strict safety. Frances Kelsey would make this point repeatedly in dealing with thalidomide. In her view an unimportant sleeping pill had to be genuinely safe.

Moulton's whistleblowing—and her call for urgent reform—caused a sensation, especially within the drug companies and at the FDA, where she had labelled the Commissioner, George Larrick, as unqualified. Her evidence also came not long after a scandal in which Dr Henry Welch had been forced to resign as head of the FDA's antibiotics division. Welch had been the editor of two drug journals focused on antibiotics, for which he told the FDA he was receiving a very modest 'honorarium'. But to Welch's disgrace it emerged that he had in fact enjoyed an ownership stake in the journals, collected a percentage of drug advertising, and had made about $250,000 over seven years from these and other extra-curricular activities.

Moulton's scathing critique and Welch's unmasking contributed to a groundswell of support for tougher drug laws and a regulatory authority with sharper teeth and a more industry-sceptic stance. Two years later that groundswell would be transformed into an irresistible force by Frances Kelsey and thalidomide, as the United States realised only Kelsey's shrewdness and persistence—not the existing drug laws—had saved it from a German-style thalidomide disaster.

• • •

Once assigned the Kevadon NDA in September 1960, Kelsey had to act quickly because if there was no decision within sixty days the drug was automatically approved for sale. Kelsey and her team thought Merrell's NDA was full of problems. Among her concerns was that doctors she had identified as hacks for hire (while working for the *Journal of the American Medical Association*) were involved in thalidomide studies. The claims made 'were too glowing' and many were 'more testimonials than scientific studies', she later said.

Frances Kelsey also had the benefit of a memo from her husband about Merrell's pharmacology. 'An interesting collection of meaningless pseudo-scientific jargon, apparently intended to impress chemically unsophisticated readers,' is how Ellis Kelsey described one section of the work. He reserved great scorn for the claim that thalidomide was so atoxic that no LD50 (the dose of thalidomide required to kill fifty per cent of test animals) could be found. 'No other substance can make that claim!' In fact part of Merrell's submission was so absurd that Ellis Kelsey concluded: 'I cannot believe this to be honest incompetence.'

Frances Kelsey and her team also wondered why the drug was effective as a sedative in humans and not in rats. Was the weak sedative effect and low toxicity in test animals because the drug was not being absorbed? If that was the case, it might be far more toxic than it appeared.

Merrell could have shed some light on these concerns. James Knox Smith, who did some animal testing for Merrell, told a later legal hearing that Merrell had been able to kill mice with large doses of the drug. But Merrell did not report this to the FDA, an omission Knox Smith criticised. Further, Merrell was able to kill twenty-two out of thirty rats with large doses of thalidomide mixed into a syrup. Again, the FDA was not told of these experiments. Instead Merrell told the FDA about separate tests in which all rats survived.

There were no tests on pregnant animals in the Merrell submission to the FDA. Like Grünenthal in Germany and Distillers in the UK, Merrell had not done this testing. Dr Carl Bunde, Merrell's director of medical research in 1960–61, told a later court hearing that 'at that time' testing drugs on pregnant animals 'was not routine. It was not usual. It was not part of the ordinary operation'. Instead, Bunde said, the 'universal' practice was to 'simply look for [deformities] when it was used in a human. The use of animals was not considered a method of solving this problem'.

Bunde was being loose with the truth. In 1959, at exactly the time it was working on thalidomide, Merrell did reproductive testing on another substance it had under investigation—the notorious anti-cholesterol drug MER-29 that, once released in 1961, caused a spate of severe injuries including skin damage and cataracts. The MER-29 reproductive testing was performed both in-house and at an external consultancy. Even earlier, in 1956 and 1957, Merrell had performed reproductive testing on another drug under development and found it damaged rat foetuses. So, contrary to Bunde's assertions, Merrell knew about reproductive testing, appreciated the need for it, and tested drugs on pregnant animals in its own laboratories and at external consultancies.

Merrell has never satisfactorily explained why no reproductive testing was done for thalidomide. But a big part of the explanation is that it was seduced by Grünenthal's false and meaningless assurances that there were no side effects of any consequence despite massive sales across Europe.

But while the lack of safety information about pregnancy did not yet worry Frances Kelsey, she had seen enough in the Merrell material to be concerned. On 10 November 1960, she marked the Kevadon (thalidomide) NDA incomplete and told the company to submit further information. The sixty-day clock started again. It was a brave move by Kelsey. Drug companies were not accustomed to being treated in this fashion and Merrell executives poured the pressure on. They telephoned and visited Kelsey and complained to her superiors, all the while stressing the need for a swift approval.

• • •

By now, though, Merrell had taken steps that ensured that no matter what Kelsey ultimately decided, millions of thalidomide pills would reach US consumers. That came about because Merrell was determined to familiarise doctors with Kevadon in advance of the FDA's green light. But how to do that when sale of the drug was still prohibited? The solution was simple. Under the still-in-force 1938 laws, a drug company could conduct as many clinical trials as it wanted prior to sale approval. This was a loophole Merrell exploited ruthlessly.

In October 1960 Merrell conducted a two-day thalidomide seminar for its salesmen. A manual distributed at the seminar—*Kevadon Hospital Clinical Program*—made clear this was a promotional campaign masquerading as a clinical investigation. Salesmen were to contact 'the most influential' doctors 'for the purpose of selling them on Kevadon and providing them with a clinical supply' and 'to perfect and develop the best possible [sales] story for the national introduction of Kevadon'.

Sales reps were told that the importance and safety of thalidomide had already been firmly established. What Merrell wanted was 'widespread confirmation of its usefulness'—good news which would be 'spread among hospital staff members'. And in case any sales reps were tempted to take the research part too seriously, there was this caution:

> You can assure your doctors that they need not report results if they don't want to…
>
> Let them know the basic clinical research on Kevadon has been done. Don't get involved [in] selling a basic clinical research program instead of Kevadon. Appeal to the doctor's ego—we think he is important enough to be selected as one of the first to use Kevadon in that section of the country.

Naturally, salesmen were also encouraged to approach doctors with the Grünenthal-inspired safety mantra. 'It is perfectly safe to state that every known hypnotic agent, except Kevadon, is capable of causing death by respiratory failure.'

Merrell's overblown claims were not limited to safety. It produced a brochure for doctors claiming that Kevadon was useful in treating 'anxiety and apprehension' arising from no less than twenty-four different conditions including bed-wetting, marital discord, nightmares, poor schoolwork, premature ejaculation and, tellingly, nausea and vomiting.

Clearly the Merrell 'clinical program' was about sales, not research. Under its guise, Merrell supplied 2,528,412 thalidomide pills to more than 1200 doctors. About 20,000 patients, including more than 3000 women of child-bearing age, received a drug that had never been approved for sale and which was appallingly dangerous. Later, when it uncovered what had gone on, the FDA argued for Merrell and its executives to face criminal charges over what the FDA believed was a blatant and illegal sales push.

• • •

One of the doctors Merrell supplied with thalidomide was Ray Nulsen, a Cincinnati GP then in his late forties, who had devoted himself to obstetrics and who enjoyed the good fortune of being Don Merrell's fraternity brother. Nulsen had been happy to oblige when Merrell, a descendant of the founding Merrell family, kicked off Nulsen's career as a drug tester by asking him to test a varicose veins treatment in about 1940.

Merrell's enthusiasm for Nulsen as a tester continued for twenty years, right up until the thalidomide disaster in 1961. He was 'very cooperative, he was competent and he was geographically convenient,' the company's medical director Dr Raymond Pogge later said, in perhaps a case of damning Nulsen with faint praise.

Indeed, Nulsen's testing had multiple shortcomings: he employed slack investigative methods, ignored and denied horrible side effects, and abdicated much of the science to his friends at Merrell. In subsequent court hearings Nulsen presented an easy target. For a start, his clinical trials were farcical. As he told it, 'one of the girls in the office keeps a running record of the patients who take the medication'. Relevant patient comments or observations were jotted down. Then—perhaps at lunch, he told a court hearing—Nulsen would hand the results to Merrell's medical director, Raymond Pogge.

It was Pogge who broached the subject of thalidomide testing with Nulsen—perhaps during a game of golf, Nulsen later ventured. Pogge told Nulsen he didn't know how thalidomide worked but that it was 'absolutely harmless'. And would Nulsen please trial the drug on women suffering insomnia in late pregnancy? As usual, Nulsen was happy to get started. He found thalidomide 'acted beautifully' and he and his family helped themselves to free samples, of which there was no shortage: Merrell sent Nulsen about 100,000 thalidomide tablets over two years. Soon Nulsen expanded the 'trial' to at least seven hundred patients. At the explicit request of Merrell he began including pregnant women suffering nausea.

One noteworthy feature of the long-running Nulsen–Merrell partnership was that Nulsen would occasionally burst into print to extol the virtues of a Merrell drug. In June 1961, an article about the use of thalidomide in the third trimester of pregnancy was published under Ray Nulsen's name in the *American Journal of Obstetrics & Gynecology*. But Ray Nulsen, as it happened, was not the author.

'Now, sir, did you physically write the article?' a lawyer for one of the United States victims asked Nulsen at a 1966 deposition.

'No,' Nulsen responded.

> Who wrote it?
> Dr Pogge or someone at the Merrell company.

Did you supply for this article any of the information with respect to the chemical facts contained in this article?
No.
Did you supply any of the footnotes for this article?
No.
Who made the original drafts?
Dr Pogge.
…
Were you [shown] a draft of the article?
Yes.
Did you make any additions to it?
I don't remember.
Did you make any changes to it?
I don't remember.
…
Who submitted the article for publication?
Merrell.

Nulsen's sloppy testing and cosy relationship with Merrell led to tragedy. The thalidomide article that appeared under Nulsen's name included this line: 'There is no danger to the baby if some of it appears in the milk or passes the placental barrier.' Under questioning, Nulsen conceded he did not write that and had no idea whether or not thalidomide passed the placenta and reached the foetus.

Merrell's Raymond Pogge had written the whole article, including the foetus line: he admitted as much under oath, adding that he had written articles for doctors up to thirty times in the past. He too admitted he had not known whether or not thalidomide passed the placenta and reached the foetus.

Nulsen's 'tests' and his ghosted article were used by Merrell to vouchsafe the effectiveness and safety of thalidomide in pregnancy. In one letter to doctors Merrell reported that 'Nulsen administered

Kevadon to expectant mothers with a sleep problem without effect on the newborn infants'. This was a very misleading précis—it carried the false implication that Nulsen had checked on the capacity of the drug to damage a foetus. On other occasions Merrell resorted to variations of these false assurances. In December 1960 it wrote to a US doctor in response to a question on the possible effect of Kevadon on the foetus. Merrell replied that it was not known 'whether or not there is any transfer of Kevadon across the placental barrier' but that even if there is 'it would be completely safe'.

Far worse was to come. During the first five months of 1961 Nulsen delivered five severely damaged children, two of whom were stillborn. Did alarm bells ring for Nulsen? Why were his patients' babies suddenly afflicted in this manner? Could it have something to do with the new pills he was using? If these thoughts ever occurred to Nulsen he never admitted it, and apparently he did not report the malformed births to Merrell. Shortly after the last of these births, Merrell wrote to Nulsen asking for his assistance in satisfying Kelsey's queries about the foetus. Had he seen any foetal abnormalities during his 'trial'? Nulsen responded that he had not.

Perhaps Merrell might have pursued Nulsen with a little more vigour. But it is also possible that Merrell could never have extracted the truth from its 'geographically convenient' pregnancy tester. After the danger of thalidomide was publicly revealed in late 1961 and the FDA and others began trying to find babies damaged by thalidomide, Ray Nulsen denied having given thalidomide to the mothers of any of the five malformed infants. FDA documents show that both it and Merrell thought Nulsen was lying. Even when the mothers swore that Nulsen had given them Kevadon, Nulsen denied it. 'Merrell does not believe him,' a 1962 FDA memo read. 'Merrell is quite sure he did dispense the drug to her throughout the period of pregnancy.' The

FDA's investigation of Ray Nulsen continued for months. At one point the FDA discovered that Nulsen had made about forty donations to an orphanage in the name of children he delivered stillborn or who had died shortly after birth between 1959 and 1962. The FDA briefly believed it had discovered a secret list of Nulsen's thalidomide victims. This theory was later discounted, though the exact number of deaths and injuries caused by thalidomide in Nulsen's practice was never ascertained.

Ray Nulsen ended up as one of the villains of the thalidomide story. But it could have been so different. He was testing thalidomide in pregnancy at the request of the drug company. He was in a prime position to connect the drug to the malformations and halt the disaster. But he didn't make the connection—or if he did, he said nothing. Had he raised the alarm, Ray Nulsen would be remembered very differently.

• • •

In February 1961, with Merrell pressuring her to approve thalidomide in time for a March 1961 launch, Frances Kelsey received some recent copies of the *British Medical Journal*. In the 31 December 1960 edition she read Leslie Florence's letter suggesting thalidomide was responsible for peripheral neuritis in his patients. The report disturbed Kelsey. First, Merrell had never told her about this side effect. Second, thalidomide was just a sleeping pill, not a lifesaving drug, and it would be widely used. Any significant nerve damage was an unacceptable side effect. In her polite but firm manner Kelsey asked Merrell why she had not been told about this side effect.

Merrell claimed it had known nothing about nerve damage and immediately dispatched a team to the UK and then on to Germany for discussions with Distillers and Grünenthal. The American team was roundly assured of the drug's safety. Grünenthal, for example, declared the condition was rare and played down its seriousness. The Merrell men appeared to swallow the Grünenthal line willingly. They returned to the US and Merrell told Kelsey that thalidomide nerve damage was very rare and 'rapidly reversible'.

Kelsey was not taken in. 'I had the feeling throughout that they were at no time being wholly frank with me and this attitude has obtained in all our conferences etc regarding this drug,' she wrote in a memo on 30 March 1961. She suspected that the frequency of nerve damage was 'very much greater' than Merrell wanted her to believe.

Merrell followed up with intense lobbying and complaints to Kelsey's bosses. Undaunted, Kelsey wrote to Merrell on 5 May 1961 and again reset the sixty-day clock on the thalidomide application. She accused Merrell of failing to be frank about the nerve-damage side effect and warned the company it had an obligation to prove the drug was safe. Within days senior Merrell management had accused Kelsey of libel, and visited her bosses to complain.

But Kelsey, not to be browbeaten, was ready to raise another—crucial—concern about thalidomide's safety. Thanks to the 1937 sulfanilamide disaster and her peripheral role in it, Kelsey knew that drug companies were capable of selling untested (or poorly tested) drugs with catastrophic results. Thanks to her World War II quinine experiments, Kelsey knew that a drug could be safe for the mother and still devastate her foetus. Thanks to her work at the AMA journal, Kelsey knew that some doctors were willing to make absurd claims for a new drug. And, obvious though it is, Kelsey was not just a doctor but a woman who had had two children of her own. She had been careful not to take drugs during her pregnancies. She regarded the health of the foetus as important, a consideration that clearly did not preoccupy the men in charge at Grünenthal and Distillers. Kelsey also had the advantage of colleagues who shared her concern about the health of the foetus. She talked with two of them, and they encouraged her to pursue this line of questioning.

So at that famous 11 May 1961 meeting, Kelsey told Merrell she wanted to know whether the drug was safe in pregnancy. Merrell subsequently tried to satisfy Kelsey with some information about late pregnancy from its soon-to-be-disgraced investigator Ray Nulsen. Kelsey rejected it. She wanted to know about early pregnancy and continued to raise the issue. At one point she said that if the drug was approved it would need to carry a warning about the 'possible hazard to the fetus if the drug is given during pregnancy'.

In the aftermath of the thalidomide scandal, Kelsey was asked to explain why she had worried about thalidomide's effect on the foetus. Her reasoning was straightforward. If the drug could damage the nervous systems of adults, what might it do to a vulnerable, growing foetus? 'We felt that the fetus might be particularly susceptible to such toxicity inasmuch as it might be exposed to a drug for as long as nine months,' and this was especially so in light of the 'rapid growth and imperfect enzyme systems of the developing [fetus]'.

Merrell saw Kelsey's complaints and queries as uninformed pig-headedness. Not content with repeatedly lobbying her directly, Merrell went behind Kelsey's back to her bosses. In total Merrell contacted the FDA fifty times between September 1960 and November 1961.

In September 1961, Merrell, in desperation, organised a meeting at the FDA of some of its medical investigators to deal with Kelsey's concerns. Kelsey asked the assembled doctors if any of them could assure the drug's safety for the foetus. None could, and one backed Kelsey, agreeing that it would be 'highly desirable' to check for a possible effect.

During this period the FDA started keeping a list of doctors submitting 'incredible' reports on behalf of drug companies. This was not for those who were 'substandard, poor reporters [or] overly enthusiastic', an FDA memo informed Kelsey and her fellow medical officers. Rather, the list was for doctors suspected of 'untruthfulness, psychosis, or dangerous incompetence and irresponsibility'. It is not known if Kelsey submitted the names of any of Merrell's investigators, but Merrell was now despairing of ever persuading Kelsey that thalidomide was safe. 'We live in hope,' a Merrell vice-president advised Grünenthal.

But events overseas were about to intervene. Kelsey had time to restart the sixty-day clock one final time on Merrell's application before the company's chief lobbyist Joseph Murray telephoned her on 30 November 1961. Thalidomide, Murray told Kelsey, had been linked to birth malformations in Germany.

• • •

Merrell executives must have been shocked by the news from Germany. But it appears not shocked enough, or not sufficiently convinced that the threat was real, to adequately warn doctors or the public.

On 1 December 1961 executives from Merrell and from Horner, a Canadian firm that had been selling thalidomide for a few months, flew to Germany. The subsequent account of a Horner executive suggests Grünenthal played down the concerns expressed by Widukind Lenz, who had finally connected thalidomide to the rocketing number of dead and malformed babies. Grünenthal treated the American visitors to a critique of Lenz's arguments and claimed that Lenz was refusing to reveal his data. '[Lenz] is supposed to have told Grünenthal that he had a "vision" indicating Contergan as the cause of all these deformities,' the Horner executive wrote. Grünenthal also appears to have engaged in a familiar dose of character assassination. '[Lenz's] father was a famous and popular geneticist in Nazi times since he had "proven" the validity of the master-race concept on genetic grounds,' the same Horner executive reported.

On 5 December 1961 Merrell wrote to US doctors advising them of the reports of malformations overseas and suggesting that thalidomide not be given to pregnant women. A further letter was sent in February 1962. Both emphasised that the link to birth malformations was uncertain. The FDA appears to have believed that this was adequate warning. What the FDA did not know was that Merrell had given thalidomide samples to more than 1200 doctors across the United States—but had sent the half-hearted warning letters to only about 150 of them. Merrell had simply left 1100 doctors in the dark, many of them armed with deadly thalidomide tablets that Merrell had previously assured them were outstandingly safe.

Merrell knew very well that the media had not alerted the doctors to the danger. On 22 December 1961 a Merrell vice-president wrote to Grünenthal mentioning there had been 'no publicity in the lay press in either the United States or Canada'. It was not until 20 March 1962, almost four months after learning of the danger, that Merrell wrote to all of its 1200-plus 'investigators' asking for the thalidomide 'research' to stop and requesting the return of all stocks. The FDA did not discover Merrell's monumental failure to warn doctors until the following month, April 1962. Up until then the FDA believed that only about 150 doctors had been given the drug and all had been warned in December 1961. This was a gross error of judgment; the FDA should never have trusted Merrell.

Bruised—and embarrassed at having been duped—the FDA began an intense investigation of Merrell's thalidomide conduct, featuring raids on Merrell offices and interviews with current and former employees. FDA staff were also sent to retrieve the drug from doctors' offices. By questioning doctors the FDA quickly discovered ten babies whose malformations had been caused by Merrell's thalidomide and another seven caused by thalidomide obtained overseas. (This search for affected babies was far from exhaustive.)

At a conference in November 1962, senior FDA officers and lawyers discussed their findings and possible action against Merrell. The FDA believed Merrell had made false and misleading claims to investigators, run a marketing program for thalidomide before getting sales approval, withheld adverse drug data, submitted false data, and misled the FDA about the drug recall.

The FDA then pushed for charges against Merrell and some of its key staff, the central issue being Merrell's thinly disguised marketing campaign for a drug it was not allowed to sell. Disappointingly for the FDA, and surprisingly given the evidence, the US Department of Justice decided not to prosecute.

The decision was based partly on ignorance of the devastation thalidomide had wrought. 'It would be difficult to prove that Kevadon's distribution in the United States resulted in grave harm,' the Department of Justice decided in 1964. 'As far as is known, only one malformed baby has been born in the United States as a result of its mother's use of Kevadon.' This was wrong—the FDA itself knew of ten cases at the time, and more would have been found with a thorough investigation.

● ● ●

Merrell's handling of thalidomide in the United States was shameful but it was not a one-off. At almost exactly the same time as its thalidomide fiasco, it was running an even more disgraceful campaign for an anti-cholesterol drug that would ultimately lead to criminal convictions for the company and three of its senior employees. The drug was MER-29, touted as lowering cholesterol and thus a weapon in the battle against stroke and heart attack.

In MER-29 material submitted to the FDA in 1959 (the year before its thalidomide NDA was submitted), Merrell extensively falsified animal test data and hid other crucial information. Unaware of this, in April 1960 the FDA allowed the drug's sale under the brand name Triparanol.

Once on sale, MER-29 caused a massive spate of injuries, including severe skin damage and cataracts which sometimes resulted in permanent eye damage and even blindness. An estimated 5000-plus people were injured during the two years the drug was on sale. Merrell pushed the drug hard and responded to reports of side effects with a grab bag of tricks: falsely denying any knowledge of similar cases; suggesting other drugs must be to blame for MER-29 damage; and keeping the FDA in the dark. In a Grünenthalesque fashion, Merrell promoted its dangerous drug as 'virtually nontoxic and remarkably free from side effects even on prolonged clinical use'. In November 1961 the FDA finally asked Merrell to withdraw MER-29 from sale. Merrell refused, saying it would defend MER-29 at 'every step'. The serious injuries continued to pile up until in April 1962, acting on a tip-off, the FDA raided Merrell's offices and found damning documents. Finally Merrell withdrew MER-29 from sale—this was only a few months after thalidomide had been exposed. Little wonder that soon afterwards the FDA raised the red flag over all Merrell applications. 'In view of [recent events] we cannot consider the information submitted by this firm as reliable without thorough verification,' a May 1962 FDA memo read.

In 1963 the company and three senior scientists pleaded no contest to criminal charges over MER-29: the company was fined $80,000 and the scientists each received six months' probation. More than 1500 victims of the drug eventually brought legal claims, and the company paid out tens of millions of dollars in jury verdicts and settlements, and millions more to its lawyers.

● ● ●

As for Frances Kelsey, she became a legend. In July 1962 a young *Washington Post* reporter, Morton Mintz, wrote an article which ran on the front page. It began:

> This is the story of how the skepticism and stubbornness of a government physician prevented what could have been an appalling American tragedy, the birth of hundreds or indeed thousands of armless and legless children.

Soon tales of Kelsey's grit and savvy were a staple of news reports across the country. On 1 August 1962 Kelsey testified before a senate subcommittee; at a press conference on the same day President Kennedy singled her out for praise, urged tougher drug laws and called for vigilance about thalidomide. A week later, Kennedy presented Kelsey with the Distinguished Federal Civilian Service medal at the White House.

By this time another American woman had received a less welcome share of the thalidomide spotlight. Sherri Finkbine was a mother of four in Arizona and the presenter of a children's television program, *Romper Room*. While pregnant with her fifth child and nervous about the pregnancy, Finkbine took some sleeping pills her husband had bought on a trip to England. Shortly afterwards, Finkbine read about thalidomide and asked her doctor to check whether Distaval was safe. 'You've been taking pure thalidomide,' was the response. Her doctor recommended an abortion. Finkbine agreed, but then gave an anonymous interview to a newspaper in order to spread a warning about thalidomide. Her identity leaked, and a brief legal skirmish ensued, during which the local county attorney, a father of nine, declared he would prosecute if the abortion took place. With time running out, Finkbine felt she had no choice but to fly to Sweden for the procedure. All of this occurred amid a blaze of publicity that caused enormous stress for a family in the midst of a crisis. Even the Swedish doctor's confirmation in August 1962 that the terminated foetus had been badly malformed was reported on front pages in the United States.

The critical and immediate result of America's brush with thalidomide was more stringent drug laws and new powers for the FDA. On 10 October 1962, President Kennedy signed into law the Kefauver Harris amendment to the 1938 Food, Drug, and Cosmetic Act. Named for its proponents, Senator Estes Kefauver and Representative Oren Harris, the law finally obliged drug manufacturers to prove their products were effective as well as safe. Kefauver had been campaigning for tougher drug laws for years and the country's thalidomide near-miss gave him valuable ammunition. Over industry protest, the new laws obliged pharmaceutical companies to report adverse drug reactions to the FDA, give consumers accurate information about drug side effects and obtain informed consent from patients participating in clinical trials. The FDA also issued regulations mandating pre-clinical trials to establish basic safety for new drugs before broader and better regulated clinical trials.

Thalidomide forced many other countries to take drug regulation far more seriously: Germany, the UK and Australia were among many to introduce a drug regulating authority with substantial powers. Over the years the testing of drugs for an effect on the foetus has become increasingly stringent. Repeat animal tests, carefully observed small-scale clinical trials, ongoing doctor reporting and an elaborate risk grading system for drugs to provide information to doctors and consumers are all part of the arsenal aimed at preventing another thalidomide. Pregnant women, too, are generally far more cautious than they were fifty years ago about what they ingest. Yet not all risks can be eliminated completely and constant vigilance is necessary. Because as Frances Kelsey realised, and even with all the animal testing in the world, the first time a pregnant women is given a new drug there is always a degree of uncertainty.

Frances Kelsey worked at the FDA for the rest of her long and distinguished career—even in her eighties she was still a part-time employee. She remains a hero there. The annual Kelsey Award recognises excellence and courage in protecting public health. Among other honours is a school named after her on Vancouver Island, her birthplace in Canada. Yet she was not without her critics. James Goddard, a highly regarded FDA commissioner from 1966 to 1968, clashed with Kelsey over organisational reform. In a 1969 interview he praised her as 'a lovely woman, a kind person'—then bent to the task of dismantling her reputation.

> In retrospect one would have to say that Frances became a Presidential gold medal award winner and heroine because she procrastinated. There had been an [application] pending on thalidomide and Frances couldn't make up her mind and just sat on the material…President Kennedy wanted to pin a medal on somebody and that somebody happened to be Frances Kelsey. So that was basically how Frances came to become a sacred cow in the FDA. You couldn't do anything about Frances…Frances couldn't make a decision. My

appraisal of her is that if it were raining, she'd drown before she could make her mind up that she ought to go indoors. Indecisive.

Goddard's analysis of why Kelsey blocked thalidomide is nonsense. But it underlines the degree of resentment Kelsey aroused, not just in industry, but even in her own workplace.

Kelsey, who turned one hundred in July 2014, was in her late nineties when Lyn Rowe's case began in Australia. We hired a former US government historian who knew Kelsey to speak to her on our behalf, but we knew we would not have to trouble her as a witness. The historical documents recording Kelsey's resistance to Merrell and thalidomide—the wisdom and tenacity that had saved the US from a full-blown disaster—would be more than enough. Kelsey's caution also proved that some doctors and scientists were capable of greater insight than the complacent drudgery on offer at Grünenthal and Distillers. In fact, Distillers appeared to acknowledge as much.

On 3 August 1962 Dr Denis Burley, Distillers' medical director, wrote to his counterpart at Merrell. Burley had just read a newspaper article which mentioned that in 1961 Kelsey had told Merrell she was concerned about thalidomide's effect on the foetus. Burley was agitated. If the newspaper was correct, Kelsey had worried about the foetus months before the drug was withdrawn. He wanted his Merrell counterpart to tell him if that was true. The letter, from Grünenthal's UK thalidomide licensee to its US licensee, can be seen as both a concession of failure by the thalidomide companies and a bouquet for Kelsey.

'You can readily appreciate,' Burley wrote, 'that we are likely now to be faced with the question, "If Dr Kelsey suspected ill effects on the unborn babies on reasonable grounds why didn't the Distillers Co. similarly suspect?"'

CHAPTER 9

Idiots and Clever People

As 1961 gave way to 1962, the executives at Grünenthal and Distillers had little to cheer. Their drug was a disaster, a killer. More victims were emerging daily. Some women who had taken just a single tablet during the sensitive window—generally reckoned to be between the end of the second and start of the sixth week of pregnancy post-conception—gave birth to grievously damaged babies. Yet some babies—exposed to far greater doses—appeared intact. The drug was terrifying and mysterious. But, astonishingly, neither Grünenthal nor Distillers had given up on it.

Within a few days of withdrawing thalidomide in late November 1961, Distillers considered resuming sales. On 7 December 1961 a senior staff member flew to Germany and told Grünenthal that Distillers would soon 're-examine the question of whether sales of Distaval could be recommenced through clinics'. Distillers believed that if sales could reach even twenty-five per cent of the previous level it would be 'a product worth fighting for'. Distillers also optimistically reported to Grünenthal that a big maternity hospital in London had seen no surge in births like those reported by Lenz, and that no further malformation cases had been published in the UK. This optimism was wildly misplaced. Distillers already knew about four of its own employees whose wives had used Distaval and given birth to malformed babies. Soon reports of malformations stretching back to

1958 emerged in great numbers as parents and doctors realised they had an explanation for the previously inexplicable. Eventually the number of surviving thalidomiders in the UK would total about five hundred. This excludes those who were never recognised, and the many miscarriages, stillbirths and deaths soon after birth also caused by thalidomide.

While the tragedy locked Grünenthal and Distillers together, there were stresses on the relationship. Distillers, which controversially resumed limited thalidomide sales to hospitals, was being flooded with vast quantities of returned tablets. It also had piles of raw thalidomide powder sitting in storage. Distillers wanted to return the powder to Grünenthal and get its money back but Grünenthal refused to accept the drug or offer a refund.

Another more serious issue also threatened to split the partners. Distillers, to its credit, very quickly accepted that thalidomide had caused the deaths and malformations. Grünenthal, by contrast, and despite overwhelming evidence, refused for years to accept the link. And of course that stance meant Grünenthal bitterly resented some of Distillers' public concessions about thalidomide's dangers.

Yet while Distillers admitted the obvious, it was also effecting some canny PR to protect its reputation and legal position. On 1 August 1962 both *The Times* and the *Guardian* carried stories about thalidomide: this was eight months after the withdrawal but the mainstream media everywhere had been slow to catch on. Distillers' staff had thoroughly briefed both newspapers and both declared the British company completely innocent of blame in the matter, swallowing the glib line that all relevant and necessary tests had been performed prior to sale. This assessment—that Distillers had acted responsibly and was blameless—was taken at face value by much of the media and was effective in providing Distillers with cover.

That same month, August 1962, Distillers' chairman Sir Graham Hayman declared that doctors still considered the drug very valuable. 'No one could possibly foresee the effect the drug would have on the unborn babies of mothers who took it.' The British Government fell into line. Health Minister Enoch Powell treated a delegation of parents of thalidomide children with little evident sympathy and refused to establish an inquiry into the affair.

Grünenthal was every bit as determined as Distillers to present itself as a model of virtue and caution. It sent a letter to its overseas agents on 30 November 1961, claiming it had acted as a 'responsible pharmaceutical manufacturer' by suspending sales even though 'the allegations [against thalidomide] lack scientific foundation'. It asked the overseas companies to cease sales, while suggesting that thalidomide might yet return to the market if future tests exonerated the drug.

The German company's business partners adopted a varied approach to the withdrawal. Some responses were outrageous. A company in Panama wrote to Grünenthal on 9 December 1961 suggesting it would do nothing about the thalidomide already in pharmacies and hospitals, and that fresh orders would be met with the response that stocks had run out.

A Jordanian company intended a similar subterfuge. On 27 Dec 1961 it wrote to Grünenthal advising that it intended to 'sneak out of this problem...without even being noticed'. It would not tell local doctors about the danger of the drug, nor would it issue a warning or retrieve stocks from its customers. Instead it would claim it had run out of thalidomide products. Later, when demand had disappeared, it would collect any remaining products from dealers' shelves. 'Although this measure may [be] unethical and against scientific rules, we believe that we should take it,' the Jordanian company advised.

A Grünenthal partner in Argentina wrote on 4 Jan 1962 saying it understood Grünenthal's desire to 'appear ethical, but you must also see the other point of view'. To cancel the product would be 'suicide'. Advertising and production had been stopped, but orders were still being filled from existing stocks. 'In case you insist on some kind of action we may, though most unwillingly, produce a new printed matter clearly stating the contraindications of [thalidomide] in pregnant women.'

The Atlas Trading Company in Khartoum (Sudan) advised Grünenthal that it would keep selling a couple of thalidomide drugs as it did not want to waste the work done by its salesmen. Grünenthal wrote back and advised the company to 'kindly stop sales'. But it was not always so prudent. In late 1961 Grünenthal's Spanish licensee advised it was not going to tell doctors the reason thalidomide sales had been stopped. On 21 December 1961 Grünenthal gave the subterfuge the green light. 'If you think such a measure is unnecessary given the relatively small distribution of [thalidomide] in Spain, we will go with your opinion.'

Some Grünenthal partners resented the company's approach. Its Mexican partner sent a strongly worded letter demanding a refund for unused thalidomide stock and accusing Grünenthal of encouraging it to keep selling the drug when it should have been withdrawn.

In Japan thalidomide was sold by about ten firms under fifteen brand names, though the Dainippon Pharmaceutical Company dominated the market. Its Isomin and Proban-M drugs were extensively advertised, very popular and accounted for about ninety-five per cent of all thalidomide drugs sold in Japan. To make matters worse, Dainippon explicitly promoted thalidomide as safe in pregnancy. Japan probably ranks third behind Germany and the UK as having suffered the greatest thalidomide disaster. The number of Japanese victims has often been assessed as about one thousand, though only about three hundred survived much past birth. The reasons for this low survival rate are unclear, but Japanese thalidomiders have previously suggested there was a significant rate of euthanasia in Japan, particularly in more remote areas.

There was also a tragic lost opportunity in Japan to cut the tragedy short. An extensive trial of thalidomide at a Tokyo maternity hospital involved 110 women at various stages of pregnancy. Some were given the drug for nausea and vomiting. Dr N—whose full name does not appear in the available documents—was the most prolific user of thalidomide. Three of his patients gave birth to severely malformed babies: two in 1960 and the third in May 1961. Dr N immediately ceased use of thalidomide at that point, as did other doctors at the hospital. Later he told investigators he could not recall why he had stopped using the drug, an obvious evasion which did not convince his interrogators. Yet while it appears clear that a number of doctors at the hospital suspected the link between thalidomide and birth malformations, it is unclear whether they passed this information to anybody outside the hospital. It seems, from the available information, more likely that Dr N and a small number of his colleagues kept their suspicion secret and did nothing while the death and injury toll continued to rise, not just in Japan but around the world.

Later events suggest that even if Dr N had alerted thalidomide's manufacturer Dainippon to his patients' malformed births, the pharmaceutical company would have been very reluctant to abandon its drug. Grünenthal notified Dainippon of thalidomide's withdrawal at the end of November 1961, and on 22 December 1961 Grünenthal offered an ill-advised update. It told Dainippon that Widukind Lenz was operating on unconfirmed assumptions.

In summary we would like to say that the assumption of Dr

Lenz is in no way scientifically proven through documents. It would be totally sufficient if an appropriate warning was added to the package insert until this question has been cleared. At the moment nobody can say if Dr Lenz's assumption will prove to be correct after extensive tests.

To what extent this reckless advice from Grünenthal contributed to the drug remaining on the market in Japan is impossible to judge. Certainly Dainippon kept selling thalidomide, a decision which later attracted fierce criticism. On 28 April 1962, having known about the malformations for almost five months, Dainippon advised Grünenthal it was still selling Isomin but in a less aggressive manner than earlier. It had not added a warning about pregnancy because a warning would effectively end sales, Dainippon wrote. Thalidomide sales in Japan finally halted in May 1962, but the retrieval of the drugs from chemists and doctors' surgeries did not begin until September 1962 and the process dribbled on for another year after that.

The long delay in removing thalidomide from Japanese shelves, for which the Japanese Government shared responsibility, added considerably to the death and injury toll in that country. Lenz described the six-month lag in suspending sales as 'if not deliberate mutilation of unborn infants' then at least 'a large scale experiment' very likely to end in deaths and malformations.

Canada was another thalidomide black spot. Frances Kelsey's sparring partner Merrell had started selling thalidomide in Canada in April 1961 because, unlike the US FDA, the Canadian Food and Drug Directorate (FDD) had swiftly approved its sale (under the Kevadon brand). Subsequently a Canadian firm, Frank W. Horner Ltd, was allowed to begin selling another thalidomide product, Talimol.

While on the market in Canada for less than a year, about four million pills were sold according to most estimates. As many as a million more were given away as samples. In fact Canada was among the countries worst hit by thalidomide—there were more than 120 official thalidomiders and doubtless others unrecognised.

In countries including Germany, the United Kingdom and Australia, thalidomide sales were (largely) halted in December 1961. But in Canada neither Horner nor Merrell saw fit to withdraw thalidomide products from sale until March 1962. Instead, in early December 1961 both sent equivocal letters to doctors, breaking the news as gently as possible. Horner's letter dated 7 December 1961 (a full week after the news from Germany had arrived) said it had 'just received sketchy information [about the malformations] from abroad' although 'whether or not thalidomide is responsible [is] unknown to us at this time'. As a 'precautionary step' doctors were advised not to give the drug to pregnant women or to 'women who may become pregnant'. The Canadian FDD approved this step and for months afterwards believed enough had been done to protect Canadians, despite having no idea whether the weak letters had even been read by doctors. The FDD's position was, at least, very unwise. Just as in the US, there was little coverage of thalidomide in the Canadian media, and many doctors did not know of the deadly impact of the thalidomide samples in their desk drawers. This is illustrated by the fact that in March 1962 a Canadian expert in birth malformations, contacted by Horner for advice, said he was completely unaware of the thalidomide disaster.

The role of the Canadian FDD was embarrassing. Defending his decision not to force the drug's withdrawal, the FDD director, Dr C. A. Morrell, later said that in December 1961 'it was all unconfirmed reports: Lenz hadn't published yet. It seemed pretty vague. It didn't occur to us to withdraw the drug'. The pressure on the FDD ratcheted up in late February 1962 when *Time* magazine pointed out that the drug was still being sold in Canada. More media attention raised the temperature further and, finally, on 2 March 1962, Morrell wrote to the companies politely asking them to withdraw their thalidomide drugs from sale. Despite being charged with protecting the health of Canadians, Dr Morrell was anxious not to cause offence to the peddlers of thalidomide. He was only asking for the withdrawal because of 'increasing demands from Canadian physicians, as well as certain other pressure'. He finished with a grovel: 'I regret very much having to take this course of action and can only hope for an early resolution of the problem.'

A few days later, in early March 1962, the drug companies wrote to Canadian doctors noting that the sale of thalidomide medications would cease. But these letters were far from effective. A month later, in April 1962, the news magazine *Maclean's* found thalidomide available at many pharmacies. On 10 April 1962, the FDD finally took direct action, writing to doctors directly and ordering inspectors to recover thalidomide from pharmacies.

The delay in getting the drug off the market in Canada had a human cost. About thirty Canadian thalidomiders were exposed to the drug after 1 December 1961, the day Merrell and Horner doctors flew to Germany to investigate the malformation question. These survivors and their families had every right to be outraged that it took another four months to raise the alarm and get thalidomide off the shelves in Canada.

• • •

Once the disaster was public, Grünenthal had no trouble seeing the future. Thalidomide was a complete and unmitigated catastrophe, shaping as the most notorious pharmaceutical disaster ever. There were thousands of victims in Germany and thousands more elsewhere. The company suspected its executives would be hit with a criminal prosecution and that victims of nerve damage and malformations would besiege it with lawsuits. Its licence partners were deeply unhappy. Grünenthal knew it had behaved shoddily in many respects—its own legal department had said so repeatedly. The company's reputation was going to take a fearful beating. Grünenthal was in a fight for survival.

Naturally it was up for the fight. Within a few days of the withdrawal, Grünenthal had efficiently switched focus from selling the drug to avoiding legal blame for having done so. One of the first orders of business was to prepare for the inevitable law suits and prosecutions. On 27 December 1961 an internal memo resolved to 'do everything we can today to not only secure expert witnesses for a legal dispute, but above and beyond this the support of all serious pharmacologists, doctors of internal medicine and neurologists'. Winning support among the medical profession included a further bout of disinformation. In February 1962 Grünenthal advised a professor at Bonn's Institute of Forensic Medicine that at the end of 1960 it had 'practically not heard any reports' about nerve damage following thalidomide use. This was a ridiculous lie.

In February 1962 Grünenthal was sounding a tougher note. It decided that all doctors who make 'negative statements have to be worked on emphatically in order to change their opinion or at least make them neutral'. Consistent with this approach, Grünenthal waged legal war against one of its key critics, the neurologist Horst Frenkel, obtaining a court order to stop him making claims about Grünenthal's negligence.

Widukind Lenz, of course, had not escaped Grünenthal's attention. In June 1962 Grünenthal thanked Distillers for refusing to provide information to Lenz. 'I am sorry to say that Dr Lenz has been making a number of false allegations at the various congresses and conventions which have been held. We do not intend to take any action in the matter at the moment, but there will certainly come a favourable opportunity for putting a stop to it.'

Many at Grünenthal saw Lenz as the enemy, rather than as a man who stopped Grünenthal's drug maiming babies. The same attitude applied to the neurologist Frenkel. One Grünenthal employee wrote:

> When considering how many countless psychic traumas have been produced by the contributions made to the discussion by Dr Lenz, and still more by the sensational reports of the irresponsible gutter press, I cannot regard Dr Lenz's behaviour as responsible. What Goethe once said applies to him as it does to Dr Frenkel. Fools and wise-folk are both harmless. Those halfwits and half-educated people who recognise only half-truths alone are dangerous.

The feeling was somewhat mutual. In mid-1962 Lenz rebuffed an attempt by Grünenthal to examine his medical reports. 'The whole material is available to interested doctors for serious scientific analysis. If you can demonstrate that you belong to this group, you are welcome to examine my collection.'

Some of Grünenthal's communications during this period were not quite as headquarters might have intended. A Grünenthal sales representative reported to her bosses that she had shocked one doctor by revealing one of the popular uses of Contergan. 'Prof. W. was initially aghast when I informed him that [Contergan] was known in Bonn as an abortive drug.' What possessed the sales rep is not known, but the claim is mind-boggling.

On 27 March 1962, Grünenthal's legal department weighed in again. It questioned the company's past enthusiasm for calling the drug non-toxic given the 'general experience that side effects of a drug often remain hidden for a long time and do not emerge until it has seen broad application, particularly since thalidomide was a new substance which was not even subject to [prescription]'. The Grünenthal lawyers gave their colleagues another lashing in relation to nerve damage but argued, hopefully, that Grünenthal was not guilty in relation to the malformations.

But there was a caution. 'This does not mean, however, that trials on account of malformations or deformities are without any risk.' If experts were to find that Grünenthal should have tested thalidomide for an effect on the foetus before putting the drug on sale, the lawyers warned, then 'it might only be a small step to being found guilty in a civil trial. Therefore, it is very important for us to prove that testing of Contergan for teratogenic properties, according to scientific knowledge at the time, was not necessary'.

By 4 April 1962 a new topic was concerning Grünenthal's lawyers: how to prepare for the likelihood of losing civil trials. The answer was to improve Grünenthal's reputation through 'intensive but very carefully and tactfully managed public-relations efforts'. Heinrich Mückter, set to face criminal charges over the drug, had another bright idea. In April 1962, he suggested the company drop the use of the trademark Contergan in all 'publications, discussions, etc.'. Instead, Mückter wrote, the 'scientific term thalidomide' should be used, thereby distancing Grünenthal from its drug.

Grünenthal's ideas for damage containment were flowing thick and fast. On 19 April 1962, it gave close consideration to the potential financial cost of the disaster, which it figured to be massive. There were some small bright spots. Some 'unsophisticated' victims who had an 'innate fear of courts' would settle for 'relatively small sums'. Other victims might be deterred by a legal argument that they had waited too long and had now lost the right to sue. But Grünenthal's lawyers recognised that this last manoeuvre would be a public-relations blunder. 'As far as the press is concerned, this would be to our detriment in a way that we would not recover from.'

Probably the most determined Grünenthal tactic of all was to keep maintaining for many years—and right through the criminal trial in 1968–70—that there was no conclusive proof that thalidomide caused malformations or nerve damage. Perhaps this was excusable amid the trauma of early 1962. But the longer it went on the more difficult it was to see it as anything other than a legal tactic. Widukind Lenz put it best (and mildly) when he wrote: 'Grünenthal continued to deny the teratogenic effect of thalidomide for years, but there was a growing suspicion that this was not due to honest ignorance but to the purpose of weakening the accusations against the firm.'

The lengths Grünenthal went to were remarkable. In the lead-up to the criminal trial it tried to promote a theory that thalidomide might actually have been foetus-saving, rather than foetus-maiming. The theory asserted that thalidomide did not damage the foetus, but on the contrary somehow allowed otherwise badly damaged foetuses to survive until birth rather than being spontaneously aborted.

• • •

If the idea of being sued by thousands of victims was a nightmare for Grünenthal, then so too was the prospect of criminal charges for its executives. The wait was brief. State prosecutors started investigating Grünenthal almost immediately after thalidomide was withdrawn from the market, and soon assembled a mountain of evidence. Some of the documents were seized during police raids on Grünenthal.

In 1967 the prosecution confirmed it would pursue serious criminal charges—including negligent manslaughter—against nine

Grünenthal executives, and produced an indictment of nearly one thousand pages. Forty-five years later the indictment and supporting material was a valuable resource for Lyn Rowe's legal team.

The trial started in May 1968, but not before charges were dropped against the Grünenthal founder and managing director, Hermann Wirtz, who was deemed too ill to stand trial. The remaining defendants hotly contested the allegations. Heinrich Mückter, the man who wanted to keep selling thalidomide even after Lenz's bombshell, declared the charges against him a 'gross injustice'.

Within days the trial descended into farce. Proving that thalidomide caused nerve damage and malformations should have been a formality, but instead proved a cesspit into which the trial sank and never fully emerged. Witnesses failed to show up, the lawyers argued bitterly over everything, experts were dragged through days of irrelevant testimony, and long hours passed as dull pieces of transcript were re-read to the court.

Amazingly, Grünenthal managed to find witnesses to assert that thalidomide did not cause nerve damage or malformations. Professor Erich Blechschmidt, a prominent embryologist, dismissed as 'pure speculation' any suggestion that thalidomide was to blame. 'From an embryological point of view one can certainly assume that thalidomide is not the cause of malformations.' This was bizarre. Serious scientists the world over were utterly convinced of thalidomide's danger. The drug had been banned everywhere. Numerous countries had changed their pharmaceutical laws because of the disaster. Grünenthal's licensee companies in Sweden and the UK were busy agreeing to pay compensation. Frances Kelsey was a hero in the US for saving the country from a massive death and injury toll. And even some of Grünenthal's own staff had admitted internally that the drug caused nerve damage and malformations. Yet Grünenthal produced a string of scientists to parade before the court denying the obvious.

How could this be? A parallel is the tobacco industry, which for years managed to find apparently reputable doctors to deny the link had been proven between cigarettes and cancer. There is an expert for just about any belief and Grünenthal found doctors prepared to argue the ridiculous.

The prosecution also underestimated Grünenthal's ruthless approach. One example illustrates the lopsided battle. Lenz, the man who exposed the drug as a killer, was in the witness stand for weeks, gave devastating evidence for the prosecution, and withstood twelve days of fierce cross-examination by Grünenthal's lawyers. At one point, Lenz was asked if a virus, rather than thalidomide, might have been the cause of the malformations. Pointing to the absence of malformations in East Germany, where the drug was banned, Lenz declared that a virus would not have stopped at the border and dismissed the theory as absurd.

But Grünenthal had the last laugh. It applied to have Lenz's evidence excluded, claiming that he was biased towards the victims, 'obsessed with his position' and demonstrated an 'almost religious conviction' in his anti-Grünenthal mission. Incredibly, the judges accepted Grünenthal had a basis for fearing Lenz might be biased, though the Court was careful not to find actual bias. Lenz's evidence was excluded, a terrible blow for the prosecution.

Characteristically, Lenz refused to be upset by the Court's decision, admitting that 'my sympathy has not been equally shared between the company and thalidomide victims'. But, Lenz said, he had been careful to give clear and unbiased evidence. 'Though the decision by the Court not to admit my testimony came to me as a surprise, I decided to take it as a compliment to my moral engagement rather than as an offence to my scientific honesty.'

• • •

In Germany in 2012 I met with one of the lawyers who worked as a junior member of the prosecution team during the 1960s. The lawyer, who asked not to be named, cited the failure to secure convictions as one of the low points of his very long career. Even forty years on, the man could recite a litany of regrets. 'It was a shame. There was a strong case against Grünenthal, but it all went wrong quickly. The public supported the prosecution because there was such horror about what thalidomide had done. But we got stuck and made little progress. And soon the goodwill evaporated.'

The elderly lawyer was right. The criminal trial was a debacle for the prosecution. All of its careful, painstaking and incredibly thorough preparation was essentially for naught. Grünenthal's numerous high-powered (and expensive) lawyers overwhelmed the government team.

The former prosecutor said one key error was spending so much effort on proving thalidomide's dangerousness. The tedious battle had been exhausting and irritated everyone including the judges. Instead, he thought, the prosecution should have trusted the judges to make the obvious finding, and quickly moved on to Grünenthal's outrageous behaviour: the lack of proper testing, promoting thalidomide as safe in pregnancy, the disgraceful response to the surge of nerve-damage reports and the mishandled malformation reports. That, the lawyer thought, would have further exposed Grünenthal, stiffened the resolve of the judges and done something to prevent the trial descending into the unedifying slog it became.

For its part, Grünenthal was leaving as little to chance as possible. Archive documents show that in July 1969 it met with the government—no victims present, though Hermann Wirtz, the Grünenthal boss excused as too sick to stand trial, apparently managed to attend. By September 1969, several government departments were discussing a solution that would end the trial: again no victims involved. By this time, quite bizarrely, the Justice Minister for the state which was prosecuting Grünenthal was Dr Joseph Neuberger: his law firm had worked for Grünenthal and he had personally represented Hermann Wirtz.

But in January 1970, with the trial in its second year and stuck deep in the mire, Grünenthal was ready to play its trump card: an offer to pay 100 million marks as compensation to the children, provided that all civil suits against it were abandoned. In April 1970 the organisation representing the increasingly desperate thalidomide parents accepted the offer, and the German Government came to the party with another 100 million marks. The money went into a foundation to make a one-off payment to victims followed by an annual pension for life.

The emotional impetus had now gone out of the trial and there was increasing pressure for it to be abandoned. The hearings dragged on, but in December 1970, with the agreement of all parties, the trial was suspended. Even Karl Schulte-Hillen, the lawyer representing the children's interests, agreed to the suspension. 'We can't afford to spend any more time on legalistic problems,' he said. 'We have other problems of education and health.' The court delivered a judgment in 1971, dismissing the proceedings and heavily criticising Grünenthal and its executives. For Grünenthal this amounted to nothing more than a light slap. The criminal prosecution was now at an end and soon it would be business as usual at Stolberg, but with a gleaming silver lining: Grünenthal was gifted protection from further prosecution or lawsuits in Germany thanks to a special law passed by the German Government.

For the drug's victims, it was a less happy story. The compensation fund proved vastly inadequate: as recently as 2012 a German victim with severely shortened arms and legs received about 15,000 euros a year from the fund—at the time about US$20,000. Poverty, depression and ill-health were rife among German thalidomiders, in part as a result of their woeful financial support. In 2013, finally, the German Government stepped in, increasing pensions by up to five hundred per cent, recognition of just how pathetic the pre-existing compensation had been. Grünenthal did not assist the German Government with this 2013 initiative, a failure bitterly criticised by some thalidomiders. Notably, Grünenthal's failure to contribute came not long after the so-called apology speech during which Grünenthal's CEO had emphasised the company's deep sympathy for thalidomide survivors.

UK thalidomiders who have met with Grünenthal in recent years seeking compensation payments are dismissive of the company's attitude. 'I don't sense they feel their responsibility even today,' one UK activist has said. 'I think they're waiting for us to die.'

No doubt Grünenthal's owners and executives—who had nothing to do with the original disaster—wish they were not haunted by thalidomide. Yet the company's ham-fisted public relations ventures do nothing to ease attacks on it. Sometimes Grünenthal's clumsy behaviour is simply astonishing. Thomas Quasthoff, who was born with dramatically shortened arms and legs as a result of his mother's consumption of thalidomide, carved out a stellar international career as a bass-baritone and also studied law and worked as a university professor. In 2012 the German newspaper *Der Spiegel* asked him if he felt anger towards Grünenthal. 'There was certainly some anger there,' Quasthoff responded. 'I remember getting a call from Grünenthal once. They asked me to sing at their Christmas party. I said: "You must be out of your minds!"'

• • •

For fifty years Grünenthal has clung to the notion that it did absolutely nothing wrong in relation to the death and damage to babies wrought by its drug. Sometimes Grünenthal has appeared desperate to exonerate itself. In 2007, Grünenthal executive Sebastian Wirtz, a member of the founding family and grandson of one of the men charged with criminal offences, told a journalist:

> It's extremely difficult with our perspective to look back to this time when the events happened. The court said there was no way Grünenthal could have known that the sedative could have these dramatic effects. According to everything I have read and heard, there was no way the tragedy could have been avoided. The tragedy for the Wirtz family is that we cannot undo it.

Wirtz's comments prompt the question: what exactly had he 'read and heard'? For example, had he read the documents which detail the red-flag queries to Grünenthal about thalidomide-related malformations by Dr K (1959), pharmacist Koch (1960) and Dr Brandt (1961)? Or perhaps Wirtz was relying on Grünenthal's sanitised version of history, 'The Thalidomide Tragedy' which read like the product of an in-house public relations team, and was full of errors and misrepresentations. For example, it claimed that it took more than two years after the tragedy to find proof of the malforming effect of thalidomide in animal experiments. The truth is that Distillers found hints within weeks and proof in just a few months.

Wirtz's claim that the tragedy was unavoidable is a fallacy. So too was any claim that the court hearing the criminal charges against Grünenthal executives had exonerated Grünenthal. First, the criminal trial was abandoned before the responsibility for malformations was properly considered. 'No actual taking of evidence has occurred,' the judgment said. Second, the court said that, had the trial continued, it 'is possible that further taking of evidence would confirm the predictability of malformations'.

Perhaps Grünenthal's most treasured claim is that it tested thalidomide properly by the standards of the time. In 2012, during his 'apology' speech, Grünenthal CEO Harald Stock issued Grünenthal's standard defence. 'Grünenthal acted in accordance with the state of scientific knowledge and all industry standards for testing new drugs that were relevant and acknowledged in the 1950s and '60s. We regret that the teratogenic potential of thalidomide could not be detected by the tests that we and others carried out before it was marketed.'

These comments might be interpreted as suggesting a diligent Grünenthal tried to check whether the drug could damage babies before putting it on the market, but, sadly, the tests were not up to the job. That interpretation would be flat wrong. Grünenthal did not bother to attempt to check thalidomide's effect on the foetus. Instead it just put the drug on the market and vouched for its safety.

Likewise, the German criminal court did not approve Grünenthal's testing. The 1971 judgment did not examine in detail what tests could have been undertaken, and said that had the trial continued it was possible the prosecution would have established that Grünenthal had grounds to suspect the teratogenic effect of thalidomide. If that were the case, the court said, Grünenthal should have conducted tests on pregnant animals and should have pointed out the lack of information about pregnancy safety to doctors and consumers. Grünenthal did neither.

Still, even the most trenchant Grünenthal critic has to admit that the company and its lawyers did a masterful job in defeating the criminal prosecution. Through a tough and determined battle, Grünenthal built the pressure which saw the trial collapse. Its executives escaped without penalty and a finding of only minor guilt. All things considered, the outcome was an unlikely triumph for Grünenthal and a glorious victory for its fleet of lawyers.

As the Australian litigation wore on I eventually came to believe that Grünenthal's success in the criminal trial had given the company a deluded sense of righteousness. The defeat of the prosecution, it seemed, had wormed its way into the company's DNA and found enduring expression in Grünenthal's absolute conviction that it had no case to answer in relation to thalidomide malformations. This 'innocence' remains a Grünenthal bedrock, a foundation stone for the modern company. And I was certain that this belief would translate into its approach to Lyn Rowe's claim. Grünenthal would concede nothing. Ever. Grünenthal believed it had done nothing wrong. A criminal court had said so. Well, it hadn't actually, but Grünenthal didn't seem to know or care.

CHAPTER 10

It's Not Contagious

'Don't worry, it's not contagious,' Lyn Rowe likes to assure people staring at her. Lyn's jokes are mostly at her own expense. She once gave a presentation to a group of gymnastics coaches, and started with: 'I don't know why I was asked to speak here because I'm not very good at the parallel bars.' Possibly Lyn's all-time favourite joke is the one she makes when she sees something expensive in a shop. 'That would cost me an arm and a leg!'

For about ten years Lyn has been speaking at schools for SCOPE (once known as the Spastic Society), trying to build awareness and understanding of disability. 'I was petrified the first time,' Lyn recalled. 'I got Mum to come into the room with me. Afterwards the feedback was good and now it's just so important to me. I love it.' These days Wendy and Ian drive Lyn to the schools, and then go for coffee while she speaks.

In recent years Lyn has spoken to up to seventy schools each year. Her message is 'see the person, not the disability', and Lyn's eyes light up when she talks about the visits. 'I go to the schools with a lovely team and they treat me like anybody else, not like a no-hoper. And I love the kids.'

Watching one of these talks is an experience. On first sight, the students are genuinely amazed and somewhat hushed, a reaction Lyn still notices. 'You can see the shock on their faces. They're thinking, wow, she can't do anything.' Lyn gives a short prepared speech and then has the students do tasks, perhaps writing with a pen in their mouth, or passing a jelly bean to each other using only a spoon held between their teeth. Her favourite part is question time. How do you go to the toilet? Do you sleep in your chair? How do you get up steps? The younger students ask questions without the filter most adults employ. 'Some of the older classes hang back. They'd love to ask, but they're too embarrassed,' Lyn said. 'The younger children ask anything.'

• • •

When Lyn was a child the Rowe family had annual holidays at a caravan park in Merimbula on the southern New South Wales coast. They stayed in tents and spent their days on the beach. Because Lyn's wheelchair could not be pushed across the sand, she was carried down to the beach in a big canvas cricket bag. In the evenings Wendy washed Lyn in a bucket or held her in the shower at the communal toilet block. 'Naturally there were the usual horrified looks,' Wendy said.

By the early 1970s Lyn was about to become a teenager and was too big to wash in a bucket or hold in a shower. The Rowes needed more privacy and for a few years holidayed in accommodation subsidised by Ian's employer. 'But after that we didn't have many family holidays. Lyn's needs made them just too difficult, and we didn't have the money,' Wendy said.

In 1980 Lyn started work at what was then bluntly called a sheltered workshop. In 2012 it was known as Knox Combined Industries. Lyn loved the place, and in the early days found it a blessed relief from school.

'I cried a lot during the first two years I was at school. I was very scared, hated being away from Mum, hated being on my [prosthetic] legs,' Lyn said. 'I was put in the too-hard basket, or at least that's what I think. They taught me how to use a sewing machine but didn't bother to teach me how to read and write properly. I was there from six to seventeen, which was eleven years too long.'

Wendy remembers the almighty fuss every school morning. Lyn howled non-stop as Wendy carried her into the bus and strapped her into a seat. 'Every single time I visited her at school she always burst into tears. She detested school and was inconsolable about being away from me and her sisters. It got to the point where a doctor prescribed Valium to try and calm her down about it.' Eventually Lyn accepted that she had to go to school, but she never enjoyed it. 'She didn't trust the staff and felt that nobody thought she was worth making an effort with,' Wendy said. By the time Lyn left school at seventeen, Wendy estimates she had progressed to about the reading standard of a ten-year-old.

Rivalling school in Lyn's horror stakes were visits to what was known as the South Melbourne limb factory, where she was regularly fitted with new prosthetic limbs to keep pace with her growing body.

> I hated my prosthetics. It was the most frightening thing in my life, worse than school. I was young and they were terrifying. They were too heavy and they wouldn't do what I wanted. The arms were gas powered and they were almost useless. They'd jerk around and I'd get very frustrated and cry.

The legs were even worse than the arms. 'Disgusting. They were getting longer and longer as I was getting older, and I was getting higher and higher off the ground.' Lyn fell off her legs about ten times over the years and, because she had no arms to break her fall, she gashed her chin each time. After her back operation at the age of fourteen, Lyn never used her prosthetic limbs again.

The doctor told me that because I had a rod in my spine I couldn't afford to fall off my legs again. He said, 'If you want to stay alive, don't walk again.' I said, 'Thank you very much, that will be just fine by me.' I dumped the arms as well. I can do a lot more with my chin and teeth and shoulders than I could ever do with those arms.

Against that background the sheltered workshop felt like freedom. 'When I started [at seventeen] it was a plant nursery. I'd take my trusty little pair of secateurs and my trusty little spoon and my apron and I'd pot plants and propagate plants. I loved doing that.' Later the workshop packaged nuts and bolts and Lyn used her mouth and nose to place the nut on the bolt and tighten it. She also put barcodes on the bolt sleeves. Sometimes she worked as a quality controller checking on her colleagues' work. 'That was a great job. I could be a little bit bossy!' Many of Lyn's friendships were made at work.

I used to have a girlfriend with cerebral palsy who had epileptic fits at work. Ninety-nine per cent of the time it was me who found her after the fits. I was shocked the first time, but then I thought I have to do something. So after that I just checked she was OK, and then asked someone to call the ambulance.

Sometimes after work a small group of managers and staff would go out to a disco.

One of my girlfriends at work would help me change into nice clothes. She had spina bifida herself and was in a chair. But we'd manage. I went on my manual wheelchair, and at the disco they'd put me in the middle and twirl me around. I don't know how I didn't fall out. Sometimes I'd have a Midori and lemonade. They were the good old days.

• • •

The Rowe family has dealt with Lyn's condition with grace and humour but it has, at times, been an exceptionally difficult journey. Every family member has led a different life than would otherwise have been the case. Wendy effectively became her daughter's full-time carer, her teaching career relegated to an afterthought. Friendships and interests became indulgences to be enjoyed rarely. Yet Wendy believes that in many ways she is a better, stronger person than she otherwise would have been. At the time of Lyn's birth she doubted she had the resilience to cope with such a profoundly handicapped daughter.

> I really didn't think I would be strong enough. I had three very lovely but dominant, arrogant, chauvinist older brothers who left me feeling insignificant. I was shy and mousey in part because I thought I could never possibly come up to their standard. They were all brilliant; they all got scholarships to university. I couldn't compete with them.

The turning point came when Lyn was a toddler. 'The doctors were always talking about her in front of me without including me,' Wendy said. 'I put up with it for a long time. Then one day they were talking about taking one of her ribs out and making her a flipper arm. I said, "Excuse me, I'm her mother, please include me in these discussions." Ever since then I've been a lot more assertive.'

The journey with Lyn also tested Wendy and Ian's faith. They met through a Christian youth group and remained believers. Yet they struggled when in 1962 some fellow churchgoers told Wendy's parents that 'the sins of the fathers' had been visited on Lyn. 'Whatever they meant by that I don't know,' Wendy said. 'But it was deeply insulting.'

For many years, the family attended church together. 'We don't do that anymore. I still believe in God and we have faith, but the church itself plays a less important part in my life,' Wendy said.

Ian dropped off [going to church] before I did, but eventually I found it hard just to get Lyn out of the house and off to church. And then we'd be patronised by people saying to Lyn, 'Oh it's very nice to see you out this morning.' In the end it wasn't worth it. It ceased to be that important for me personally to get there. Maybe I'll come back to it—there's still time!

Lyn's sisters—Merrilyn, Alison and Andrea—also felt the impact of a family life completely dominated by Lyn's needs. And the shock of Lyn's birth had a severe impact on her father Ian, as did the pressure and financial struggle that followed.

What Ian and his family told us about his struggles was in one respect surprising. Ian Rowe was an impressive character. Clearly an intelligent man and a deep thinker, he kept close tabs on the progress of Lyn's litigation and asked frequent and insightful questions. Ian was also the family's nominated spokesman, fronting several crowded press conferences and giving assured performances in what is, for almost anybody, an intimidating setting. He was also warm and courteous in conversation, unfailingly and genuinely interested in the well-being of whoever in our office he was speaking with.

But Ian also suffered from what he called 'nerves' and his family saw as anxiety. Several times after the start of the litigation Ian suffered panic attacks and the family called an ambulance. Small details, such as parking arrangements when the Rowes drove to our office, could cause him stress. Wendy and Lyn, with the ease of family members, sometimes gave Ian stick about his 'worrying'. Once when Ian was talking about his concern about how Lyn would be cared for when he and Wendy were 'no longer here', Lyn interrupted. 'If you're no longer here then you won't have to worry about it Bugsy.'

Ian always took the ribbing with good humour, and joked about having been the only male in a house dominated by five forceful women.

Lyn would laugh and remind her father that they did have a male dog for a while—'so you can't say you've never had any male company'. But in developing his witness statement for the court case, Ian was perfectly frank about his struggles in the aftermath of Lyn's birth.

• • •

The birth itself was an obvious shock. 'Afterwards I often struggled to cope at work, and found stress and pressure very hard to deal with,' Ian said. Some people appeared to distance themselves from the family, even if they were sympathetic. 'They seemed a bit reluctant to come to our house, and we always got stares and odd looks when we were out with Lyn,' Ian said. Despite all this Ian was successful at work for some time after Lyn's birth. He was promoted to head of the superannuation department at AMP, then to head of sales information and then to head of collector records. But stress and anxiety were constant problems.

'At times over the years I really battled to get to work at all. There were periods I cried quite often, and at other times I stayed home because I felt too emotionally distressed to go to work.' Social situations were a particular problem. 'On one occasion I stayed home from a work Christmas party and Wendy and Lyn went in my place.'

But by 1969, with the birth of Andrea, the couple had four children, so Ian often worked overtime for extra money. His escape from pressure during these years was playing cricket on summer weekends, but it wasn't enough. Things got worse slowly throughout the 1970s until in 1983 matters reached a head. Family relationships were strained. Merrilyn and Alison had left home after periods of rocky relationships with their parents. Ian was busy and stressed at work and it all boiled over.

I had a breakdown. I couldn't go to work for long periods. I found it hard even to walk to the shops. I was very distressed. At some point during this period my boss at AMP telephoned me at home and I burst into tears. It was an extremely difficult time for me, and for the whole family. AMP was offering early retirements and I applied for one because I was convinced the best thing for me was to find a low-pressure job.

Ian knew he could not remain unemployed for long: the family needed his income. So he got a job at a local hardware store. But that too was stressful—ordering and pricing and unfamiliar relationships. So he quit and began looking for something else and fortunately AMP came to the rescue with an offer of part-time work. 'So I started back again, in charge of just a few staff. I coped much better. Everything was much less stressful.'

But life was a constant financial struggle. When Alison got married in 1983 in New South Wales, Wendy and Ian could not afford to go. 'Ian and I sent what money we could to help pay for the reception, but we were devastated to miss it and have always regretted it,' Wendy said.

In 2002, when Ian Rowe stopped working, the family had no savings at all. Any extra money had been spent on Lyn's needs. To make ends meet, Ian and Wendy took out a $40,000 mortgage on their home. They were unable to make repayments and by 2012 the mortgage had risen to $80,000.

During 2012, the year that we spent many hours taking the Rowes' witness statements, Ian and Wendy were both on age pensions. Wendy received an extra carer's payment of about one hundred dollars per fortnight. Lyn was on a disability pension plus twenty dollars for each of her school visits. She also earned thirty cents an hour at the workshop, where she greeted visitors and occasionally did some typing. For a five-and-a-half-hour day she earned $1.65. In short, the Rowes' financial position was parlous.

Ian Rowe never got any effective mental-health treatment. In the early 1980s he was prescribed an antidepressant, which he stopped taking after he saw a television program about its side effects. He also self-medicated with Valium over the years. Once his GP suggested he see a psychologist. 'I thought that would be weak and I didn't do it. I now know it might have helped but at the time I couldn't see that. I've still never had any counselling at all.'

Wendy Rowe had a similar regret. 'If the same thing happened to a young couple today they'd be offered all sorts of assistance, including counselling. Having that would have done Ian a world of good, and me as well.' Over the years Wendy did the vast bulk of care work for Lyn, though it became more of a joint effort after Ian retired. 'Prior to that Wendy did almost all of it,' Ian said. 'Wendy has been incredible.' Retiring from work helped Ian's mental health. 'But I worry and stress and forget things. And when I feel under pressure I don't cope at all.'

• • •

In March 2012, Lyn Rowe celebrated her fiftieth birthday at the Yarra Yarra Golf Club in Melbourne's south-east. Family and friends arrived from around the country, and Lyn revelled in the attention. Ian Rowe gave a short eloquent toast, and Lyn's school friend Mary Henley-Collopy, the thalidomider who had suggested the family contact Peter Gordon, gave a warm and funny speech, at the conclusion of which Mary and Lyn pretended to high-five each other, quite a feat for a woman without arms and a woman with her fingers at her shoulders.

Lyn's eldest sister Merrilyn had driven down from her home in country Victoria, middle sister Alison had flown in from Queensland, and youngest sister Andrea (whose husband Paul was the superintendent at the golf course) had provided the venue. While Lyn beamed all night, she never appeared happier than when surrounded by her sisters.

Growing up, Lyn and her sisters were close, and Lyn hated it when one by one they moved out of home as young adults. With her sisters she was one of the girls, whereas in public she was the girl with no limbs. 'Lyn could be a pain just like the rest of us,' Merrilyn laughed.

> When she wanted to get one of us, she'd bite us, or drive her chair over our toes or clamp onto us with her chin. And we were just as mean back. Lyn didn't get any special treatment. We thought it was really funny to unplug her wheelchair, or put something out of her reach and tell her to get it herself. Once or twice, I might have even pushed her face into her food. You had to be quick though. She's got such a strong neck that if she knew you were coming there's no way you could budge her.

Lyn loved the give and take. 'I was treated like everyone else in the family. Nobody said "poor old Lyn" and put me in cotton wool. I have a really good relationship with my sisters. I'm definitely a people person, I like having people around, having company, especially my sisters.'

When Alison, who is just over a year older than Lyn, was about eight years old, she took Lyn to school to present her to her classmates at show-and-tell.

> I wanted to put my hand up and say, 'This is my sister, check her out.' Lyn came into class with me and I made a bit of a speech and then Lyn and I answered questions. There was a bit of staring at first but it was a big success. I didn't have

to worry about the other kids whispering and pointing after that.

Alison, who is now a kindergarten teacher, described her childhood as 'different'. Life unavoidably revolved around Lyn and each sister responded in her own way. 'Merrilyn was defiant and gave our parents a hard time. I fought back against everyone and was pretty verbally aggressive at times. Andrea struggled with it, but stayed at home much longer than Merrilyn and I did. We moved out as soon as we could.'

Alison described Lyn as an inspiration. 'I think she's amazing. I'm so proud of her. I have her picture up at work. My parents are incredible too. Somehow they kept going and they're still together. I'm in awe of that.'

Merrilyn, who is three years older than Lyn, echoed Alison's description of their 'different' home life. 'When I brought friends home for the first time I felt obliged to warn them that I had a sister without arms or legs. That's not something you expect to hear when going around to a friend's place.'

Friends and extended family members were fine with Lyn, Merrilyn said, but the public was often a different matter. All three sisters said that strangers frequently made cruel or unthinking comments. Merrilyn remembered a trip to the city as a teenager. 'We took Lyn in a wheelchair and pushed her around, carried her up and down stairs. This was normal for us, but I can still remember the comments we got. They were disgraceful. It was as though we shouldn't be taking Lyn out in public.' More than thirty years later Merrilyn was still appalled by the memory. 'When it's little kids reacting, it's not so bad. When it's their parents, that's the worst.'

Alison remembered chasing other children who had made insulting or mocking remarks. 'It happened all the time. Kids were cruel.' Wendy even recalled strangers shielding their children's eyes in Lyn's presence.

The person least upset by the stares and comments was Lyn. 'I can't recall Lyn saying even once, why did this happen to me?' Merrilyn said. 'I don't remember her being depressed. She is amazingly positive.'

Merrilyn's teenage years were difficult. 'Mum says she neglected me and that's what made me a horrible teenager. It's true that I was awful and I did give my parents a very rough time. But who knows, I might have been like that anyway. I can't put it down to Lyn.'

Merrilyn dropped out of school at seventeen and moved out at eighteen. 'I wanted to earn my own money and get out of home.' Recently she returned to study and is completing an accountancy degree. She thought she might have been a better student the first time around if circumstances were different. 'But I have no regrets about that. Mum and Dad did the best they could in a very difficult situation. They sacrificed everything to give Lyn as normal a life as possible. I could not have done what they did.'

Because of Lyn's condition all three of her sisters had somewhat traumatic pregnancies. Merrilyn's first child, Troy, was born when she was twenty years old.

> I was absolutely paranoid during the pregnancy. There was no way I was taking any medication. I was seriously worried that my baby would not have arms or legs. Reasoning didn't help—I was just panicked. First thing I asked the doctor when Troy was born was: does he have everything, is he OK?

Alison admitted to being 'terrified' during her first pregnancy, and Andrea was convinced something would go terribly wrong.

> I told my doctor about Lyn and he said I'd be fine, but still I worried. What if it wasn't thalidomide? What if it was a genetic thing and I had it too? I really didn't believe I could have a healthy baby. I had ultrasounds and everything else,

but still I thought something was going to go really wrong. And even when Aleisha was born I could barely believe it. She was perfectly healthy, but I kept checking her to make sure there was nothing wrong.

Andrea, the youngest of Lyn's three sisters, lived at home the longest, not moving out until she was twenty-four. Andrea was shy and having Lyn as a sister made her feel she was always in the spotlight. 'You could never hide when you were out with Lyn, always lots of stares and comments. Mum and Lyn seemed to be able to switch off to it, but I never could. I always noticed it. It was relentless. There was no reprieve.' During school holidays Andrea sometimes escaped to Queensland to stay with Alison.

Andrea remembered her parents being somewhat preoccupied when she was a child. 'They were surviving and never thought far ahead, they just got through it day to day. When we were teenagers we all got away with a lot. Mum and Dad were so distracted.' The close bond between Wendy and Lyn sometimes made the other girls feel like outsiders. 'Mum and Lyn can finish each other's sentences,' Andrea said. Alison described Wendy and Lyn as sharing an 'intense fifty-year connection, they're a package deal'. The bond is so close that when Lyn went into supported accommodation for a week each year to give her parents a short break, Lyn would 'just have a total meltdown', Andrea remembered. 'Hysteria, sobbing, screaming. She's much better now, but back then she couldn't bear to be parted from everyone, especially Mum.'

When Andrea moved out of home she sought counselling.

Lots of it. I knew when I was in my early twenties that I had a few issues. My central problem was with self-esteem. I had this ingrained belief that what I wanted or needed didn't matter: in fact, I wasn't entitled to even have wants or needs.

Lyn was so needy, her situation was so serious, that anything I wanted or felt was trivial by comparison. Plus there was crippling guilt: guilt that Lyn was so damaged and I was OK. What right did I have to be happy? The way I felt wasn't Mum and Dad's fault—they did the absolute best they could. And Lyn was almost always happy and positive. But what could anyone do?

Andrea studied environmental management and worked as an integration aide during university. She has a strong relationship with her parents and is amazed at their lives. 'Mum just put her head down and worked. So did Dad, even though he struggled a lot. People just accepted their lot then and got on with it and that's what Mum and Dad did. They are outstanding people.'

Wendy Rowe is very grateful that the family remains close. 'There's no doubt at all that the three girls didn't get as much attention as they wanted or I wanted to give them. Lyn probably got eighty per cent of my time herself, and it was a very unusual family home they all had.' Wendy feels some guilt about her daughters' childhoods, but they have all talked about it openly. 'There have been some difficult moments, but we have a great relationship today, and have had for years now. All four of them are exceptional women.'

The Rowe family's struggle with the impact of Lyn's condition was far from unusual. In fact, given the severity of Lyn's malformations the family survived remarkably well. There are many stories of family break-up and worse. Sadly notorious is the UK case where the father took one look at his thalidomide-damaged baby at the hospital and told his wife: 'If you bring that monster home, I leave.' In Australia, one father disappeared on a three-day bender after seeing his baby daughter. Many marriages buckled and broke under the strain. Guilt and recrimination were commonplace. In some families the subject was taboo and children were never told the cause of their condition. Many thalidomide babies were handed over to the state or given up for adoption.

In rare cases parents took more drastic measures. In November 1962 a Belgian woman was acquitted of murder after she admitted having killed her week-old baby who was born with misshapen hands growing from her shoulders. Suzanne Coipel-Vandeput's trial became a cause célébre in Belgium and a crowd of two thousand gathered at the Liège court to hear the verdict. Coipel-Vandeput's doctor, Dr Jacques Casters, was charged with complicity, as were Coipel-Vandeput's husband and two other family members. Dr Casters, who had prescribed his patient thalidomide during early pregnancy, was accused of prescribing a strong dose of barbiturates after the birth, which Coipel-Vandeput mixed with milk and honey and fed to her baby Corinne.

None of the defendants denied the essential facts of the case. Coipel-Vandeput in particular had been open about her intention. When questioned by police after Corinne's death, she wept and said: 'At least she's happy now.' Despite the apparently strong prosecution case, the jury needed less than two hours to find all five defendants not guilty, a verdict greeted by cheering and chanting in the courtroom and by the crowds outside.

• • •

In early 2012 Lyn's legal team hired a filmmaker to document a day in Lyn's life. We planned to use the film during the trial, to demonstrate the exceptional level of care and attention Lyn received from her elderly parents. Also, plans were afoot to replace the Rowes' ageing home, and it was important to capture the conditions in which Lyn had lived for her entire life.

The footage is extraordinary and confronting. So too is Wendy's account of caring for Lyn, which we took to match the film. At that time Wendy was seventy-six. Ian was seventy-nine and taking medication for blood pressure, for his prostate and for a hernia. Yet they were both Lyn's full-time carers.

'Every weekday, Ian and I are up at 6.30 to be ready in time for the carer, who comes to shower Lyn,' Wendy told us.

> In the past I've done all of the showering, and we've both done the toileting. But now we've started getting a carer for the showering because it's too hard for me to do it alone. I help the carer get Lyn into a sling, which winches her up into the air. She gets pushed along the railing which we have installed in the roof of her bedroom. She's then lowered into her chair and taken to the shower. In the past, before we had a sling, Ian and I physically lifted Lyn in and out of bed, and her chair and so on. While Lyn has her shower, I make her lunch, and cut it up so that she'll be able to eat it. Then I find the clothes she wants to wear that day. While I'm doing that, and helping the carer to dress Lyn, Ian gets Lyn breakfast. She usually has stewed fruit and Ian spoons the fruit onto a device that my father made about forty years ago. It's a circle of spoons, welded together at the ends of the handles, fixed to a base which sits on the table. Lyn can turn it with her head and feed herself with it, as long as someone has put the mouthfuls onto the spoons.
>
> After breakfast, I take Lyn to the bathroom and brush her teeth. On days when Lyn goes to the workshop, Ian puts Lyn into the converted van, and takes her to work. If it's a school-visit day, Ian and I drive her in our van to the school,

and go for coffee while she's there. If it's not a school-visit day, while Lyn's at work I do the washing, ironing, cleaning and some cooking and grocery shopping. There is usually a lot of washing to do, as Lyn's sheets need to be washed regularly because of accidents. I also do some sewing for Lyn. I make her underpants, and have to adapt almost all of her other clothes. Ian or I collect Lyn from work at about 3.15. She usually needs a trip to the toilet and something to eat and drink when she gets home. After that, Lyn likes to play on her computer. She hits the keys with a pen held between her teeth. Or she watches some television or writes to her pen pals. While Lyn's doing that, I cook dinner.

After dinner, I sometimes give her a sponge bath. Because of her lack of body surface area Lyn gets hot and sweats easily. Lyn usually goes to bed at about 9.30. I brush Lyn's teeth. Then Ian and I get her out of her chair and into the sling, and hoist her into bed. We put her into her pyjamas. Ian takes her chair and puts it on the charger.

Any time Lyn is at home during the day, I don't leave for more than about half an hour. If I need to go to the shops and Ian's out, I take Lyn with me. Once, many years ago, when Lyn was hoping to have a bit more independence, I left her alone for part of a morning and went to play a game of tennis. While I was gone, Lyn's chair ran out, and when I got home, she was stuck in the corner of the room, unable to move. Since then, I have not left her on her own for an extended period.

During the night, if Lyn needs to go to the toilet, she calls out and I have to help her with a pan. She probably needs to go to the toilet two or three times a night, and sometimes she's uncomfortable and calls out so we can move her. For the past forty-nine years I've got up several times a night for Lyn. Lyn weighs around forty kilos and it's more and more difficult for me to move her if she's uncomfortable in bed.

Except for when she's sleeping, Lyn is strapped into her motorised chair. She sees the chair as the avenue to the only tiny bit of independence she has.

• • •

From the very early days of the thalidomide disaster, Lyn's malformations—completely absent limbs—were seen as one of the things that thalidomide could quite clearly do to a foetus. But doctors did not know with certainty all of the things that thalidomide could do. That was because doctors and scientists were responding to a tragedy, not running a carefully controlled trial. So they made the best decisions they could in difficult circumstances.

In the early 1970s Sydney radiologist Janet McCredie was contacted by Dr William McBride, the Australian doctor who, along with Widukind Lenz, first connected thalidomide and birth malformations. McBride, whose famous and controversial role in the thalidomide story is explored in chapters 12 and 13, was acting as a consultant to the compensation scheme for Australian thalidomide victims. In some cases there was no clear information about whether the mother of the malformed child had taken the drug. So McBride had been asked to help determine which children were thalidomide afflicted and which were not. McBride asked McCredie for advice. Could anything be deduced about whether the children were thalidomide damaged by examining their X-rays?

McCredie studied the X-rays of some accepted thalidomide victims in Australia and the UK. Based on her reviews and research, McCredie developed a theory that was later labelled the neural crest hypothesis. McCredie reasoned that just as thalidomide was capable of damaging nerves in adults taking the drug, so too did it attack and halt nerve growth in the embryo. In summary, her theory proposed that thalidomide acted on the neural crest, damaging foetal nerve growth and causing the failure of normal bone growth in the limbs in a pattern that was somewhat predictable.

McBride claimed to have come up with the theory at the same time, and indeed the two co-authored a paper on the subject. However, after a public spat and the fracturing of their relationship, McCredie was given the credit for the neural crest hypothesis and she has written and lectured extensively on it over the years.

Certainly, McCredie's thesis was widely praised at the time. In the years after the disaster, thalidomide had resisted the efforts of scientists to pinpoint its mechanism of action, the precise way in which it caused birth malformations. Even today, with all the tools and sophistication of modern science, thalidomide's mechanism is only partly understood and still resists the best efforts of scientists to fully unlock its secrets.

But in 1973 McCredie believed she had solved the riddle. She became confident in her ability to spot thalidomide cases by checking the X-rays of children over whom there was a question mark.

McCredie's thesis was also embraced because it provided a scientific explanation for the observations clinicians had made in the wake of the disaster. In thalidomide's aftermath, doctors in several countries decided who was and was not a thalidomide victim, based in part on the availability of evidence that the mother had taken the drug and on whether the child's injuries matched a frequently observed pattern. The medical orthodoxy which developed was prescriptive. It asserted that thalidomide usually caused damage to corresponding limbs on both sides of the body, far more often to the arms than the legs, sometimes to all four limbs, but rarely, if ever, to an odd number of limbs. The thumbs were the first of the digits to be affected, and in the forearm the radius was damaged before the ulna bone. There was a host of other injuries also said to be 'typical', including damage to the spine, eyes, ears and feet. But they all fitted into a loose framework, backed by the doctors' observations and later by McCredie's hypothesis.

This understanding of thalidomide's 'typicality' helped guide who was offered compensation during the early litigation in the 1970s and in the years afterwards. Some people with 'atypical' injuries but with solid evidence of maternal consumption were given the benefit of the doubt. But others were excluded because their injuries, even if severe, did not fit the accepted range.

The problem with all that, Peter Gordon realised in 2011, was that nobody had ever been able to check, let alone study, the full range of injuries caused by thalidomide. The strict application of a 'typical range' was nonsense: a fiction that applied a scientific rigour which had never existed, Gordon decided.

> In short, there was a massive thalidomide tragedy. Lots of foetuses were damaged. Lots died in utero and miscarried. Lots of babies died shortly after birth. Maybe half survived, though even that's a rough guess. The doctors then studied some of the survivors. So to boil it down, the early doctors studied a fraction of a fraction of the children who had been exposed to thalidomide.
>
> Remember this was not a planned epidemiological study. This was doctors responding to a disaster, saying, 'Quick, let's try to work out what the drug has done.' They seized on the children with the obvious malformations, the most common and the most severe problems. Stunted or absent limbs, anuses without openings, missing ears, missing thumbs. The doctors could not go back to the start and examine the child of every woman who had taken thalidomide in pregnancy. They

didn't know who had taken the drug. So they did what they could and identified the most obvious and common injuries. That's fair enough. But the glaring mistake some of them then made was to conclude that the most common injuries were everything, the whole lot. That was wrong.

Gordon likes to use a tobacco analogy to point out the error.

The strict limits that were imposed on what thalidomide does to a foetus was like saying, 'Smoking causes lung cancer and that must mean it doesn't cause anything else.' It's just an error in logic. Smoking also causes heart disease. It causes oral cancer and larynx cancer and oesophageal cancer and throat cancer and emphysema and a lot else. Those diseases are not as numerically apparent or often as graphic and confronting as lung cancer but they're still there and still caused by smoking. And that's what was missed with thalidomide. They got part of the range but not the whole range.

Ultimately Gordon and Sally Cockburn put together a densely reasoned fifteen-thousand-word document marshalling all of the evidence about where the early medicine went wrong, poking holes in the orthodox view of thalidomide typicality and critiquing McCredie's neural crest hypothesis.

Gordon found support for his arguments in surprising places. In the late 1970s the claims of about seventy-five UK children, earlier rejected for compensation, were re-evaluated by an expert panel to see whether any of them should be accepted as victims. About twenty were accepted and notes were kept of the deliberations. One of the most esteemed of the early thalidomide physicians, Dr Claus Newman, was recorded as voicing his doubts about aspects of the medical orthodoxy.

'Dr Newman went on to explain the difficulties of deciding which

Birth drug $89m win

Aussie thalidomide victims finally reach legal settlement

**DANIEL FOGARTY AND
DAVID WILCOCK**

WHEN Monica McGhie's mother hurt her hand and she was given the latest "wonder drug" to ease the pain, she had no idea she was pregnant.

Then when her baby arrived months later, a devastating shock was in store: little Monica was born without arms or legs — one of multitudes worldwide to fall victim to heart-rending birth defects wrought by a drug that proved anything but wonderful.

Yesterday, more than 100 Australian and New Zealand victims of that drug, thalidomide, triumphed in a long legal battle for compensation — to the tune of $89 million.

Monica McGhie — who proved she was a fighter at birth after refusing to fulfil doctors' predictions that she would die — was there.

Ms McGhie travelled all the way from Perth to be with her friend, fellow thalidomide victim Lynette Rowe, at Victoria's Supreme Court for the announcement.

Ms Rowe, who was also born without limbs, last year reached her own multimillion-dollar settlement.

"I nearly cried," Ms McGhie said of her reaction on hearing news of the settlement.

"I never thought this day would come."

Today, she has her own art studio; she has been scuba diving; and she is an advocate for people with disabilities.

"Life has been a daily struggle for 50 years," she said.

"This settlement will not take that hardship away, but it means I can look to the future with more confidence, knowing I can afford the support and care I need."

But yesterday's settlement has been reached only with the drug's distributor, Diageo, not thalidomide's German manufacturer, Grunenthal.

A class action against Grunenthal, which apologised for the first time in August last year, will no longer proceed, following the settlement.

But the victims' lawyers say Grunenthal has behaved appallingly in not paying up.

"Every single Australian thalidomider was injured by a drug made by Grunenthal in Germany," lawyer Michael Magazanik said.

"Despite that, Grunenthal still will not pay a cent to its Australian and New Zealand victims. Fifty years on, Grunenthal will still not 'fess up to its shameful behaviour."

Lawyer Peter Gordon said the sum of the settlement, without Grunenthal's inclusion, was adequate and vindicated the victims' courage.

Thalidomide, withdrawn from sale in 1961, was distributed in Australia and New Zealand by Distillers, which became part of Diageo.

If the settlement is approved in February, victims may receive some payments as early as March.

And then, Ms McGhie hopes she may be able to buy a home — and take her mother, now aged 86, on a cruise.

Lynette Rowe and Monica McGhie with lawyer Peter Gordon (far right) outside the Supreme Court yesterday. Picture: JANINE EASTGATE

Herald Sun

This is a long-overdue outcome for innocents whose lives have been blighted by the failures of the Grunenthal company, with its former shadowy links to the Nazis

FULL EDITORIAL, PAGE 20

Pictured, from left: Lyn Rowe, Michael Magazanik, Monica McGhie, Peter Gordon. NEWSPIX

The Rowe family in the 1960s.

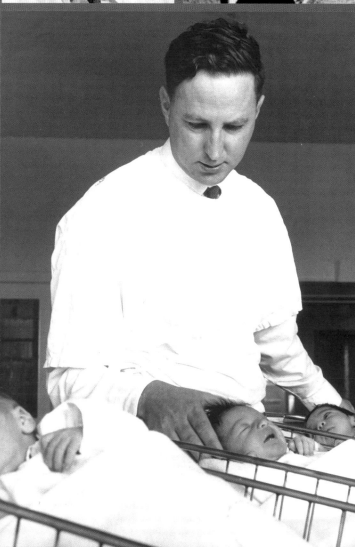

Clockwise from far left:

Heinrich Mückter. Photo published in 1967, just before the German criminal trial began.
© BETTMANN/CORBIS

Otto Ambros at the time of the IG Farben trial, 1946.
© DPA/DPA/CORBIS

Dr William McBride checks a baby at Crown Street Hospital for Women, December 1962.
NEWS LTD / NEWSPIX

1954 DEC. 31, 1960   CORRESPONDENCE   BRITISH
MEDICAL JOURNAL

Is Thalidomide to Blame ?

SIR,—I feel that four cases which have occurred in my practice recently are worthy of mention, as they may correspond to the experience of other practitioners. They all presented in more or less the same way—each patient complaining of : (1) Marked paraesthesia affecting first the feet and subsequently the hands. (2) Coldness of the extremities and marked pallor of the toes and fingers on exposure to even moderately cold conditions. (3) Occasional slight ataxia. (4) Nocturnal cramp in the leg muscles. Clinical examination in each case has been essentially negative, and during this time I have not noticed similar cases in my practice.

It seemed to me to be significant that each patient had been receiving thalidomide (" distaval ") in a dose of 100 mg. at night, the period during which the drug had been given varying from eighteen months to over two years. Thalidomide is generally regarded as being remarkably free of toxic effects, but in this instance the drug was stopped. Three of the patients have now received no thalidomide for two to three months, and there has been a marked improvement in their symptoms, but they are still present. The fourth patient stopped taking the drug two weeks ago, and it is therefore too early to assess the effect of withdrawal.

It would appear that these symptoms could possibly be a toxic effect of thalidomide. I have seen no record of similar effects with this drug, and I feel it would be of interest to learn whether any of your readers have observed these effects after long-term treatment with the drug. I might add that I have found it otherwise to be a most effective hypnotic with no " morning hangover " effect. It has been especially useful in patients with skin pruritus and discomfort.—I am, etc.,

Turriff, Aberdeenshire.   A. LESLIE FLORENCE.

Monika Eisenberg outside the Grünenthal plant, 2012.

Lyn with Mary Henley-Collopy.

Frances Oldham Kelsey.
US FDA / NIH

Drug Detective

● Her skepticism and insistence on having "all the facts" before certifying the safety of a sleep-inducing drug averted an appalling American tragedy — the birth of many malformed infants.

○ ○ ○ ○ ○ ○

She resisted persistent petitions of commercial interests who presented data supporting claims the inexpensive drug was harmless. The facts finally vindicated Dr. Kelsey, as evidence piled up to show the drug — thalidomide — when taken by pregnant women, could cause deformed births.

Her action won her the President's Award for Distinguished Federal Civilian Service.

FRANCES O. KELSEY, *M.D.*
Food and Drug Administration

The Federal Civil Service

Four Score Years of Service to America

1883·1963

Widukind Lenz in 1967.
© DPA PICTURE ALLIANCE / ALAMY

Lyn's fiftieth birthday with (l-r): Andrea, Wendy, Merrilyn, Alison, Ian.

were typical and which were atypical injuries,' the 1978 notes read.

> The original descriptive work done on populations known to
> have been thalidomide-damaged did not give a very compre-
> hensive picture. The doctors involved had looked for the very
> obvious signs of thalidomide damage such as anotia [absent
> external ear] and flipper limbs. They did not look for and so
> did not describe other minor defects.

In that same year, 1978, the UK trust responsible for paying
compensation funds to victims was being confidentially offered the
same advice. Dr Philip Quibell, the trust's medical officer, wrote that
literally hundreds of victims of thalidomide had been missed because
most of the initial surveys lacked merit and could not 'estimate the
real impact of the thalidomide disaster'. Even the better early studies
were deeply flawed, Quibell wrote in an unpublished manuscript.
Only children who fitted the 'alleged thalidomide syndromes' were
included and no follow-up was performed to identify latent defects,
meaning the 'clinical spectrum is incomplete'. As a result, Quibell
wrote, the scale of the epidemic had been greatly underestimated. He
guessed there could 'really be twice the present number of thalidomide survivors'.

This confidential 1978 advice was saying exactly what Gordon
came to believe thirty years later. It reinforced Gordon's concern about
what everyone in Lyn Rowe's team came to call the 'old medicine'.
Our office was being contacted by many people who believed they
were thalidomiders, but had been told they could not be by doctors
conditioned to look for 'typical' injuries like bilateral shortened arms
or absent thumbs. Many of these people had unilateral injuries (to
one side of the body: say, a single arm), a category of injury seen as
'atypical' but which, when Gordon delved deeper into the historic
literature, had always been a feature of the thalidomide disaster.

McCredie's neural crest hypothesis, which gave backing to the traditional injury view, also had its critics from very early on. In another unpublished 1978 document for the UK Thalidomide Trust, the distinguished developmental biologist Professor Lewis Wolpert described the neural crest hypothesis as possessing a 'very weak foundation [which] is contrary to all known embryological studies'. He dismissed it as 'most unlikely' and suggested 'damage to the vascular system of the early limb bud' as a much more likely mechanism. Time would prove Wolpert correct.

• • •

In 1972, Trent Stephens, a young developmental biologist from Idaho, started work on thalidomide's mechanism as part of his interest in embryonic limb development. Stephens, too, grew to doubt Janet McCredie's theory. A decade later, in 1983, he and one of his students authored a paper describing a study in which they used foil barriers to prevent nerves entering the developing limbs of chick embryos. If McCredie's theory that thalidomide damaged bone growth by blocking nerve development was right, the chicks' limb bones, deprived of nerves, would not develop. But the chick bones developed normally, strongly suggesting that the neural crest hypothesis was not the explanation for thalidomide's effect. During the 1980s and '90s a mass of work by other scientists followed, which supported mechanisms of action other than the neural crest hypothesis.

Stephens, one of the better known of thalidomide's many investgators, and a scientist we retained as a consultant, says that over the last fifty years almost forty different mechanisms for the drug have been proposed: 'Some were ridiculous and some have been experimentally evaluated and dismissed.' McCredie's neural crest hypothesis, says

Stephens, was a clever contribution to the science, but one that has been set aside.

Modern experts, says Trent Stephens, believe thalidomide is capable of wreaking havoc on the foetus in multiple ways. The most prominent of these are through damaging blood-vessel growth in the foetus (angiogenesis); causing oxidative damage to the tissue and cells of the developing foetus; binding itself to the DNA so as to block the production of specific proteins needed for embryonic development; and by binding to (and disrupting or disabling) a specific developmental control protein. 'The fact that it seems to act by multiple mechanisms at different biological levels might well explain why it has caused so many more birth deformities than any other pharmaceutical,' Stephens observes. 'Thalidomide really can be seen as the perfect storm of teratology.'

The drug's terrifying and mysterious effect also made it, in the early 1960s, a fascinating drug for scientists; its comeback began almost immediately after it had been withdrawn from sale. Doctors and scientists quickly wondered whether it had caused limb malformations by hindering cell division in the developing embryo. If that were the case, then perhaps it might be effective against cancers, which feature uncontrolled cell division. Soon experiments were underway but without any real success.

The first discovery of a useful application came by chance. In 1964, an Israeli doctor, Jacob Sheskin, was treating a patient with the painful, weeping boils (ENL, erythema nodosum leprosum) that often afflict sufferers of severe leprosy. Sheskin decided to see if a leftover bottle of thalidomide would allow his tormented patient some desperately needed sleep. The drug had a miraculous effect. The patient slept and, even better, his sores quickly began to heal. The drug had a similar effect on others at Sheskin's Jerusalem leprosy clinic. Further trials followed and the results were persuasive. Thalidomide was generally providing complete remission from the painful boils by the second week of treatment. To this day, thalidomide remains a primary tool in treating ENL in some parts of the world (though it's not recommended by the World Health Organization).

In 1991 US researcher Dr Gilla Kaplan found the explanation for thalidomide's success in leprosy. Thalidomide reduced the level of a particular signalling protein, a cytokine called TNF-alpha which makes inflammatory diseases worse, and is found in high levels in ENL victims. TNF-alpha is also often found at high levels in HIV/AIDS sufferers. Soon an underground network was smuggling large quantities of thalidomide into the United States to give relief to people with HIV/AIDS. This created a conundrum for the FDA. Large quantities of a dangerous and banned drug were being used for worthy purposes.

In 1997, Celgene, a US-based pharmaceutical company, submitted an application to the FDA for thalidomide sale approval. A week later a conference was held at which thalidomide survivors, scientists, doctors and members of the leprosy and HIV/AIDS communities expressed their views. Frances Kelsey was there, more than three decades after the first ill-fated application for thalidomide had landed on her desk. After much negotiation, in July 1998 the FDA approved thalidomide for sale for use in leprosy under the brand name Thalomid.

Strict conditions developed by Celgene accompanied the use of the drug, including multiple warnings, detailed information for doctor and patient, a video presentation featuring a thalidomide survivor, a limit on the number of capsules provided at any one time, regular feedback from patients, and a telephone hotline. Females of 'childbearing potential' had to return a negative pregnancy test in the twenty-four hours before starting treatment, and thereafter take regular pregnancy tests.

After legalisation the drug's popularity for HIV/AIDS soon diminished. Thalidomide's sedative effect often had a severe impact on already weakened patients. But further uses were found. Thalidomide (and more recently its analogues, lenalidomide and pomalidomide) became important in the treatment of multiple myeloma, a cancer that inhibits the production of normal blood cells. The analogues have also been investigated, and are currently under investigation, as possible treatments for many other conditions.

Yet resurgent thalidomide is still dogged by its side effects: its tendency to cause nerve damage in adults and, much more terrifyingly, its capacity to malform the foetus (its teratogenic effect). In some countries the risk of unintended tragedies is a reality. Brazil, with one of the biggest populations of leprosy victims in the world and thirty thousand new cases every year, is now the epicentre of modern thalidomide births. Leprosy is most common in poor, remote areas of Brazil. The people being treated with thalidomide sometimes do not appreciate or understand the dangers of the drug, and it has frequently found its way into the hands of newly pregnant women. There are also anecdotal reports of women taking the drug as a birth-control measure after misunderstanding the picture on the pills of a pregnant woman with a line through the image.

A recent study in Brazil counted about one hundred possible thalidomide-damaged babies in the period between 2005 and 2010. During that same period more than five million thalidomide tablets were thought to have been distributed in the country. Some people believe that the speculated thalidomide toll in Brazil may in fact be an underestimate.

One of them is Dr Neil Vargesson, a developmental embryologist who is investigating whether a safe form of the drug could be developed.

'I know the Brazilian researchers and they fear they may have only seen the tip of the iceberg,' Vargesson says. 'Thalidomide gives great relief to people suffering terribly with leprosy. So nobody can blame patients for using it. But when the safeguards are not used the drug is dangerous. Many of the leprosy victims in Brazil are poor, they live in remote areas, illiteracy is common, they share medicines and that's how these births happen. It's a total tragedy.'

Vargesson, who works at the University of Aberdeen in Scotland, has had a longstanding interest in thalidomide but his intense focus on the drug began in 2006 after he saw news reports highlighting cases of children born with thalidomide-like damage in Brazil and Africa. Despite its historic significance, thalidomide's mechanism was not fully understood and Vargesson decided to investigate.

> I wanted to know what it did inside the embryo and how it caused birth defects, and I knew advances in pharmacology and molecular biology would help do that. I hoped we could learn general lessons about drugs and how they act in the body and hopefully how to make them safer. Most importantly, though, I wanted to try to develop a form of thalidomide that does not cause birth defects. If we could keep the anti-inflammatory qualities which make it so effective in leprosy, but get rid of the birth defect risk, then we'd be able to stop the terrible birth of thalidomide children in Brazil and other places.

Vargesson is fighting a valiant but lonely battle. Even Celgene, the thalidomide manufacturer—a company built on the drug's revival—is not researching a safe but leprosy-effective form of the drug. Of Celgene's $6 billion-plus global revenue in 2013, more than two-thirds came from the sale of a single thalidomide analogue, lenalidomide. But Celgene is not the source of all thalidomide-related medicines. Thalidomide is off patent, meaning that generic forms of the drug are produced all over the world. In Brazil it is the generic brands being used in leprosy cases that are causing malformations. Celgene says it does not sell any of its own thalidomide in Brazil, nor does it license any other company to sell the drug there.

Celgene's Australian vice-president George Varkanis said in a 2014 interview that the company regards the Brazilian situation as a tragedy. 'It's a drug we have been deeply involved with and it is tragic to see it's still causing birth defects. Our programs have shown that when it is strictly controlled it can be used safely.' Celgene says that only a tiny portion of its revenue comes from the use of thalidomide in leprosy cases and that wherever it sells thalidomide or its analogues, it includes a local version of its pregnancy prevention program.

Vargesson, who largely uses chicken and zebrafish embryos in his experiments, is confident that his team is making progress towards a better version of the drug for use in leprosy. 'You have to understand the drug in order to improve it, and we're getting there. Thalidomide inhibits the formation and growth of blood vessels in the embryo. In my view that's the key way it causes damage to the embryo. So if we get rid of that property then it might be safer for the embryo and by extension a much safer drug for use in leprosy.'

Both Vargesson, at the cutting edge of modern thalidomide research, and Trent Stephens, whose research interest in the drug began in the early 1970s, agreed to act as expert scientific consultants to Lyn Rowe's legal team. Vargesson travelled to Australia just before Christmas 2012, trading freezing Aberdeen for Melbourne's summer heat. Stephens, who twice made lengthy visits to Australia with his wife Kathleen, is a man of many parts. Since retiring (largely) from his academic life, Stephens has run a costume shop, the Party Palace, in Pocatello, Idaho. He has also written a book in which he reconciled his dedication to science, and embryology in particular, with his devotion to the Mormon Church and its strictures, including the existence of life after death. While in Australia, Stephens spent time in our office, often dressed in colourful Hawaiian shirts, and was accompanied by lawyers Sarah Roache and Brett Spiegel on several trips around Australia and to New Zealand to meet and examine more than seventy of our thalidomide claimants.

Another key medical contributor was Ravi Savarirayan, a charismatic professor of clinical genetics at Melbourne's Royal Children's Hospital. Malformations can have a host of causes, known and unknown. The known causes include genetic conditions, amniotic bands (where strands of the amnion break off, float around the womb and wrap around part of the foetus, causing damage), alcohol, drugs and malnutrition.

Where possible we wanted to eliminate competing causes for a client's condition. Savarirayan was critical in that he was able to advise on the likelihood of a genetic condition and whether a genetic test was available. We ordered genetic tests for about ten of our clients, and the negative results strengthened our claim that the cause of the malformation was thalidomide.

The work by Peter Gordon and Sally Cockburn in dismantling the rigidity of the 'old medicine'—assisted by the medical experts we consulted—opened up the field for many of our clients whose claims might have foundered under a strict application of the old notions of thalidomide typicality.

But this was only one hurdle facing us. Another key task

was dealing with the myth that the thalidomide tragedy was an unavoidable disaster. To do that we would have to establish that, in the early 1960s, Grünenthal and Distillers should have been worried about giving thalidomide to Wendy Rowe and every other pregnant woman.

CHAPTER 11

Grünenthal's Accidental Pregnancy Test

In 1952, an especially bizarre medical experiment featured in the pages of the *American Journal of Obstetrics & Gynecology*. The author of the paper was John Thiersch, a doctor and pathologist who thought he might have found a way to perform non-invasive abortions by simply giving pregnant women a few doses of aminopterin, an anti-cancer drug. Thiersch had used the drug to produce abortions in animals, and if it had the same effect in humans, thought Thiersch, then it might be an effective path to population control. Women could regularly take a small dose of aminopterin, preventing pregnancies advancing beyond the first few weeks. (By contrast, the contraceptive pill, which came a few years later, prevents conception.) In effect, Thiersch was trying to develop an early abortion pill, which he believed would be useful in many countries with poverty, booming populations and inadequate food supply.

To put his thesis to the test, Thiersch ventured into a fraught arena. Over an extended period, he administered aminopterin to twelve pregnant women in whom terminations had been suggested for medical reasons: tuberculosis, mental illness, cancer and muscular dystrophy.

Thiersch's experiment was radical, groundbreaking and in some respects a profound disaster. In ten of the twelve women the drug worked and the women expelled the dead foetuses. But this took as long as thirty days. The lengthy delay between foetal death and expulsion meant some of the embryos 'underwent partial resorption and dehydration'. On examination one of these babies was found to have a brain/skull malformation. These cases, according to Thiersch, were the successes.

The failures, Thiersch wrote, were cases eleven and twelve. Here aminopterin did not induce foetal death and surgical abortions were required. Both foetuses, when extracted, were found to have been damaged by the drug. One had hydrocephalus (fluid on the brain) and the other had a cleft palate and harelip.

Viewed today, Thiersch's report makes uneasy reading. In Thiersch's defence, he made great efforts by the standards of the times to obtain informed consent and engage independent medical oversight for his experiments. It was also a different era, one of bold and aggressive experimentation. Siddhartha Mukherjee has reported in *The Emperor of All Maladies* on the controversy surrounding the brutal treatment of cancer victims in the 1950s and '60s with increasingly toxic combination doses of anti-cancer drugs. The leukaemia ward at the National Cancer Institute became known as the 'butcher shop'; Mukherjee reports two researchers being labelled 'insane, incompetent and cruel' for proposing the 1961 trial of a cocktail of four cytotoxic drugs on children with leukaemia, a trial which took a terrible toll on patients but led in some cases to unprecedented remissions.

But the historical context can only explain so much. Even Thiersch admitted that the audience was horrified when he detailed his human experiments at a 1954 conference. Perhaps in part because of its shock value, Thiersch's report quickly became famous and was much cited.

And the report—indeed Thiersch's whole career—was clearly a weapon to be used in Lyn Rowe's legal battle with the drug companies. Thiersch's work starkly demonstrated that it was well known in the early 1950s—years before thalidomide went on sale—that a drug given to a pregnant woman could be non-toxic for the mother and fatal (and/or malforming) for the foetus. This was going to help us with one of the most bitterly contested issues in Lyn Rowe's claim: should Grünenthal and Distillers have checked the effect of thalidomide on the foetus?

The companies have always claimed such tests were simply not required at the time, that such checks were not commonly done, and that there was no reason to suspect thalidomide might cause damage. In 2013 the following statement could be found on Grünenthal's website: 'In the period before and during the thalidomide tragedy, it was the pharmaceutical manufacturer's responsibility to decide how to test new drugs. Medicines did not have to be tested for their propensity to harm unborn life.' Distillers has made similar statements.

In a literal sense, the Grünenthal statement is correct. There were almost no laws governing what a pharmaceutical company had to do in terms of testing. But pharmaceutical companies then and now had a clear legal obligation to ensure their products were safe. And that means taking sensible precautions, whether or not obliged to by government regulation.

It's also fair to say that Lyn Rowe's legal team did not ascribe much weight to protestations of innocence from Grünenthal and Distillers. But scepticism does not equal proof, and we had to produce evidence. Our research tasks were clear. When did doctors realise that embryos and foetuses could be damaged by substances ingested by pregnant women? Was it before the thalidomide era? Did sensible, responsible drug companies of that period try to investigate whether their drugs might harm foetuses? What if the drugs were being promoted for use in pregnancy, as was the case with thalidomide? And had Grünenthal and Distillers chosen to investigate thalidomide's effect on the foetus, what would the tests have found?

To answer these questions we spent months searching through medical texts and journal articles from the 1930s, '40s, '50s and '60s, talking to elderly doctors and reviewing piles of material in various archives. Soon it became clear that some pervasive myths were still current. Thalidomide was such an epochal disaster that in its wake many doctors and scientists divided knowledge about drugs and pregnancy into pre-thalidomide and post-thalidomide eras. According to that view, pre-thalidomide was a time of darkness and ignorance when, supposedly, nobody realised that drugs taken by a pregnant woman could harm a foetus. When it was unknown whether drugs even passed through the placenta and reached the foetus. When drug companies just had to hope for the best.

But then came the thalidomide disaster and, according to the story, everything changed. Prompted by the tragedy, drug companies began assiduously testing on pregnant animals, conducted rigorous clinical trials and kept a careful watch on their drugs once they were released for sale.

It's a good story, and one that pays appropriate homage to the shock and scale of the thalidomide disaster. But, we discovered, it's largely fiction.

• • •

Human fascination with physical difference is ancient. Giants, dwarfs, monsters, mermaids, cyclopses, albinos and two-headed creatures. The name given to the study of birth malformations is teratology, from the Greek for the study of monsters, an unfortunate though accurate historical reference. Even in the 1960s the reporting of the thalidomide disaster was occasionally blighted by resort to the offensive 'monster' terminology. 'One out of every two women who took the drug bore a freak,' a US headline screamed in 1962.

In 1959 teratologist Josef Warkany surveyed the history of his profession, and noted that over the centuries enlightened thought had tussled with superstition in seeking to explain birth defects. For much of recorded history it was believed that what a mother looked at during pregnancy could cause defects in her baby. Pregnant women were sometimes encouraged, for example, to gaze at beautiful statues and avoid looking at monkeys. This idea of mental pictures moulding the unborn child finds expression in Genesis, where Jacob and Laban reached a deal entitling Jacob to all speckled and spotted lambs and goats born to Laban's flock. Jacob cunningly peeled some branches, creating a streaked and speckled effect, and then 'set up the branches in front of the flocks when they were in heat and came to drink'. The scheme worked. 'When the sheep mated in front of the branches, they gave birth to young that were streaked or speckled or spotted.'

These notions were not confined to the lay population. The sixteenth-century French surgeon Ambroise Paré wrote *On Monsters and Marvels*, an illustrated treatise dealing with birth defects. Paré listed expectant mothers' mental imagery as one cause of birth malformations, and also 'Seated Too Long, Having Had Her Legs Crossed, or Having Bound Her Belly Too Tight While She Was Pregnant'. But even then Paré was headed in the right direction, devoting a chapter to 'monsters that are created by hereditary disease'. He also speculated that the foetus's vulnerability to maternal vision was confined to the first six weeks of pregnancy because after this the embryo was largely formed.

Other pre-modern ideas about the cause of birth malformations included the agency of demons, witches and divine anger. Breeding between humans and animals was another culprit. Warkany reported the execution in 1642 of the unfortunate George Spencer of New Haven, Connecticut. Spencer had a malformed face and eye and, unluckily for him, a piglet stillborn in the same town with a twisted face and single eye was said to bear Spencer a startling resemblance. Spencer was accused of having sired the pig and given a very dubious trial. Despite the lack of any evidence against him, the vengeful officials of New Haven executed both Spencer (by hanging) and his putative paramour, the mother pig (via the sword) on the same day in April 1642.

Eventually though, the intellectual forerunners of today's embryologists and teratologists began to advance their theories. During the seventeenth century the interruption of embryonic development began to be seen as a cause of birth malformations. This was in part the work of English doctor William Harvey, more famously credited with properly describing the circulation of blood in the body, who spent much time dissecting pregnant deer killed during royal hunting expeditions.

By the nineteenth century science was ascendant. In France, Étienne Geoffroy Saint-Hilaire, often seen as the father of experimental teratology, created abnormal chicks by subjecting eggs to all sorts of indignities: shaking, pricking, turning upside down, and altered atmospheric conditions. Others took up this work with further animals and techniques. By the early twentieth century defects in mammals were being produced by measures including radiation and altered maternal diets. In 1933, for example, Fred Hale, of the Texas Agricultural Experiment Station, reported in the memorably titled article 'Pigs Born Without Eyeballs' that a pregnant sow fed a diet deficient in vitamin A had given birth to a litter of eleven pigs, none of whom had eyeballs. By this time heredity via genes (and, increasingly, genetic disorders) were also established as prime causes of birth malformations.

A seminal contribution was made by an Australian paediatric ophthalmologist, Norman Gregg. In 1941, Gregg noticed an exceptionally high number of babies with cataracts among his patients. The story goes that one day he overheard a conversation between two mothers in his waiting room. Each had a baby with cataracts and each mentioned having had German measles (rubella) during pregnancy. Gregg searched his records and questioned his infant patients' mothers. The results were astonishing. Close to ninety per cent of the mothers of children with congenital cataracts had suffered rubella during pregnancy. Gregg published his work in a little-known journal, and then a follow-up paper connecting congenital deafness with maternal rubella.

Clearly the foetus was vulnerable—not only to maternal illness—and this was well known. In 1939 Dr Harold Speert at Johns Hopkins Hospital in Baltimore worried about the effect that sulfanilamide—used to treat infection—might have on the foetus when given to pregnant women. He conducted a series of sophisticated experiments with pregnant rats and found increased mortality in their offspring, decreased litter size and reduced birth weight. Dr Speert published his findings, and strongly advised that sulfanilamide should only be used with 'extreme caution' in pregnancy until further observations of the drug's effect in human pregnancy could be made. This was almost twenty years before thalidomide, untested in pregnancy, was spruiked by Grünenthal as utterly safe.

During the late 1940s and '50s any number of medical texts recognised the capacity of drugs taken by the mother to pass the placenta and reach and damage the foetus. Some texts also pointed out that a dose which was non-toxic for the mother could damage the foetus. 'Many drugs pass from the mother to the child, and this is to be borne in mind, because quantities that are insufficient to poison the former may have more serious effects on the latter,' one 1954 text warned.

It was also understood that the risk to the foetus was greatest in the early months of pregnancy (when medically the foetus is often referred to as an embryo). For example, a 1948 article in the *Journal of the American Medical Association* recognised the potential risk of medicating pregnant women during the first trimester. 'We would be hesitant to advise administration of streptomycin during the first trimester because of the generally accepted sensitivity of the fetal structures in…that period.'

The effect of drugs on the foetus was also the subject of study in Germany. In 1956, working a short drive from Grünenthal headquarters, Dr Ernst-Albrecht Josten wrote a paper that appeared in one of Germany's most widely read medical journals, *Münchener Medizinische Wochenschrift*, under the heading 'The Effect of Medication on the Unborn Child'. Dr Josten's six-page article included an English summary that began: 'In cases where pregnant women undergo treatment by medicaments, one must consider whether any harm can thereby be done to the fetus.'

The examples from the German literature are too numerous to mention, but mirrored publications elsewhere. In 1960, more than a year before thalidomide's deadly effect was exposed, 'The Effects of Drugs on the Foetus' by Dr J. Baker of the Charing Cross Medical School in London was published. It included references to 354 previously published articles on the same or related subjects. Such was the interest in birth defects prior to the thalidomide disaster that two international conferences on the subject were held in London in 1960.

Both featured multiple presentations and discussions on the effect of drugs on the foetus.

One additional document surely demolishes the theory that the era prior to thalidomide was an age of darkness with an entrenched ignorance about drugs damaging the foetus. In May 1961, six months before the thalidomide disaster was revealed, the US Committee on Fetus and Newborn drafted a statement, 'Effect of Drugs upon the Fetus and the Infant'. The statement was so prescient and wise, that looking at it down the telescope of history it appears the committee saw the thalidomide disaster coming.

> The fetus and the newborn infant often behave so differently as to warrant consideration as separate categories of the human species…data obtained from tests in mature animals and human adults or older children cannot be accepted as a satisfactory basis for recommendations concerning the fetus and infant.

The committee called for careful animal testing of the effect of drugs on the foetus. 'Physicians who administer drugs to the fetus and the infant must be alert to unusual effects in this subdivision of the human species.'

The connection between drugs and birth defects was clearly not a dark mystery. Yet Grünenthal and Distillers promoted thalidomide to doctors, including obstetricians, as specifically suitable for use in pregnancy, without ever having tried to check the drug's effect on the foetus. And mere months after the statement of the US committee, when thalidomide was outed as a birth defect drug, Grünenthal and Distillers started claiming that they could have done nothing to avoid the disaster.

It was spin: a completely spurious claim. Yet it was accepted without investigation or query by large sections of the media, industry, government and public alike. This nonsense remained entrenched fifty years later and we understood it would pose a serious obstacle to Lyn Rowe's claim.

We knew that Grünenthal and Distillers would find 'experts' to come to court and talk about the pre-thalidomide dark age of medical knowledge. But we believed we had assembled the evidence to demolish such claims. The documents referred to in this chapter are a tiny fraction of the material we gathered. Copies of articles flooded in from libraries in Australia and overseas; Amazon made a tidy profit as we searched for and collected ageing medical texts. The material piled up in our offices and we hired casual staff to sort and file it electronically.

The mountains of material made clear that by the time thalidomide went on sale it was well known and well publicised around the world that drugs taken by a pregnant woman could pass the placenta, reach the foetus and cause damage. Scientists and researchers had for many years conducted experiments on pregnant animals to determine whether drugs might damage the foetus. Many doctors had for years urged caution in medicating pregnant women. Anti-cancer drugs were most obviously capable of damaging the foetus but other widely used drugs were also considered potentially dangerous.

In the era before thalidomide, best practice was enlightened. But by no means had all pharmaceutical companies adopted this best practice. Many were, like Grünenthal and Distillers, unenlightened. What the thalidomide disaster really did was to make public in the most dramatic fashion what was already known in informed circles about the vulnerability of the foetus to drugs. It also rapidly accelerated study of the subject. 'Thalidomide changed the lives of the small band of experimental teratologists who [previously] worked quietly in their laboratories,' one leading expert later wrote. 'Now government, industry, and the media called on them for advice.'

• • •

All of this led to another important issue. Was the complacency of Grünenthal and Distillers universal in the industry? Did any drug companies of that era try to check the effect of drugs on the foetus? The work of John Thiersch, the man who used an anti-cancer drug to procure abortions, held some of the answers.

Thiersch grew up in Germany before making his way to Australia via a teaching stint in China. In Australia he developed his interest in cancer and leukaemia, worked as a pathologist in Adelaide, and in 1946 authored an article about his attempts to establish whether acute leukaemia might be transmissible. He must have been a very persuasive man. In order to test the possibility, Thiersch took bone marrow from patients suffering acute leukaemia and injected it into the bone marrow of volunteers. In other words, Thiersch set out to infect people with leukaemia. Thiersch's volunteers were suffering from various cancers and perhaps he persuaded them that their situations were dire and would not be significantly worsened by adding leukaemia to their burdens. Thiersch later said his volunteers were terminal patients with less than two years to live, and that he had obtained 'informed consent' and consulted with the hospital authorities. In any event, none of the recipients developed leukaemia.

Thiersch then left Australia and found a job at the Sloan Kettering Institute in New York, a key cancer research centre. In 1947 in Boston, the doctor and pathologist Sidney Farber had pioneered the use of aminopterin to produce remissions in children with leukaemia. Aminopterin inhibits the body's absorption of folic acid (thus 'folic acid antagonist'); folic acid stimulates the growth of leukaemia cells (and is vital for the health of the foetus). Inspired by Farber's successes in Boston, researchers at the Sloan Kettering Institute were working hard in the same field. It was in this environment that Thiersch found work.

In 1948 Thiersch fed a dose of aminopterin to a dog as part of an experiment. Unknown to Thiersch, the dog was pregnant and to Thiersch's surprise it bled vaginally and aborted. 'I took this single observation seriously and followed it up with a number of experiments in mice, rats and dogs studying the effects of folic acid antagonists in pregnant animals and fetuses.'

Thiersch soon realised that mother and foetus responded differently to drugs at different stages of pregnancy. Further, drugs taken by the mother could cause embryos to die and be reabsorbed into the lining of the uterus (resorptions), increase the number of stillborn, reduce litter size, reduce the birth size of babies, and cause malformations. Thiersch published the results of many of these experiments, reports that were widely available, including to the drug companies. Much of Thiersch's research was funded by influential organisations: the Population Council and Planned Parenthood. Finally though, Thiersch had to give up on his abortion pill. 'The entire approach was too dangerous,' he concluded.

By the time the thalidomide scandal broke in the early sixties, Thiersch was one of a small group of scientists in Europe, Japan and the United States at the forefront of experimental teratology. So, understandably, the lawyers for thalidomide victims sought Thiersch's expertise. He was happy to oblige, ultimately giving evidence in Swedish, Japanese and US thalidomide lawsuits. Thiersch had strong opinions, and they were strongly critical of Grünenthal. More than forty years after those lawsuits, and almost twenty years after his 1993 death, we found copies of Thiersch's advice and evidence in various archives around the world.

In a lengthy written opinion for the Swedish lawyers, Thiersch said that thalidomide could and should have been tested in animals for its effect on the foetus. If this testing had been properly conducted it would at the very least have resulted in reduced litter sizes and increased embryonic death. This would have put the drug under suspicion and led to further tests and inquiry, and the terrible effect of the drug would have been discovered. By skipping reproductive testing in animals, Thiersch believed, Grünenthal had in effect experimented on vast numbers of humans.

Thiersch also provided important evidence about drug companies. During the 1950s major firms including Merck, Lederle, Burroughs Wellcome, Parke-Davis and Smith Kline & French all investigated the teratogenic potential of their drugs, Thiersch said. Thiersch himself had been asked to perform reproductive work, including tests on Diamox (a diuretic) for Lederle and on Daraprim (an antimalarial) for Burroughs Wellcome. 'Many drug houses were aware of a potential effect on the fetus of their drugs, and actively supported investigation of this nature,' Thiersch wrote.

Thiersch's research and his controversial abortion experiments occasionally caused him grief while in the witness box for the thalidomide victims. The drug company lawyers seized on his work, trying to paint him as an 'abortionist'.

'You went to Seattle and started using aminopterin in human beings?' Thiersch was asked by Merrell's lawyer in one US thalidomide trial.

'Yes. This requires an explanation.'

'I am sure it does, doctor,' came the response.

On another occasion, Thiersch was being questioned about his

Australian work experimenting with leukaemia on cancer victims. The lawyer for the thalidomide victim stepped in, objecting that Merrell was trying to portray Thiersch as 'some sort of beast'.

But Thiersch was an impressive witness: tough and assertive and never willing to apologise for his work. In one case he gave evidence that it would have cost just one hundred dollars and taken less than a month to run a test with thalidomide in pregnant rats or mice—a test, he pointed out, that would have shown up signs of a damaging effect on the foetus.

• • •

None of this is to suggest that reproductive testing in animals for new drugs was mandatory, or even an industry standard. Rather, the point is that some responsible drug companies were doing it.

In 1954 Rhône-Poulenc performed reproductive testing on rats with chlorpromazine, which had an anti-nauseant effect, and the results were published in 1954. 'This research seems to us to be more than ever justified since this product is frequently administered to pregnant women,' the article observed.

A Smith Kline & French memorandum from April 1956 (prior to the sale of thalidomide anywhere in the world) about the drug prochlorperazine sets out some basic common sense that should have occurred to thalidomide's manufacturers. 'Since [it] may be a useful drug in the treatment of nausea and vomiting during pregnancy, it appeared advisable to determine the effect of daily administration... on male and female rats during mating and on pregnant females and their young after impregnation had taken place.'

In 1956 and 1957 Richardson-Merrell performed reproductive testing on a non-steroidal oestrogen antagonist and found severe interference in rat pregnancies: embryonic death, stillbirths and neonatal deaths. In 1959 Richardson-Merrell did reproductive testing with Mer-29 (Triparanol, the controversial anti-cholesterol drug) on rats, both in-house and at an external consultancy. Merrell of course had a close relationship with Grünenthal as its US thalidomide licensee. Had Grünenthal been interested it could have asked Merrell about reproductive testing.

When the *Sunday Times* journalists conducted their investigation into thalidomide in the 1960s and '70s they questioned many pharmaceutical firms about their procedures. Hoffman-La Roche said that since 1944 it had routinely performed reproductive testing on all of its new drugs and published some of the work. For example, a 1961 article on the new tranquilliser Valium concluded: 'The results of [the rat] breeding experiment indicate that Valium does not exert a deleterious effect on the process of reproduction or normal development of the newborn.'

Edward Paget, the former head of pathology at British company ICI, told the newspaper that during the 1950s ICI had conducted tests on pregnant animals with every drug that might be used by a pregnant woman. In the aftermath of thalidomide's withdrawal, Paget was approached by Distillers to give evidence for the drug company. Paget told Distillers of ICI's longstanding policy. He added that he considered Distillers at fault for recommending the use of thalidomide in pregnancy without having tested the drug in pregnancy. Understandably, Distillers did not pursue Paget as a witness.

There was also much reproductive testing that never saw the light of day. In 1959 the leading teratologist James Wilson wrote that 'pharmaceutical laboratories test many new drugs on incubating eggs and pregnant rodents but do not publish the negative observations'. To be sure, testing new drugs on pregnant animals was neither universal nor even standard in the late 1950s. It was also an inexact science. A lot of run-of-the-mill drug companies did not bother with it. But many responsible drug companies were making the effort, knowing that it was the best way to investigate a crucial issue: what might the drug do to a vulnerable foetus?

Of course Grünenthal and Distillers would argue that these diligent companies were the exception. But that's a largely meaningless legal defence. Just because lots of companies were negligent does not excuse that negligence. Asbestos companies all over the world were negligently exposing their employees and workers to deadly carcinogenic fibres throughout the 1960s, often without warning or precaution. Many of those companies have now paid out vast sums to their victims. It never assisted their legal position to argue, 'Our competitors were also exposing everyone to cancer so it can't be our fault that we did the same.'

And anyway there was nothing far-fetched about testing the drug in pregnant animals. Grünenthal and Distillers knew how to do it and each had animal laboratories. The first thing they and other drug companies did when forced to confront the likelihood that thalidomide was maiming foetuses was to test the drug on pregnant animals.

By January 1962, only weeks after thalidomide's withdrawal, tests by Distillers pharmacologist George Somers showed thalidomide had a dramatic impact on litter size in rats and increased the number of stillbirths. Somers pressed on with further tests. Grünenthal, meanwhile, was less successful in finding an effect on animal foetuses. It is hard to understand this failure. Perhaps its scientists were not very skilful. Perhaps its test animals were freakishly resistant to the effects of thalidomide. Or perhaps, a cynic might think, Grünenthal was not trying as hard as it might have.

While Grünenthal's unsuccessful tests dragged on, Somers at

Distillers quickly cracked the case. A colleague later recalled 'a very excited' Somers telephoning in March 1962 and demanding he drop everything and rush to Somers' laboratory. 'Like a conjurer producing a rabbit from a hat, he removed the cloth covering a dish to reveal a malformed rabbit!' Somers did not plan to keep his work quiet, despite a request from Grünenthal that he delay publication. 'Now we have succeeded in producing deformities in rabbits remarkably similar to those seen in humans,' he wrote to *The Lancet* in a letter, with photographs, published on 28 April 1962. Somers promised further detail on these and other experiments with mice, rats and hens' eggs.

Grünenthal was outraged. Somers was behaving like a scientist! First, Heinrich Mückter (now rich thanks to his personal share of thalidomide profits) wrote Somers an insulting letter. Then in May 1962 another Grünenthal executive, like Mückter also later charged with thalidomide crimes, wrote to Somers' boss. 'Unfortunately, Dr Somers' publication on deformities in rabbits…is more the work of a free, independent scientist than that of a researcher working within the compass of a pharmaceutical firm.' The Grünenthal letter warned that Somers' coming publications would 'lead to harm being done to both our firms, which is neither in your interests nor ours'.

Grünenthal has never accepted that it should have tested its drug on pregnant animals prior to sale or even during the period it was on sale. And Grünenthal insists that even had it done so, tests in pregnant rats, the likely test species, would have given no cause for concern. This is yet more propaganda. John Thiersch was one of the world's foremost experts and he has stated that proper tests on pregnant rats, mice or rabbits, using the appropriate dose, would have detected a significant rise in resorptions, where the foetus dies and is absorbed into the placenta, leaving behind a scar. Competent scientists would have seen this as evidence of a possible teratogenic effect on the foetus, said Thiersch. Further tests would have followed, and the danger would have been exposed.

Yet despite the weakness of its argument against pregnancy testing, Grünenthal prefers to focus on this rather than on what happened once thalidomide was on the market. It is easy to see why. The reports of nerve damage that reached Grünenthal (and Distillers) after the drug went on sale established that thalidomide was not as safe as claimed. Obviously pre-sale testing had not picked up this major problem. The drug was neurotoxic, a serious problem, but exactly the sort of problem that could emerge once a drug was in widespread use. Drug firms were supposed to keep their drugs under close surveillance for just that reason. FDA commissioner George Larrick said in 1960 that pre-marketing animal experiments and clinical studies were merely pilot studies. 'Untoward reactions may not become manifest during the treatment of two or three thousand patients during the period of clinical study, but may show up only after the drug has been subjected to use by millions of patients,' Larrick said. 'The undesirable properties sometimes show up tardily.'

Once the nerve-damage effect showed up, it would have been sensible to ask what a neurotoxic drug might do to a foetus. Years earlier exactly the same concerns had arisen about streptomycin, an antibiotic which was neurotoxic to the eighth cranial nerve, thereby damaging hearing. Grünenthal and Distillers had both been in the streptomycin business and should have been aware of this issue. A 1948 article warned against the use of streptomycin during the first trimester of pregnancy because of the sensitivity of the embryo. In 1951, three doctors in the United States published their investigation into streptomycin's effect on the foetus. 'Since streptomycin crosses the placenta, the possibility of fetal damage from prolonged administration of the drug required consideration,' the doctors wrote. The doctors then checked on a series of children exposed in utero to streptomycin and found that, at least in mid- to late pregnancy, it seemed to be safe for the foetus.

Why did a similar concern never motivate Grünenthal or Distillers in relation to thalidomide? Why did they not worry, like Frances Kelsey, what might thalidomide be doing to a vulnerable foetus? If the drug had been pulled at the point at which its neurotoxicity became clear, about ninety per cent of thalidomide's death and malformation toll would have been avoided.

As well as a vast number of nerve-damage reports, Grünenthal received reports of possible links to malformations. But still nothing was done: no investigation, no belated animal tests, no survey of pregnant women. Even after the drug went on sale, proper care and concern could have avoided much of the tragedy. Grünenthal's response, however, was to sell, sell, sell. It's an approach that still amazes fifty years later. Even several years of exposure to Grünenthal's historic modus operandi did not reduce our team's astonishment at the company's conduct.

• • •

There is one further—remarkable—footnote to Grünenthal's position on animal testing, which only emerged late during our research in the German archives. In September 1961, not long before it was forced to pull thalidomide from the market, Grünenthal accidentally—*accidentally*—conducted a test with thalidomide in pregnant rats. How did it happen?

By this time, Grünenthal had become sufficiently worried about the nerve-damage issue that it had started testing the drug on rats to see if it did indeed cause nerve damage. Three of the rats turned out to be pregnant, a development that surprised the Grünenthal scientists. In early October 1961 the rats gave birth: the first two gave birth to six and five babies respectively, the third to just one dead baby. These were small litters, and in the case of the third rat, dramatically so.

The accidental test was a model in miniature (albeit inadequate and unintended) of the sort of research John Thiersch said should have been done before the drug went on sale. Thiersch said thalidomide would cause reduced litter size and increased embryonic death, leading to suspicion about the drug. But Thiersch had vigilant scientists in mind, not Grünenthal's team.

While the documentary record is sketchy, it appears that nobody at Grünenthal registered any concern about the three anomalous rat litters. This was despite the fact that reports of human birth malformations possibly linked to thalidomide had already been brought to Grünenthal's attention. Further, some people inside Grünenthal were by then calling for animal testing to determine whether thalidomide could have any effect on the foetus. Weeks later, in November 1961, Lenz blew the whistle and Grünenthal was forced to halt the sale of thalidomide.

At that point the Grünenthal scientists who had conducted the accidental pregnancy research must have looked back at the episode with growing concern. But, fortunately, exoneration was at hand. In January 1962 an internal Grünenthal report dealt reassuringly with the unintentional pregnancy testing: it speculated that the small litter size of the first two rats was probably a result of the advanced age of the mothers, and made no reference to the third rat's single dead baby. Thalidomide was not identified as a possible culprit.

This episode perhaps gives a prism through which to view some of Grünenthal's subsequent self-serving statements about thalidomide.

The fact is that Grünenthal accidentally performed a small-scale pregnancy test with thalidomide at a time when alarm bells were ringing in Stolberg about the danger of its drug. The results of the accidental test might have worried another company. At Grünenthal HQ it was business as usual.

CHAPTER 12

Like Lollipops

In 2011 preparations for Lyn's trial were in full swing but the outcome, naturally, was uncertain. All of the members of Lyn's legal team were hopeful, even optimistic, but it would be an overstatement to say we were certain of victory. So in late 2011 Peter Gordon and his wife Kerri O'Toole began thinking about what they could do to ensure the Rowe family emerged with something even if the case failed. Their focus quickly fell on the old weatherboard house in Nunawading. Home to the Rowe family since 1954, it was now in a bad way. The floors had cracked and sloped. Yawning gaps had opened up between the skirting boards and the walls and floors. The back door was permanently jammed shut. The Rowes had never had the money to improve their home, and even maintenance was a stretch when any extra funds were spent on basic necessities for Lyn, like a specially fitted-out van. The house predated Lyn's birth and had never been wheelchair-friendly. Thanks to the deterioration over the years, it was now exceptionally wheelchair-unfriendly.

Gordon talked with Melbourne-based building company Watersun Homes about an extensive renovation. Watersun took a look and its assessment was blunt: demolish it and start again. The home was simply too far gone to be saved. From that assessment grew a charitable push to build a new home for the Rowes. If that could be done, then even if the worst were to happen in court, the Rowes' plunge into the legal system would not be for naught.

Watersun attacked the job enthusiastically. Soon it had persuaded dozens of its usual suppliers and tradesmen to pledge time, materials or expertise, and in many cases all three. Watersun's designer worked closely with the Rowes and an occupational therapist to assess Lyn's care requirements and make provision for modern aids and automation. Large sums of money were donated by some individuals—on the proviso of anonymity—to buy what could not be donated, including new furniture. These donors also covered the five months' rent for the Rowes' temporary accommodation.

In March 2012 the Rowes watched as their home of fifty-seven years was demolished. Lyn shed tears as the old house came down, the only home she had ever lived in. Over the next few months Lyn and her parents made frequent visits to the site as the new home began to take shape. A month after the demolition the slab was poured and by the end of April 2012 the frame for the new building was up.

At times the construction site had a community feel. The neighbours put on morning tea for the tradesmen, and the concreters wrote 'Best wishes Lyn' on the slab. In the rush and enthusiasm to get the job done, tradesmen went the extra mile. Landscape gardeners worked almost around the clock for three days, finally finishing the front garden late on a Sunday night, working in the glow provided by their truck's headlights. In July 2012, just eighteen weeks after the old home was knocked down, the Rowes moved back in. The difference between old and new was enormous, a contrast highlighted by the fact that the address had not changed. 'I feel amazed to be here,' Lyn said after moving in. 'I just wish everybody who worked on it could see how happy I am.'

Whereas the old home had no specific features for Lyn's benefit beyond a retro-fitted hoist in the bathroom, the new home was fully twenty-first century. Ramps, a voice-controlled front door and extra-wide hallways and doorways catered for Lyn's wheelchair. An expanded ceiling hoist system connected Lyn's bathroom, bedroom and study. Cameras and monitors allowed Lyn to know what was going on in other parts of the home. Lyn's bedroom and that of her parents were at separate ends of the house, giving them all extra privacy. Lyn's quarters included a separate bedroom for an overnight carer, and a private entry. Of course with the court case still in progress, there were no funds for private care. To afford that, Lyn would have to win her case. And increasingly our attention had been turning to uncovering thalidomide's Australian story.

• • •

In 1959 the men in charge at Distillers in London turned to Bill Poole to make thalidomide a bestseller in Australia. It must have seemed a sensible choice. Poole was a lawyer, a pharmacist and an Australian. And after many years in the UK, Poole was willing to return home.

He set up base just north of the Sydney Harbour Bridge, hired a sales team and set about putting thalidomide in every pharmacy and doctor's surgery in the country. Thalidomide was Poole's big chance, his ticket to success at Distillers, and he was not going to miss his opportunity. For two years he worked hard and impressed his bosses. But then disaster: in late 1961 Poole learned that a Sydney obstetrician suspected thalidomide was damaging babies. Horrified but undaunted, Poole rose to the occasion. He acted quickly and responsibly, withdrew the drug and assured the government, the media and his own employees that Distillers had acted with great care.

Poole is long dead, but that was his story. It is, however, a giant lie. The truth about Bill Poole—when it finally emerged—was one of the most stunning outcomes of our investigations. It reframed the way we viewed Distillers' responsibility for the thalidomide disaster. Until then, Grünenthal appeared to Lyn's legal team to have behaved far more outrageously than Distillers. But Poole's behaviour went some way to balancing the ledger.

The fact is that at one of the critical moments of the unravelling thalidomide saga, Poole chose to put his career and profits above lives. Despite learning in mid-1961 that thalidomide might be killing and maiming babies, Poole kept selling more and more of the drug for almost another six months, including specifically for use in pregnancy and to obstetricians and maternity hospitals. When thalidomide's deadly effect could be kept secret no longer, Poole realised he might be in deep, deep trouble. So he lied on an industrial scale to cover up his disgraceful behaviour: in writing to the Australian Government, to his colleagues, and to the media. He even lied on oath in court documents. Bill Poole lied and kept lying.

It is not known whether his bosses at Distillers in London knew the real story. Certainly they could easily have discovered it afterwards, and one has to wonder whether they did. But nobody in the inner circle blew a whistle. Poole's behaviour was covered up. And the blame that should have been heaped on Distillers was deflected as a result.

The only witnesses to Bill Poole's lies are now gone or very elderly. Distillers' internal documents remain largely under lock and key. If Lyn Rowe had not decided to pursue the drug companies in 2011, Poole's outrageous behaviour and the extent to which he and his bosses could have stopped the thalidomide death toll would never have been exposed.

• • •

Right from the start, Distillers was anxious to get a licence from Grünenthal to sell thalidomide in Australia and New Zealand. Distillers was a British company and the antipodean countries were very firmly part of the British Commonwealth. Distillers saw it as only right that it be given the chance to exploit thalidomide in the far-flung corners of the empire.

But starting in the late 1950s, Distillers' entreaties were repeatedly rebuffed. Distillers persisted and finally, in early 1960, Grünenthal relented, granting Distillers the much-sought-after Australian licence, throwing in New Zealand as part of the bargain.

Under the agreement, concluded on April Fool's Day 1960, Grünenthal insisted that Distillers hire at least twelve salesmen in Australia to promote thalidomide. Distillers also made an important concession. According to the original 1957 contract with Grünenthal, Distillers could have been manufacturing thalidomide at its factory in Speke, Liverpool. But it had never bothered to do that. Instead it had been buying raw thalidomide from Grünenthal which it mixed with other ingredients to make the finished medications. As part of the negotiations over the Australian licence, Distillers gave up the right to make its own thalidomide and agreed to keep buying it, thereby handing Grünenthal a financial windfall. The move also ensured that everyone who took a Distillers thalidomide pill in Australia (including Wendy Rowe)—or the UK or anywhere else Distillers exported its products—was swallowing Grünenthal-made thalidomide.

Relieved to have the licence, Distillers swung into action. A team was already on the ground in Sydney and soon an office-warehouse was established and staff hired. Senior Distillers employees arrived from London to train the Australian recruits. Thalidomide drugs had been dribbling into Australia for some time, but they were now shipped in bulk and stockpiled. Doctors were given advance samples and promotional material. In July 1960 all of the new sales staff were flown to Sydney and given a week of instruction in the art of selling. All was ready for the official launch in August 1960.

It was always clear to Lyn's legal team that what went on in Australia in 1960 and 1961 was crucial. Our claim was in an Australian court, for an Australian woman whose Australian mother took the drug in Australia. Clearly events in Australia would loom large in the court case. We searched for the twenty or so people employed by Distillers in Australia in 1959–62, and after months of intensive effort managed to find a handful. Many had passed away. All of those we found were happy to speak with us. They offered us a priceless insight into what actually went on.

I found Phil Lacaze's name on a fifty-year-old letter that the father of one of our thalidomide clients had kept. Lacaze had headed Distillers' Melbourne sales team in 1961. Fortunately Lacaze is not a common name and there were only a few in the telephone directory.

I cold-called a P. Lacaze in a Sydney suburb one morning in March 2011. After introducing myself and warning that this was a very left-field call, I asked the man who had answered if he had ever worked in the pharmaceutical business. Yes, the man replied. Did he happen to work for Distillers in the early 1960s? 'Yes.' I launched into my prepared speech: 'I'm a lawyer working for victims of the drug thalidomide…' The man heard me out. 'I'd be happy to talk to you,' he responded. 'I'm sure I have some useful information and I have a pretty good memory.'

A few days later I pulled up outside Phil Lacaze's unit in a rented car after an early morning flight from Melbourne. Phil, then eighty-two, handsome and slightly stooped, welcomed me and ushered me inside, where I met Johnny, his wife of fifty-nine years. I had brought a good bottle of red wine as a gift, and a quiche for morning tea. But since neither drank, and both were on restricted diets for health reasons, my gifts fell a little flat. Then I found the pen in my pocket had leaked all over my shirt and in the ensuing slapstick the ice was broken. Unfussed, Johnny insisted I change my shirt (I had a spare) and quickly removed the stain.

In the months that followed I spoke regularly with Lacaze and met with him several times. Both he and Johnny, who died suddenly in June 2011, were welcoming and all too happy to help. Lacaze had studied medicine for several years before becoming a pharmaceutical salesman and had a deep knowledge of drug chemistry and the pharmaceutical industry in Australia. He was a man with an inquiring mind and was keenly interested in Lyn's claim.

Lacaze only worked for Distillers in Australia for about a year, but fate dictated that it was the critical final year that thalidomide was on the market. Early on he told me he had spent the subsequent fifty years regretting having worked for Distillers.

Another salesman I tracked down, also in March 2011, was Hubert Ollyet Woodhouse, known to all as Woody. Woodhouse was eighty years old, and had spent the last twenty years of his career running his own pharmaceutical company before retiring in 2000. I visited him at the beautiful home in Sydney's northern suburbs he and his wife Ursula had bought about forty-five years earlier. The house was perched high on a wide tree-lined street. At the bottom of the hill were picturesque sea baths where the couple's three children had learnt to swim.

Woodhouse and Phil Lacaze had known each other only slightly in 1961, when Lacaze worked for Distillers in Melbourne and Woodhouse in the Sydney head office. In the aftermath of my meeting them, they arranged to have lunch, meeting for the first time in half a century. Both men were interested in Lyn Rowe's personal story and empathetic about her circumstances. Both were willing to help Lyn and her parents by telling me all they could remember about the thalidomide operation in Australia. Woodhouse and Lacaze were delighted by our eventual success on Lyn's behalf, and wrote warm personal notes to the Rowe family in the aftermath of the settlement. The litigation gods could not have delivered us two more willing witnesses, both of whom had front-row seats at crucial times during the thalidomide story.

Woodhouse was a charming man, fond of a good story and conversation. This, I soon realised, is a feature of many former pharmaceutical salesmen. It makes sense of course: salesmen rely on their charm and wit for appointments and sales. Woody, as he insisted I call him, initially seemed a little cautious. I had no problem with that. I was grateful that he was talking with me at all. Every potential witness I spoke to about thalidomide would have been entirely within his or her rights to say, 'No thank you, not interested.' Woodhouse did not do that. But he did seem to hold back a fraction.

I thought I knew why. Woodhouse had worked at Distillers headquarters in Sydney. I had seen documents revealing that in the late 1960s the German criminal prosecutors had tried to get a statement from Woodhouse to help in their prosecution of the Grünenthal executives. Woodhouse refused, on legal advice from his former employer Distillers. Obviously the German prosecutors thought Woodhouse might know something of value, and, I suspected, even all these years later that thalidomide would remain a somewhat painful topic. As it would for anyone intimately involved in selling it.

• • •

Woodhouse had started medicine at Sydney University in 1949, but after three years dropped out and entered the pharmaceutical industry. For five years he worked as a sales rep in Sydney and Adelaide, and then in April 1957 he and his wife Ursula moved to London. Ursula, an actress, had a role in the movie *Robbery Under Arms*, which had been part-filmed in South Australia and was to be completed at Pinewood studios in England. The couple had wanted to live overseas so they traded Ursula's first-class return trip to London for two economy-class one-way tickets and pocketed the change.

After a few casual jobs in London, including selling soap, Woodhouse found work with the Distillers pharmaceutical offshoot, Distillers Company Biochemicals Ltd (DCBL) as an assistant in the sales manager's office. Woodhouse looked after about eighty sales reps all over the UK, read their reports, highlighted anything interesting for the attention of the sales managers, and ensured the reps were kept supplied with drug samples and promotional literature. Woodhouse would later perform much the same role for Distillers in Sydney.

Woodhouse's first brush with thalidomide came in early 1958, when Distillers started selling Distaval in the UK. In early 1959 Woodhouse left Distillers for another job, but soon afterwards he and Ursula started talking about returning to Australia. By now they had two children and were missing the Sydney sunshine.

So in early 1960, Woodhouse was delighted when he heard that Distillers was setting up an Australian arm. This was his ticket home. After an interview he was quickly employed as assistant sales manager in the Australian business.

The Woodhouse family arrived back in Australia in June 1960 and Bill Poole met them at Sydney airport. Ursula's celebrity was such that their arrival home was noted in the newspapers. Woodhouse started work immediately at Distillers' premises on Campbell

Street in Artarmon, where the small staff featured some memorable characters.

Fred Strobl, a Czech fluent in five languages who claimed to have played water polo at the Olympics, was the national head of sales. Trading on his good looks and charm, Strobl had moved to Australia during the 1950s and after a series of jobs in the pharmaceutical industry was hired by Distillers. Strobl's former colleagues at Distillers remember him as an entertaining charmer, a 'cool customer', according to Woodhouse. One of Strobl's party tricks was to arrange dates with multiple flight attendants on short interstate flights.

In a career arc that is hard to believe, Strobl later became a famous film star. Two years after the thalidomide disaster was exposed, Strobl was holidaying in Bangkok when he was approached by a French film director. The director is said to have offered Strobl a career in the movies solely on the strength of his movie-star looks. 'Why not?' Strobl apparently replied. He subsequently adopted the more debonair nom-de-film Frederick Stafford, starred in a series of French action films and was dubbed the French James Bond. He also played the lead in Alfred Hitchcock's *Topaz* and married the German film star Marianne Hold. Not bad for a former salesman whose biggest claim to fame until then had been promoting the most notorious drug of the century. Strobl's acting was sometimes panned as wooden but he appeared in about twenty movies before his death at fifty-one, in a light plane crash in Switzerland in 1979.

Another big personality working for Distillers in Sydney, and almost universally disliked, was Walt Hodgetts, the senior New South Wales sales rep. Hodgetts was responsible for visiting the city's leading medical specialists and the major hospitals. One former Distillers salesman remembered Hodgetts ordering him to steal drinking glasses from a city hotel where the pair were meeting. Hodgetts wanted them as a gift for his wife. Curiously, for a man reviled by his colleagues who took delight in sacking staff, Hodgetts later felt so overcome by guilt over thalidomide that he turned up at an early meeting of the afflicted families.

Hodgetts' remorse had another outlet. In April 1963 he voluntarily presented himself at the German embassy and offered to give a statement for use in the German trial of thalidomide executives on the sole condition that Distillers not be told what he had done. A copy of Hodgetts' statement is still in the Düsseldorf archive of the German trial papers. While an unpleasant man, known as a bully and a racist, Hodgetts does not appear to have been a liar, at least not about thalidomide. His various accounts of the thalidomide disaster often reflected poorly on himself and appear entirely truthful.

The Australian operation was only ever a sales office. There were no doctors or scientists on staff and any medical questions were referred to London, if indeed anyone bothered to refer them at all. Poole, Strobl, Hodgetts and every other member of the Australian team were focused on selling thalidomide. The company's sales staff fanned out across Australia, visiting hospitals, doctors and pharmacists in cities and country towns alike, always spruiking Distaval as a new wonder drug, perfect for a wide range of maladies. Extravagant double-page advertisements in medical journals promoted the sensational and ultra-safe product. The first and most popular thalidomide drug was Distaval, a sedative and hypnotic, which also came in a stronger version, Distaval Forte. But the thalidomide range ultimately included Valgraine (for migraine), Asmaval (asthma), Valgis (headache) and Tensival (PMT).

The Distillers team in Australia was following the UK lead in promoting thalidomide as overdose proof and free of significant side effects. 'This safety quality was its main selling point and contributed enormously to its popularity,' Woodhouse remembered. 'Our ticket into doctors' surgeries,' is how another former salesman puts it. The drug was also popular among Distillers staff. At least four salesmen in Australia and New Zealand ultimately suffered family tragedies as a result.

Soon Distillers was asking Australian doctors to run 'trials' with Distaval. These were essentially promotional gimmicks designed to introduce doctors to the new product and build sales. There was a further reason for the trials. Distillers' Australian team was desperate to get Distaval onto the 'free list'. Drugs judged vital in health care were 'free listed' by the Australian Government—placed on the Pharmaceutical Benefits Scheme, thereby attracting heavy government subsidies, which in practical terms meant increased sales. Australian trials and doctor testimonials would help Distillers persuade the Australian Government that a thalidomide subsidy was warranted.

But then during the second half of 1960, Distillers salesmen in Australia began approaching obstetricians and maternity hospitals, promoting thalidomide for use in pregnancy. The drug was now being aimed squarely at pregnant Australian women who were effectively, if unintentionally, being used as laboratory animals.

• • •

On 18 August 1960, Distillers sales manager Walt Hodgetts visited John Newlinds, the medical superintendent of the Crown Street Women's Hospital, the biggest maternity hospital in Sydney, where almost five thousand babies were born every year. When we visited Newlinds in retirement at his outer-suburban Sydney home in 2011 his memory of the events of 1960 and 1961 was very clear, seared into place by subsequent developments.

Once installed as medical superintendent, one of Newlinds' new duties was to meet the drug reps selling new products, and so it was that one Thursday morning Newlinds saw Walt Hodgetts about a drug called Distaval. 'Hodgetts tried to persuade me of its value as a sedative generally and especially for use in pregnancy and labour. Certainly he said nothing about any significant side effects.'

Newlinds was not especially interested in Distaval as there were many satisfactory sedatives. 'I agreed, however, to try Distaval. Hodgetts left me a large bottle of pills which I sent to the hospital pharmacy. I did not give Distaval much further thought in the months after this.'

Pregnancy was a lucrative market opportunity for the drug, and Distillers was just getting started. On 16 September 1960 Fred Strobl (the future movie star) and Hodgetts (the bully later consumed by guilt) visited thirty-three-year-old William McBride, a well-known obstetrician. McBride had a flourishing private practice and often delivered his patients' babies at Crown Street. Distillers wanted McBride to adopt its drug, and, hopefully, write a positive report that could be used to boost sales. Hodgetts and Strobl gave McBride the prepared speech about how effective and safe Distaval was, and they handed over promotional literature and samples. The visit was a success. Hodgetts' report noted that McBride had agreed to do a Distaval trial at the Crown Street Hospital.

That meeting set McBride's life aboard a rollercoaster of adulation and bitter controversy. McBride would later be feted as the hero of thalidomide, and, later still, found guilty of doctoring the results of scientific experiments and stripped of his licence to practise medicine. But all that lay ahead. Within weeks of his meeting with the Distillers salesmen, McBride was enthusiastically dosing his pregnant patients with thalidomide, certain that it was relieving morning sickness. Why was he so taken by the drug? McBride offered one explanation in his autobiography, written during the 1990s as he attempted to repair his tattered reputation. He wrote that one of his pregnant patients had been vomiting non-stop for several days, to the point where he feared a miscarriage. On a whim McBride gave the woman a prescription for Distaval. The vomiting stopped, and McBride became perhaps the most prolific prescriber of thalidomide for morning sickness anywhere. As one journalist who interviewed McBride in the 1970s observed: 'He was, by this time, handing it out like lollipops.'

McBride offered a further explanation for his initial experiment with thalidomide when I visited him at his home in Sydney in April 2013.

> This [1960] was before the [contraceptive] pill and women did not have much control over whether they got pregnant. So a lot of the women I saw were either very distressed to be pregnant or really giddy with excitement. Some were worried they were going to lose the baby. In any event a lot of them had high emotions and that contributed to anxiety and nausea. So it stood to reason that an effective sedative or sleeping pill would work. It would calm them down and lower their emotions.

By modern standards that's an odd view of morning sickness, but it was a very common approach at the time and McBride was far from alone. Whatever their reasoning, a lot of doctors used thalidomide for morning sickness. Some doctors were told it was useful for nausea by drug salesmen, some by other doctors, and some struck out on their own. No blame attaches to the doctors. Distillers and Grünenthal had both pitched the drug as a revolution in drug safety, so doctors felt reassured that it was fit for use in pregnancy. And both Distillers and Grünenthal clearly wanted pregnant women to take their drug.

McBride, meanwhile, had thoroughly embraced thalidomide. Believing it was the cure for morning sickness, he prescribed Distaval for scores of pregnant patients in 1960 and during the first months of 1961. McBride kept Distillers informed about his success with morning sickness, and Distillers salesmen began promoting the drug particularly for that use. On 9 May 1961, McBride wrote Distillers a note. 'I have used your Distaval tablets for an extended period, both in the treatment of morning sickness and hyperemesis gravidarum [uncontrolled vomiting in pregnancy], and have found that it is extremely efficient in controlling these conditions.' McBride added that he would be 'only too pleased' to support Distillers' application to have the drug placed on the government's pharmaceutical benefits scheme.

Distillers was delighted and Strobl responded with a note of his own. '[I] would like to take this opportunity to express our appreciation for your interest and cooperation. Should there be an occasion when we can be of service to you, please do not hesitate to contact this office.'

All very lovely. But even before McBride wrote his testimonial for Distillers, he had started to see the catastrophic consequences of his thalidomide 'trial'. Five days earlier, on 4 May 1961, McBride had delivered a baby with malformed arms (the radius, one of the forearm bones, was absent in each arm), and a bowel without an opening. The baby died within a week. McBride had not previously seen this combination of malformations and justifiably assumed it was a random and thankfully rare occurrence.

Three weeks later, on 24 May 1961, McBride delivered another baby with almost identical malformations. That baby also died within days. And then on Thursday 8 June 1961, came the third of McBride's babies with similarly devastating limb and bowel malformations: as with the two earlier babies, death soon followed birth.

Now McBride was seriously worried. Something was maiming and killing his patients' babies. In McBride's retelling of the story, he took the files home and spent the whole Queen's Birthday long weekend puzzling over the cause. McBride has recounted how he pored over the medical literature, wondered whether radioactivity from a nuclear reactor in Sydney or polluted food could be the villain, and searched for signs in each of the mothers' medical histories, before finally his gaze fell on Distaval, which he had prescribed in each of the cases. McBride examined the Distillers information about thalidomide, and read John Thiersch's 1952 work on aminopterin, the cancer drug which had caused severe foetal malformations and had a superficial similarity to thalidomide. McBride then found a medical journal note about thalidomide's damaging effect on nerves, before finally deciding, late at night in his study, that thalidomide must be the culprit. He went to bed confident he had cracked the riddle, and resolute about taking action the next day.

The story is no doubt an approximation of what actually happened. And McBride certainly deserves credit for an astute clinical observation. But the story raises several questions, not least about the notion later pushed by McBride and some of his allies that unmasking thalidomide and his subsequent research was a work of genius. 'Make no mistake about it, there is a Nobel Prize hanging on this,' McBride once wrote to a colleague.

For a start, McBride had not chanced upon thalidomide. He was trialling it on his patients at the request of a drug company. A doctor trialling a drug must above all be alert to any negative side effects. McBride had been enthusiastically giving heavy doses for morning sickness, starting in about September 1960. His patients receiving the drug started giving birth in about May 1961, delivering severely malformed babies at an astonishing rate. What had changed in

McBride's management of his pregnant patients? One thing: he was giving them large doses of a 'trial' drug. No wonder he noticed. And it's a little surprising that, according to his recounting of the dramatic events of that long weekend, it took him so many hours of agonising to suspect thalidomide.

On the Tuesday after the June 1961 long weekend McBride visited Crown Street Hospital to talk with Newlinds, the medical superintendent. Newlinds himself had been growing increasingly concerned about the rising malformation rate at the hospital.

'McBride told me he was certain that the drug Distaval was causing the malformations,' Newlinds recalled.

> He said it was the only common factor in the cases of the three malformed babies in May and June. He suggested that the drug was interfering with glutamic acid metabolism in the embryos. McBride appeared convinced. His explanations seemed reasonable, or more reasonable than anything I had heard or considered previously, and I respected his judgment. I knew that drugs could cross the placental barrier and that drugs could damage the embryo. It was also well known that the embryo was particularly sensitive during the first trimester of pregnancy.

Newlinds decided that he had to act, even though the evidence was not overwhelming. 'Distaval was not a crucial drug—it did not save lives. This aspect should be stressed. The decision to withdraw a basic sedative in case it caused malformations, even if it was only a small chance, was easy.' Newlinds telephoned Mrs Sperling, the hospital pharmacist, and told her that Distaval should no longer be used.

Then he and McBride discussed what further steps should be taken. 'We agreed he would contact Distillers and tell them that Distaval had been withdrawn from use because we suspected it of causing malformations. I also understood that McBride would write to one of the medical journals with his suspicions. I was quite sure that Distillers would take action to withdraw the drugs while investigating McBride's concerns.'

At some point that week McBride telephoned Distillers. For many years he thought he had spoken with Bill Poole, but when Bill Poole denied it, McBride said he just asked for the man in charge and assumed it was Poole. McBride says the man at the end of the telephone was sceptical that Distaval could be maiming and killing babies and told McBride that the drug had been on sale in Europe for years and nothing similar had been reported. The man told McBride that he would pass the concerns on to head office in London, but was not receptive to McBride's suggestion that Distillers stop promoting the drug until his thesis had been checked.

This was the week starting Monday 12 June 1961. Across the world thalidomide sales had peaked and more (perhaps many more) than two thousand malformed babies had been born in Germany alone. About half of them subsequently died. The toll was rising fast in a dozen other countries as well. Yet the epidemic of death and injury had barely been noticed, and nobody had publicly connected it to thalidomide. Had McBride's report quickly led to the withdrawal of thalidomide, at a bare minimum one thousand survivors alive today might have avoided their fate, as would a roughly equal number of babies who were either stillborn or died shortly after birth. Thousands of others who died in utero would have survived. The scale of the disaster would have been far smaller.

Lyn Rowe was one of the babies who could have been saved. Wendy Rowe took thalidomide in the last week of June or the first week of July in 1961. Had Distillers taken McBride seriously in early June 1961, immediately got the word out to the medical profession, including Wendy Rowe's doctor, and withdrawn the drug, Lyn Rowe would have been born with normal, functioning limbs. Her life and the lives of her family would have been radically different.

But nothing happened. Nobody at Distillers got back to McBride. The drug remained on the market. McBride has claimed that he took a second step in June 1961 to get the warning out. He said he posted an article briefly outlining his concerns to the prestigious British medical journal, *The Lancet*. Sadly, McBride said, *The Lancet* wrote back, rejecting his article.

McBride's claim angered *The Lancet's* deputy editor Ian Munro, who vehemently denied it. Munro claimed the journal had never received any such letter from McBride and therefore, obviously, had never rejected it. McBride could produce nothing to prove he had written to *The Lancet*. It is impossible to know with certainty where the truth lies, but in view of McBride's later troubles, there has to be a question mark over his account.

After telephoning Distillers, and possibly writing to *The Lancet* in London, McBride decided he had done enough to raise the alarm. He did not try to contact Distillers' London headquarters, nor did he contact any Australian medical journal. He does not appear to have warned other doctors to stop using the drug. Instead he started testing his thesis on laboratory animals at the Crown Street Hospital by force-feeding Distaval to pregnant mice and guinea pigs.

McBride was not a scientist, certainly not a teratologist, and did not really know what he was doing. He had only a small number of test animals, not even enough for a control group. That meant he couldn't compare litter numbers between dosed and non-dosed groups, or look for resorption sites (certain drugs, including thalidomide, reduce the litter size in some laboratory animals by killing a number of the foetuses, leading to their resorption into the placental lining). All he was able to do was stuff Distaval into pregnant animals and then look for malformations in their offspring. He found none, and as his experiments wore on he began to wonder about the accuracy of his theory.

But on 6 July 1961, prior to doubt setting in and while still convinced that thalidomide was a killer, McBride bumped into the Distillers sales rep Walt Hodgetts on a Sydney street. He asked Hodgetts to walk with him to his surgery. Once there he told Hodgetts that he believed Distaval was causing shortened limbs, internal malformations and other injuries in babies, problems so severe the babies had subsequently died. McBride told Hodgetts that thalidomide drugs should be taken off the market.

Hodgetts was shocked. He told McBride he would immediately report the matter to his company. Later that day he wrote a report of the meeting for his bosses, somehow turning McBride's three dead babies into four.

> I interviewed Dr W. G. McBride...this is what he said: 'I have discovered that Distaval is the answer for morning sickness. When the early symptoms of nausea come I can stop the vomiting...I have had 4 deaths at birth in the last 8 weeks. One baby was born with 6 fingers, one with fingers joined together, one with malformed toes but all four died from intestine collapse. I studied all four case histories of the mothers and there was nothing abnormal. The only common thing I found was that all four had received Distaval for morning sickness. I am now waiting for this next two weeks to seek any further information, with my fingers crossed. I would like some 100 mg for myself and I want this information confidential as I have a responsibility to myself. I know Distaval is not indicated for morning sickness but it is not contra-indicated.' They were his words to me.

Hodgetts later said that on arriving back at the office that day, he told Fred Strobl about McBride's report and then the two of them went to see Bill Poole. Hodgetts' memory, years after the event, was that Poole telephoned Ernie Gross, Distillers' senior employee in Australia, to report the potential disaster. Hodgetts then left, confident he had done his duty. Later Poole denied on oath that Hodgetts ever said a word to him about McBride at that time. Poole would forever claim that Hodgetts kept McBride's terrible news to himself, or maybe shared it with Strobl. Had he known, Poole claimed, he would have responded immediately.

What is clear is that throughout the second half of 1961 Distillers in Australia kept promoting the drug: including specifically for morning sickness.

• • •

Phil Lacaze joined the company in early 1961 and was given the standard company sales pitch. 'Distaval was safe at any dosage. I was told that people who had tried to commit suicide by taking an overdose of Distaval woke after a long sleep feeling physically well.'

Not long after starting with Distillers in Melbourne, Lacaze was told by the Sydney office to start pitching Distaval as a morning-sickness drug. '[Strobl] told me that Dr McBride in Sydney had trialled Distaval on patients with morning sickness and had had great success. He suggested that we promote Distaval as a morning-sickness drug—in addition to its other indications. I thought that was a ridiculous suggestion, and I told Strobl I thought it was a ridiculous suggestion.'

Lacaze, who had studied medicine for three years, said he thought 'one doctor's feedback' did not give an acceptable basis for promoting Distaval for morning sickness, and he refused to do so. Decades later when we interviewed him Lacaze was happy to concede that his refusal was not as a result of safety concerns. 'In Melbourne we promoted Distaval as a safe and effective drug, including to obstetricians and GPs for use in pregnant women. But so far as I was aware we did not promote it specifically for use in cases of morning sickness. There was no medical basis for doing that.'

Meanwhile McBride's experiments with animals during the middle of 1961 wore on and none of his mice or guinea pigs gave birth to malformed offspring. And among his patients, the expectant mothers to whom he had prescribed thalidomide also gave birth to healthy babies. McBride began to wonder about his thesis. Was he missing something? But then in September two more of his patients gave birth to babies with malformations very much like the May–June babies. McBride sought advice from Professor Roland Thorp, a renowned pharmacologist at Sydney University who was unconvinced by McBride's thesis and wanted more evidence.

McBride's recounting of what he did next has varied. He has said he telephoned Distillers in Sydney in October and adopted a tougher line, demanding action. While there's no independent proof of that, it is certain that on 14 November 1961, McBride spoke to another Distillers salesman, described the malformations and somewhat angrily said he had already reported the matter to the company but nothing had been done. That salesman went back to headquarters and reported his conversation to Poole.

Woodhouse takes up the story: 'Poole told me I should arrange to go and see McBride and get further detail about his cases of injured babies and the connection with Distaval.' Woodhouse spent a couple of hours with McBride, who was happy to cooperate. 'When I got back to the office I talked with Poole and put together a fairly detailed report. It mentioned six injured babies all of whom died shortly after their births.'

The report was mailed to London. Poole apparently did not think the report important enough to telephone his bosses. Woodhouse's report reached London just as Widukind Lenz in Germany was reporting multiple thalidomide injuries and deaths to Grünenthal. 'Within a week or so Poole got word back from London that we were to stop selling thalidomide pending the results of investigations into whether thalidomide really did cause birth defects,' Woodhouse said. 'We stopped selling thalidomide drugs immediately.'

So that's the Distillers story in a nutshell. McBride's June–July 1961 report of malformations got stuck with one or two irresponsible salesmen. McBride then laid low. It was not until October–November 1961 that McBride made another effort to bring his concerns to the attention of the Australian branch. This time Poole learned of McBride's fears. He performed, via Woodhouse, a quick investigation, reported the concerns to London, and the drug was withdrawn from sale.

Except that's not at all what happened.

CHAPTER 13

The Humane and Proper Thing

By April 2012 I was finally ready to ask Woody Woodhouse to swear an affidavit as to what he knew about thalidomide in Australia. I had spoken with him many times, asked him hundreds of questions. I had also to come to like him a lot. Woody was quick and clever and interested, and I enjoyed visiting him and Ursula at their home. I also suspected there was more he could tell me. I had never believed Poole's story that Hodgetts and Strobl had kept their dark secret to themselves. Hodgetts had written an extensive report about his meeting with McBride. Why would he keep that secret? It was a farcical notion.

Woodhouse, though junior at the time, had worked at head office, worked closely with Poole, and worked with the salesmen. I thought it likely that Woodhouse would know something about McBride's first report and why it was not acted on. But I knew that talking about this would be hard for him. After more than a year of working with thalidomiders and their families I was very aware how painful the subject was for many people. Still, it was getting late in the piece. Lyn's trial was only six months away. I wanted a sworn statement from Woodhouse and could not wait much longer.

So in early April, I flew up to Sydney to see Woodhouse again.

Was there any further information he might volunteer? I showed him a statement I had drafted for him, which covered his university days, Ursula's period as a film star, living in London, moving back to Australia to work for Distillers, the drug disaster and his reflections on the whole sorry thalidomide saga. Woodhouse read it carefully. Then he suggested we go for a drive and look around his neighbourhood. 'We can talk about this again when we get back.' I was happy to do that. Woodhouse was good company, and he lived in a beautiful corner of Sydney. On the drive he pointed out former prime minister Bob Hawke's spectacular harbourside home and the playing fields where his own sons had played football as children. Then we drove to the bottom of the hill, parked and walked down the steep path to the sea baths.

It was a stunning Sydney autumn day, sunny and bright. The baths sparkled and a couple of tough elderly locals churned up and down in the chilly water. Hundreds of tiny fish flitted in the shallows. I remarked how lucky Woodhouse's children were to have grown up here. After lingering on the boardwalk beside the sea baths, we walked back up the hill to Woody's car.

I told Woodhouse I'd love to see the Distillers building in Artarmon where he had worked in 1961. Would he be able to find it? No problem, Woodhouse replied. It was a short drive, and true to his word, Woodhouse immediately identified the building. It was now a car rental premises, painted a garish green. Woodhouse and I walked across to the building. Pointing up at the second level, Woodhouse said: 'That's where my office was, over there. Poole was over in that far corner and Skinner [the accountant] and Strobl were in the middle. Often the four of us would stay after work for a drink. Around the back was the warehouse. We had a lot of thalidomide in there.'

Standing outside the building with Woody felt like peering into the past. It helped me understand what went on: not just who did what to whom, but the colour and movement; the extra, ostensibly irrelevant, detail. Woodhouse had been in his early thirties when he worked in the building, with a young family and a long career ahead of him. Now he was in his eighties, comfortably retired, and helping a lawyer who he knew was going after the company he had worked for. I was grateful to him. We talked for a while and then, after I took a few photographs, we drove back to his home. At the small dining table where he and I usually talked, Woodhouse got right down to business. 'This affidavit is pretty right so far as it goes,' he said, gesturing at the stapled pages in front of him. 'But it's not everything.'

OK, I thought, I knew that.

'We have to talk some more about McBride's warning in the middle of 1961,' Woodhouse continued. 'I know that's what you're really interested in. What I have to tell you is this: I knew what McBride had told the company. So did a lot of other people.'

I held my breath. What Woodhouse was volunteering was dynamite. I desperately wanted it for the court case, for Lyn, for Wendy. And after more than a year of digging into thalidomide history, I badly wanted to hear confirmation of what I suspected.

Woodhouse was not going to disappoint. 'I don't know how Bill Poole found out about McBride's concerns but he definitely knew about them. Bill Poole and Ron Skinner [the accountant] were both aware around the middle of 1961 of what McBride believed.'

There it was. Confirmation that Bill Poole had been lying and the authorised Distillers version of history was a fiction. But Woodhouse, who later swore an affidavit detailing the information he provided that day, continued. He painted a picture of mid-1961 at Distillers' Sydney office that was ever more compelling. 'There were only a few employees at [head office],' Woodhouse said.

Often in the evenings after work Poole and Skinner—and sometimes Strobl—and I had a whisky and a chat together. These chats could go on for some time and sometimes I arrived home quite late.

At that time, about June or July 1961 and afterwards, Poole and Skinner—and Strobl when he was there—often talked about McBride's concerns that thalidomide was causing the deaths of babies and the implications for the business and our sales if McBride's suspicions about that were correct. The conversations were sometimes lengthy and Poole and Skinner especially expressed great concern at the possibility McBride was right. Both Poole and Skinner believed, and stated, that the future of the business hinged on whether McBride was right or wrong.

At the time these conversations were going on I assumed that Poole had referred McBride's report to [Distillers] in London and that it was being investigated. While it was just one doctor and the report was not confirmed by anyone else, it was a very serious matter with major ramifications. It was a matter that should obviously have been immediately reported to London. We were not equipped to assess or investigate McBride's report [in Australia]. We had no medical or other technically qualified staff. On the other hand [the London head office] had a well-staffed medical division plus pharmacologists and others.

Woodhouse, it must be stressed, was a junior employee in 1961. Poole, Skinner and Strobl were older and far more senior. Poole ran the drug business in Australia and reported to (and frequently met with) Ernie Gross, the Distillers board member with responsibility for all of the Australian operations, including alcohol and pharmaceuticals.

Poole had clearly understood the gravity of McBride's report.

There was no doubt about that. He insisted that Woodhouse speak to nobody about it. 'Poole told me I was not to discuss McBride's report with other staff or anyone else. The only reason that I unofficially knew about McBride's report was because Poole, Skinner and Strobl discussed it frequently and openly during our after work drinks.'

So Distillers' three key men in the Australian drug arm—Poole the boss, Skinner the money man, and Strobl the national sales manager—knew that a Sydney doctor they had asked to trial their beloved drug now thought that it might be malforming and killing babies. The three senior men sat around drinking and talking about how, if McBride were right, it would devastate their business. 'During this time I thought we were waiting for London to conclude some investigations or give us instructions,' Woodhouse said. 'Poole and Skinner discussed McBride's concerns in front of me from time to time during this whole period.'

Remarkably, as these drinking sessions continued through the second half of 1961, Poole and Strobl kept telling their salespeople to promote thalidomide as safe and effective, including to obstetricians. And, incredibly, they were still fighting to get a government subsidy for the drug, which if granted would have seen sales rocket, and a far worse thalidomide disaster in Australia. In anticipation of the government subsidy, and the sales surge sure to follow, Poole had built up a huge cache of thalidomide drugs. Government records show just how big the stockpile was. In the aftermath of the disaster, when sales had been suspended, there were more than eight million pills plus 30,778 bottles of liquid thalidomide in Distillers' warehouse. Poole had been planning to flood the market with a drug he knew might be a baby killer.

The government's final refusal to admit Distaval to the free list came in October 1961. By this time, Poole had known of McBride's report for three or four months and not a word had been mentioned to the government.

In late October or November 1961, McBride complained again, and Woodhouse was sent to see him. Woodhouse is quite clear that McBride's November 1961 complaint was not his first. 'I was aware that McBride had first voiced his suspicions to [us] some months earlier.'

Woodhouse's revelations were critically important: a major advance of Lyn Rowe's claim. We could now prove, with sworn evidence, that Distillers' Australian arm had received a clear warning from McBride in June 1961. This warning, which might have saved Lyn Rowe and thousands of others, had not got lost with two foolish salesmen. The warning had in fact ended up with the senior men running the business: Bill Poole, the managing director, and Ron Skinner, the accountant. Poole had a direct line to his bosses in London and to Ernie Gross, the Distillers board member in Australia. We could now mount a variety of legal arguments that the UK parent company was liable for Bill Poole's disgraceful behaviour.

• • •

When Phil Lacaze, who was in Melbourne, received the shocking news from Sydney headquarters about thalidomide's withdrawal, his sales team was dispersed around Victoria, visiting country towns. Lacaze sent word that they were to return to Melbourne immediately and they met at his home the next day. 'I told them that Distaval was suspected of causing birth deformities [and] would no longer be available for sale and we were not to promote it.' Lacaze described the news as 'a bomb', which ultimately shattered the company. 'I knew the implications were terrible.'

Throughout 1962, Lacaze continued to visit specialists on behalf of Distillers. Several obstetricians told him they had delivered malformed babies who died before or shortly after birth. The doctors now knew that these births were the result of Distaval. 'They said that these babies were often not shown to their mothers, who were told only that the babies had died.' Lacaze quickly realised there was 'a greater number of thalidomide deaths than was publicly known'. Disillusioned with Distillers, Lacaze quit the company in October 1962. Very helpfully for us, Lacaze had kept some material, including a letter Bill Poole wrote to him in December 1961, immediately after the sale of thalidomide had been suspended.

At the time Poole was in full damage control, which meant lying constantly. Poole crafted his letter to make Lacaze feel he was being admitted into the inner sanctum of thalidomide knowledge. 'I think I had better put you fully into the picture in so far as I know it myself and the facts are as follows,' Poole began. He dishonestly claimed that McBride had told only Hodgetts about his thalidomide suspicions in mid-1961, and that Poole himself did not find out until October or November 1961. 'You may imagine the concern with which I later received this news,' wrote Poole. 'Certainly I think we have done the humane and proper thing in discontinuing sale of the product and a long road now stretches before us...to see if there is any foundation for the theory.'

Poole then set out Lacaze's orders: as little information as possible was to reach the public about the disaster. 'We must take every precaution to see that no news of this information leaks out to the public generally or to the national press or to the weekly magazine press.' Poole was paranoid about publicity—publicity which would have helpfully alerted pregnant women not to take the drug that may have been lurking in their medicine cupboards.

Even the sales reps who reported to Lacaze were to be kept in the dark. 'It would be as well not to give very much information to the other representatives. I am sure they are all very sound people at heart but I can see no useful purpose being served by telling them too much at this stage and, knowing human nature, some of them will be sure to pass too much information on to other people.' Poole also told Lacaze not to mention that the 'weight of evidence' against the drug came from Australia: instead he was to refer to 'circumstantial evidence' received in London.

Poole's next mission was to sell his lie to the Australian Government. On 28 February 1962 he wrote to the director-general of health complaining of 'sensational and rather distorted reports' in some newspapers. Poole wanted to correct the record by providing the 'full story'. First Poole offered a self-serving account of how safe the drug had proved during clinical trials in Germany: 'completely non-toxic'. Then he got down to his central purpose. 'On the subject of the malformed babies, we received a telephone call from the Sydney consultant Dr W. G. McBride, sometime in October [1961] and as a result of that we paid several personal visits to him.' McBride's information had been 'extremely worrying and I lost no time in sending it to England for evaluation and instructions'. No mention of Poole's personal knowledge from June 1961, or his drinking sessions where he worried that McBride's report would destroy his business, or his insistence that staff keep McBride's warning secret.

The fictional history Poole provided to the government concluded with a flourish: 'I think this puts you in full possession of the true story. I am sorry to have written at such length but I feel that you will at least now be in a position to inform the Minister, or anybody else, of what actually happened.' Soon afterwards, Poole received a note from a senior government bureaucrat assuring him that his letter would be a 'most valuable aide memoire on the subject'. Mission accomplished for Poole. His letter deceived the Australian Government, which thereafter showed no inclination to investigate the disaster.

In July that year Poole was still lying—but now to the media. The *Sunday Truth* of 29 July 1962, under the headline 'Sydney Doctor Stopped Horror', carried Poole's insistence that he had acted promptly on receiving McBride's warning. 'Mr Pool [sic] said the doctor's report shocked him so much he sent it to England and the drug was withdrawn from sale two days later.'

Poole never gave up on this fairytale. In the 1970s Poole swore an affidavit in the UK litigation between the *Sunday Times* and Distillers over the thalidomide story. Poole denied ever knowing about McBride's concerns until October 1961, denied that thalidomide had been withdrawn at the Crown Street Hospital in June 1961, and accused Hodgetts and Strobl of keeping McBride's devastating report to themselves. Lying on oath held no fears for Bill Poole. Distillers adopted Poole's fiction, advising inquirers that Poole knew nothing about McBride's suspicions until October 1961 at the earliest. If Distillers did not know this was fantasy, it should have. A few questions of any number of its own staff in Australia would have elicited the truth. As an exercise Lyn's legal team tallied the number of people in Distillers' Australian office who knew in mid-1961 that McBride believed their number-one drug was maiming and killing babies. We counted eight staff, and there were in all likelihood more.

Some people have always known Bill Poole was a liar. Barbara-Ann Bishop (later Hewson) was born in July 1961 with severely malformed hands and arms. Her father, John Bishop, was another Distillers salesman who had studied medicine before becoming a pharmaceutical salesman. A spitfire pilot during World War II, he had joined Distillers in June 1960. He later developed a great deal of resentment towards his former employer and was writing a book that covered his thalidomide experience at the time of his death in 1978. During our investigations we were disappointed to discover that this material had been largely destroyed. Fortunately an affidavit survives in which Bishop recounted critical aspects of his employment with Distillers.

Marie-Louise Bishop had given birth to the couple's sixth child in July 1960. In October 1960, she was upset to learn she had fallen pregnant again, and was given thalidomide tablets by her husband to calm her anxiety. Then, during June 1961, just before the baby was due, John Bishop and his immediate boss John Creswick had dinner with Bill Poole, who had flown in from Sydney. According to Bishop's affidavit:

> During the course of the dinner Mr Creswick mentioned to Mr Poole that the Children's Hospital in Adelaide was very pleased with thalidomide. Mr Poole then said 'don't count your chickens before they are hatched. We had a report from a doctor in Sydney last week about Distaval and abnormalities in the foetus.' It was plain that Mr Poole was worried and disturbed about this report. He was clearly not taking the matter lightly.

Shortly after the dinner, on 28 July 1961, Barbara-Ann was born with severe malformations. Her parents were devastated. Then Bishop remembered giving his wife Distaval tablets. 'I also remembered what Mr Poole had said a few weeks earlier over the dinner table. It looked to me as if thalidomide might very well have been the cause for my child's deformities. I mentioned this to Mr Creswick, my immediate superior.' Bishop had no doubt whatsoever about the timing of his dinner with Poole: it was just weeks before his daughter was born, and the warning Poole gave at the dinner only assumed terrible personal significance with the birth of his daughter.

Nothing came of Bishop's report to Creswick and Poole did not contact him. Years after the disaster, Bishop was still angry with Poole and Distillers, and willing to help the *Sunday Times* in its fight with his old employer. Poole's response to Bishop's allegations? He swore that he had never said any such thing to Bishop and had not known about the potential danger of thalidomide until much later. It amounted to accusing Bishop of lying. Poole had no shame.

John Bishop's daughter Barbara-Ann has never had any doubt about her dad's story, but was pleased to hear that Woodhouse's account made it clear her father was right. 'Dad was a highly principled man, honest to a fault,' she said. 'Poole was a liar, plain and simple. And the liar tried to smear the good man. You have to wonder how Poole lived with himself.'

• • •

Shortly after the sale of thalidomide was halted in Australia, London head office asked the Australian branch to get hold of a thalidomide-damaged foetus and send it to London so that Distillers' medical advisers could examine it. Why the Australians were asked to supply a foetus is unclear: there was a much greater epidemic of malformed and dead babies in the UK. Perhaps the Australian branch had developed a can-do reputation within the Distillers organisation.

The Australian office set about the task and somehow managed to procure the required foetus, which was duly packed up and shipped to London. There is no clear information about the source of the foetus, however a curious letter written by McBride a decade later suggests that he may have assisted.

In 1973, McBride wrote to Distillers asking what had happened to the Australian foetus sent to London eleven years earlier. Distillers wrote back advising that on arrival in London the foetus had been sent out for post-mortem at Queen Charlotte's maternity hospital. The fate of the foetus was now unknown. The Distillers letter writer concluded: 'I am told that it is unlikely that the foetus itself will have been preserved but there may well have been some slides.'

Another issue for the Australian office in the wake of the disaster was what to do with the eight million thalidomide tablets at its Sydney warehouse. The company's first move was to attempt to persuade the Australian Government to assume responsibility for the dangerous pills and use them for medical research. The only condition attached to the proposed 'gift' was that the tablets be repackaged in plain cartons, without Distillers' name mentioned anywhere.

The government refused. Distillers then lobbied various other medical research bodies, but could find no takers. Finally the company had no choice but to destroy the surplus thalidomide, and in July 1963 the job was given to Woodhouse (he now worked for Eli Lilly, to whom Distillers had sold its pharmaceutical business). Woodhouse organised for a truck to make repeated trips carrying the millions of pills from the storehouse to a furnace at Pyrmont in Sydney. 'The truck tipped the pills in their glass containers straight into the furnace,' Woodhouse remembered. 'This went on for so long that the manager of the furnace complained that the amount of molten glass in the furnace had clogged it and the furnace had to be turned off and the glass allowed to cool before it was removed.'

The generosity and cooperation Woody Woodhouse extended to Lyn Rowe and her legal team did not end with his sworn affidavit. In 2013 he welcomed me and a filmmaker into his home for several hours, where we recorded him reading his statement and answering questions about his thalidomide experience. Woodhouse's evidence was so crucial we wanted to preserve it on film. We were also considering showing it to Diageo's lawyers to forcefully impress on them the strength of our case, the lengths we had gone to in preparing it, and the risks they faced at trial. Later that year I had dinner with Woody and Ursula Woodhouse. I told them I was planning to write a book and that if he agreed, Woody's revelations would form an important part of the story. Woodhouse was enthusiastic and supportive, but I still had gnawing concerns about revealing his role. Would he be criticised for speaking out after so long, for opening old wounds? Would he be criticised for not speaking sooner? The fact is that Woodhouse's willingness to speak the truth about a matter he could easily have left forever buried was courageous and laudable. Many Distillers employees who knew that McBride's ghastly report had been ignored for months had taken that secret to their graves. Some, like Poole, had actively lied about it. Woodhouse had peeled away the deceit and exposed the truth. In doing so he played an important role in winning compensation for many thalidomide survivors.

• • •

I met with Bill McBride just once: in March 2013 at his Sydney apartment. His health was fading and his memory was not running at full speed. Initially he mistook me for an electrician he had booked to fix a hallway light. Once that was cleared up he ushered me into his lounge room, which enjoyed a spectacular view of the Sydney Harbour Bridge. Books about medical greats were stacked on the coffee table, including a thick tome about the scientists who unravelled the mystery of DNA's double helix structure and won a Nobel Prize as a result. Once McBride imagined himself achieving similar distinction, though that had been long ago. Much of his wealth had been spent on court battles and his name conjured up fame and infamy in equal measure.

Yet, back in his glory days, McBride revelled in the attention his thalidomide triumph brought. In 1962 a Sydney newspaper named him man of the year. In 1971, he flew to Paris to accept a 250,000 franc prize from L'Institut de la Vie for his thalidomide work. In 1972 he was named Australian Father of the Year and used the occasion to promote a 'good smack on the backside' for errant children. Honour piled upon honour.

Were the fame and adulation deserved? As we've seen, McBride was conducting a 'trial' of the drug for Distillers. He was therefore obliged to be on the lookout for problems and that takes some of the shine off his achievement. But it was still a clever deduction. In the UK, there had been hundreds of thalidomide births by that time. In Germany there had been thousands. Yet no doctor in the UK or Germany implicated thalidomide before McBride. As Hans-Rudolf Wiedemann, one of the German investigators who helped identify the epidemic and who came close to identifying thalidomide as the cause, wrote years later of McBride's June 1961 observation: 'It is astonishing that in Germany where by [early 1961] far more than a thousand similarly malformed infants had been born, no obstetrician had then suspected a similar connection.'

Once McBride realised that thalidomide was maiming babies, however, his attempts to raise the alarm were mixed. McBride immediately reported his concerns in June 1961 to the Crown Street Hospital, telephoned Distillers and possibly wrote to a medical journal. A month later he warned another Distillers salesman. Several months later, after further malformations, and after a delay, he warned the company again and wrote (definitely this time) to multiple medical journals. Later in life McBride regretted not having forced the immediate withdrawal of the drug in mid-1961.

Now compare McBride's efforts with those of Widukind Lenz, who did not suspect thalidomide might be maiming babies until early November 1961. Unlike McBride, Lenz did not have the advantage of having given thalidomide to dozens of his own pregnant patients. Yet within two weeks Lenz had done enough to force the drug's withdrawal in Germany. In that period he worked feverishly gathering evidence, consulting with other doctors, confronting Grünenthal, involving the health authorities and speaking publicly, which ensured the thalidomide story got into the media.

So despite suspecting thalidomide almost five months after McBride, it was Lenz who, within days, compiled the evidence and created the pressure to have the drug withdrawn. That meant McBride, despite his head start, always shared with Lenz the distinction of having been the first to connect thalidomide with disaster.

McBride's attitude to Grünenthal in the years afterwards also appears to have differed from Lenz's. During the lead-up to the German criminal trial, McBride met with Grünenthal executives twice. The German company was especially interested in enlisting McBride to help with the offensive argument that thalidomide was a drug which somehow saved malformed babies from aborting and thereby allowed them to survive to birth. (As Grünenthal put it in a 1968 letter to McBride, the theory was that far from being a malforming agent, thalidomide might actually 'protect' an already damaged foetus from 'early death'. Grünenthal told McBride this perverse thesis was 'based primarily' on McBride's cases; McBride had not raised this thesis himself.)

As it turned out McBride did not give evidence at the trial, which was halted mid-stream. But he obviously felt his advice had been valuable to Grünenthal. Years later, in 1974, he tried to persuade the company to pay him for his work and was met with a firm refusal.

•

In 1972, at the height of his fame, McBride established Foundation 41, so named for its focus on the forty weeks of pregnancy and the first week of life. McBride courted publicity, leveraged his reputation to raise funds, and combined his work as a doctor with scientific research at the foundation. To what extent that research added to the sum of human knowledge is the subject of some debate. One respected embryologist has spoken of his excitement at meeting McBride in the 1970s.

> I was young and McBride was the hero of thalidomide. So when he came into my lab to spend an hour with me I was thrilled and honoured. We started talking and within about five minutes I felt shattered. It was clear that McBride had only the most basic grip on embryological concepts. I soon realised he was a medical doctor who'd been in the right place at the right time and had cleverly connected thalidomide with the deformities he'd seen. But he had no claim to being a medical researcher.

McBride also developed a reputation for making public pronouncements about drugs without having assembled compelling evidence. Perhaps he was determined to avoid another thalidomide-type tragedy. Or maybe he was determined to have a second heroic success. In 1972 he caused a media storm, and a flurry of activity by health authorities, by accusing a well-known antidepressant of causing birth malformations. McBride produced no persuasive evidence for his claims, and the drug is still not classified as a teratogen. Yet that episode was only a warm-up for the career-ending disaster which followed.

In the late 1970s McBride became convinced that the morning sickness medication Debendox (Bendectin in the US) was a 'low grade teratogen' capable of causing severe limb damage. He gave evidence in several high-profile US trials for alleged victims of the drug, once clashing with Lenz, who gave evidence for the manufacturer. There was never clear proof the drug was a teratogen, and a significant body of research has proclaimed it safe. The FDA, for example, even today considers it safe for use in pregnancy. But McBride's status as the man who had unmasked thalidomide carried great cachet. The number of claims against the manufacturer ballooned, and eventually the drug was withdrawn from sale. In the course of this anti-Debendox crusading, McBride had researchers at his Foundation 41 do some research on an anti-cholinergic drug (Debendox had an anti-cholinergic component). Two years later the researchers were shocked when a journal article appeared under McBride's name and theirs about the work. Their shock turned to horror when it became apparent to them that McBride had manipulated the data—changing figures, creating control rabbits when none existed, and exaggerating the number of birth malformations. The manipulated results gave support to McBride's contention that Debendox was a teratogen.

The controversy found its way into the media, and in 1988 a Foundation 41 inquiry declared McBride 'lacking in scientific integrity' and guilty of 'deliberate falsification'. Amid a chorus of condemnation, McBride quit the Foundation. But that was not the end of his public shaming. The next year a health department inquiry began; in 1993 McBride was again found guilty of manipulating data and reprehensible conduct, and his licence to practise medicine was revoked. (His licence was restored in 1998.)

When I met McBride in 2013 he reminisced about his horror as a medical student when confronted with the preserved malformed foetuses at the university. 'Strange that I should have devoted my life to congenital malformations after that.' He was reluctant to look back at the ups and downs of his career. Would he have been better off without his thalidomide encounter? 'No, not at all,' he responded.

But it was clear that he missed the adulation that for years had been his prize. When his telephone rang he was startled and joked that people rarely rang him anymore. 'It's much better being in the public spotlight than all alone,' he concluded sadly.

• • •

In the early 1970s, while he was still an icon of Australian medicine, McBride examined Mary Henley-Collopy, a young girl who was a candidate for thalidomide compensation. At the time there was no evidence that Henley-Collopy's mother had taken the drug—that did not emerge until later when her birth parents were located and interviewed. But McBride was utterly convinced by Henley-Collopy's highly typical and very severe injuries and said he would 'stake my reputation' on thalidomide having been the cause. A doctor's note not long after her birth described Henley-Collopy's injuries this way: 'Has some fingers on stumps coming from each shoulder, feet from thighs an inch in length.' In 1974 Henley-Collopy was granted a modest lump sum in an out-of-court settlement with Distillers.

In the years afterwards, Henley-Collopy overcame enormous hurdles to carve for herself a successful career, build a supportive network and travel overseas. And in 2010 it was Henley-Collopy who, after listening to Peter Gordon speak at a Sydney conference, encouraged Wendy Rowe to seek legal advice for her daughter Lyn.

Over the course of the litigation Henley-Collopy became a good friend to our office, often visiting when she travelled to Melbourne from her home in a country town about six hours away, a trip she usually made alone by bus and train. Occasionally, she drove her own modified van. Frequently Henley-Collopy and I had coffee together, always taking an outdoors seat so that Henley-Collopy could indulge her nicotine addition, 'something I've been trying to break for about thirty years'. Like many thalidomide survivors, Henley-Collopy is dextrous and makes best use of what she has, employing a combination of her mouth, fingers and toes to light and smoke a cigarette, use her mobile phone or rifle through her handbag.

As a recognised thalidomider, Henley-Collopy was not part of the group of uncompensated survivors headed by Lyn Rowe. But Henley-Collopy had known Lyn since childhood and was a valuable source of information and advice for Lyn's team. Henley-Collopy was also a potential witness in Lyn's case because she offered us a nuanced insight into the experience of being a profoundly injured survivor. It was an insight we wanted to present at trial, but not one easily gained from Lyn herself. One of Lyn's great strengths is that she is relentlessly positive. 'I don't really think about what might have been,' she told me once. 'To be quite honest, I can't change anything, so why think about it?' Of course Lyn does get frustrated and unhappy and frightened and resentful like everyone else. But she never gets down for long, and she does not like to talk about it. 'Lyn keeps going,' Wendy said. 'She gets unhappy if her chair breaks down, for example, but she doesn't let herself dwell on the fact that she doesn't have limbs, and she certainly doesn't complain about it.'

Henley-Collopy has led a very different life from Lyn Rowe. Unlike Lyn, she does get some assistance from her massively damaged limbs and digits. She also has a sharp mind, which she has used to get a university education, and she has worked as a social worker and grief counsellor, frequently with other people with disabilities. Lyn, of course, suffered brain damage before her first birthday, compounding her already overwhelming disadvantage.

Henley-Collopy was raised in foster homes and has fought a complex struggle for everything she gained, including an independent life and a relationship with her birth parents. As we got to know her we understood more of her own remarkable story, a story she related with deep insight and honesty.

Mary was born in Perth in October 1961, the child of an unmarried couple, thirty-four-year-old Dulcie Henley (a 'housekeeper' according to government records) and thirty-five-year-old William Collopy, a railway worker. While Dulcie was anxious to marry William, 'circumstances were preventing it', according to a carefully worded and somewhat obscure government file note. Perhaps the 'circumstances' contributed to Dulcie's self-described 'highly strung and nervy' state during the pregnancy, a state which led a Perth doctor to prescribe her sedatives.

A government investigator later found a note on Henley-Collopy's surgery card which made reference to her tiny limbs: 'Seal baby due to Distaval.' Many years later when Henley-Collopy accessed her government files, she discovered that her mother held her for just two hours at the hospital after her birth. 'Baby Mary' became a ward of the state and remained so until her twenty-first birthday.

Henley-Collopy lived in a number of group homes in Perth, and then with foster parents who were paid forty-five shillings a week to care for her. She was removed from that family after an inspector found the foster mother 'tends to flaunt the child's disability in public, and glories in the reflected notoriety'.

At twenty-one months, Henley-Collopy was, according to a child welfare department memorandum, 'a bright looking child, fat and healthy looking, although reported to be mentally retarded. She rolls in the cot and holds rattles in her flippers'.

The Western Australian authorities wanted Henley-Collopy to have access to the latest in prosthetic limbs. An attempt was made to find her a place at Chailey House in the UK, where many thalidomide children were treated, but no places were available. So Henley-Collopy was sent across the country for treatment at Melbourne's Royal Children's Hospital. Before she departed Perth there was a determined effort to raise money to cover her costs. Rocker Johnny O'Keefe performed a fundraiser at a Perth radio station, and together with some lottery proceeds and public donations, almost eight thousand pounds was collected.

Henley-Collopy's parents visited her before she left for Melbourne. A social worker supervised the visit, described the parents as 'reasonable people', and speculated that Mary might one day be returned to their care. After that pre-departure visit, Henley-Collopy did not see her birth parents for almost thirty years.

On 19 September 1963, not yet two years old, Henley-Collopy flew to Melbourne accompanied by a nurse. Sister Ellis stayed in Melbourne for two weeks, and noted Mary was 'withdrawn with other people and was not eating as much as when in Western Australia'. Henley-Collopy lived at the hospital for eighteen months, surely a barren and austere home for a very young child. Finally, in April 1965, she was able to move into less irregular surroundings. A former physiotherapist at the hospital, Margaret Green, set up a home for disabled children, which she named the Christian Service Centre, and Henley-Collopy lived there for twenty years.

'I still remember the day I went there and Margaret Green became my mother. She was a very strong woman with a very rigid Christian faith. She never married, never had any biological children of her own and we became her children. We all called her Mum,' Henley-Collopy recalled. 'There were usually about eight children living there. Some of us stayed for years, others for much shorter periods.'

There were two bedrooms for the children, one for the boys and one for the girls. 'I remember my surprise years later when I first saw a queen-size bed. I didn't even know such things existed.'

Margaret Green was a fundamentalist Baptist and ran a very tight ship. 'We said grace before every single meal, and then every night after dinner we'd sit around the dinner table and have bible readings, songs and prayer,' Henley-Collopy said. 'As we got a bit older we learned to ask for the shortest songs. Once I asked for "God Save the Queen" and everybody laughed at me. I said, "Well it has God in it!"'

On Sundays Margaret Green 'went into overdrive', Henley-Collopy said. 'There was no television, no outings, no knitting, nothing was allowed that could be regarded as fun or work. We went to a church service in the morning, then Christian youth group at the church in the afternoon and then back to church again on Sunday evening.'

Margaret Green believed it was wrong to seek funding for the home, or to ask for payment. She believed God would provide. In a letter about Mary, she wrote: 'We pray about each child we take, and believe it is right for Mary to be with us, and we trust God to supply all her needs as He has done for others.'

A visitor to the centre in July 1965 described Mary as a 'charming little girl, with soft brown hair, a frequent smile and friendly manner, full of chatter and using her malformed limbs in such a remarkable way that she finds her prostheses somewhat irritating'. The visitor found Miss Green devoted and caring, but somewhat over-possessive. 'She wants to weld these children into her family and I had the feeling that she did not want them to have too many outside contacts.'

In July 1969 a government report described Henley-Collopy as 'extremely intelligent' and 'reading very fluently for a child in grade two'. Despite this glowing assessment Henley-Collopy attended a primary school for disabled children, Yooralla. This was where she met Lyn Rowe.

Finally at fifteen she swapped to a mainstream school, Balwyn

High. 'I was desperate to get there. I was far behind—academically and socially—but I loved it. I just wanted to learn.' After high school Henley-Collopy suffered her first bout of depression when she could not find work. 'Nobody would help, it seemed hopeless. I spent a year thinking, what am I going to do for the rest of my life? I was living with Mum in Box Hill, nowhere near public transport, isolated and depressed.'

But the next year Henley-Collopy started a two-year diploma in welfare studies. 'Getting to and from college was a nightmare but the course was great.' After graduating in 1983, she was offered a student placement with the Australian Government's Department of Social Security, and she ultimately worked there for twenty years, initially as a locum but then full-time. Along the way Henley-Collopy also did a degree in social work and qualified as a grief counsellor.

It was not until she was in her late twenties that she first raised with Margaret Green the possibility of getting in touch with her birth parents. 'I'd been nervous about it, because I didn't want to upset her. But she was great. She said she knew I needed to do it.' With the help of a government agency Henley-Collopy managed to obtain an address for her birth parents, who were living in Sydney. Margaret Green, who Henley-Collopy often refers to as her Melbourne mum, wrote them a letter asking whether they would agree to contact with Mary. 'I thought that might be a better, less confronting approach than me contacting them out of the blue,' Henley-Collopy said.

Months passed without a response. But Henley-Collopy and her Melbourne mum were not giving up. Remarkably, Margaret Green decided she would take the train to Sydney and find her way to Henley-Collopy's birth parents' home. 'It was brave of her,' Mary remembered. 'I got some photos taken of me doing normal things like pouring a kettle and knitting and gave them to her. I wanted my parents to know that I could do things for myself. I saw Mum off at the train station and spent the next twenty-four hours on tenterhooks. Every bone in my body said this might not go well.'

But the November 1989 visit was a success. Her birth parents were put at ease by Margaret Green's message that Henley-Collopy bore no grudge about having been given up at birth, and that she very much wanted to meet them. So, a few months later, Margaret Green and Mary Henley-Collopy flew to Sydney, where in February 1990 Henley-Collopy met Dulcie Mary and William John for the first time since 1963. It was the first meeting with her birth parents in Henley-Collopy's memory.

'The first thing my mum, Dulcie, said to me was I'm sorry for giving you Mary as a name. I said I'm just glad you didn't call me Dulcie.' The meeting was emotional but rewarding. 'Most of all I wanted them to know I was OK,' Henley-Collopy said. She quickly forged a bond with her father; a bit more slowly with her mother. 'I already had a mother, but I always craved a father. I used to cry all day on Father's Day. Mum probably also had a bit more emotional baggage about giving me up than Dad did.'

Henley-Collopy kept up weekly contact with her birth parents afterwards and added Collopy to her name: until then she had been Mary Henley. She feels grateful she found her birth parents when she did because her father died two years later in 1992 and her mother in 1996. Henley-Collopy's Melbourne mum, Margaret Green, died in 1999. 'Many of the children who had grown up in that home gathered at the hospital right at the end. It was quite a scene. All these adults in wheelchairs calling this unconscious woman Mum. The nurses didn't know what to make of it.'

Henley-Collopy is a direct and forthright woman, and is open about some of her struggles. 'There was a time when my friends were partnering up and going on dates and having fun. Eventually they got married and had families. I got the same sort of crushes as anybody else but I knew it wasn't going to happen for me. That hurt very badly.' Through grit and determination, Henley-Collopy did some of the things she wanted to do, such as living alone and travelling overseas. 'But it's a struggle, things happen slowly when you're in a wheelchair and it's expensive.' As she ages she is ever more reliant on care and help.

Henley-Collopy receives an annual pension from Diageo (Distillers), though she worries about her future. 'Diageo has tried to do something about the shocking thing that was done to us. It can't be fixed, but Diageo's cheques help us lead better lives. On the other hand Grünenthal won't give us a dollar. Ask the Grünenthal bosses what they think my arms and legs are worth. See if you can get an answer to that.'

Her central concern, Henley-Collopy said, is living with dignity.

> Death doesn't scare me. I grew up around death. Lots of children I lived with and went to school with died young. So the end doesn't hold any great fears for me. But I want to live the time I have left with dignity and independence, and we need money and help to do that. I reckon I have done all right with what I have, but nobody would choose to be born this way. It's hard. Life's a struggle. It's trite to say it's not fair, and I don't say that. But it's not bloody right. It should never have happened to anyone.

CHAPTER 14

Greedy Hearts

In March 1972 the parents of six thalidomide-damaged British children were told by a London judge that they no longer had the right to make key legal decisions for their children. This low point in thalidomide legal history did not arise because the parents were guilty of mistreatment or neglect, or indeed of any failing of any sort. The parents' common sin was that they wanted to reject an utterly miserable compensation package offered to them by Distillers.

To call the offer miserable is to praise it highly. The Distillers offer amounted to less than £10,000 to cover a lifetime of care for a catastrophically injured child. Yet those parents with the nerve to reject the offer were first pressured by their own lawyers to change their minds, and then taken to court so that a substitute guardian could accept the deal in their place. The reason for all this pressure on a few holdout families? Distillers had insisted that every last set of parents had to accept the deal or it would be withdrawn.

This was the sad state of play in the UK in March 1972, more than ten years after thalidomide had been exposed as a deadly drug. The legal battle between Distillers and the children had been a no-contest. The children's lawyers were overwhelmed and underprepared. The mismatch had limped along for years, effectively going nowhere, largely in secret and protected from comment and publicity by the English contempt-of-court laws, which banned publication of any material that might influence a legal proceeding.

For Lyn's legal team the history of the vexed UK litigation was something of a touchstone. We were determined to learn its lessons and avoid its pitfalls. One of the keys, obviously, was to avoid the apparent passivity of the UK lawyers. Their job was to force Distillers to pay compensation, either through a settlement or by winning at trial. Yet, partly through the force of circumstance, they seemed to adopt a reactive approach that translated into years of delays and little progress. Meanwhile the traumatised families became increasingly frustrated and desperate. In the finish, it was only the decisive and wholehearted intervention of the *Sunday Times* newspaper, and the political and public campaign that followed, that led to a half-decent settlement.

The UK thalidomide litigation had its start in mid-1962 when a small group of the parents met and formed the Society for the Aid of Thalidomide Children. The parents agreed to apply for legal aid so that they could find lawyers and start a legal action. But from the outset they were beset by problems. The Law Society, which administered legal aid, believed the children's claim had no hope. It agreed to dribble out funding for just one test case. A child was selected, and after years of snail-like progress the trial was scheduled for early 1968. But the lawyers were not even close to being ready. In fact, by the eve of the trial they had become deeply pessimistic they could defeat Distillers.

Years later the *Sunday Times* journalists exposed some of what appears to have gone wrong. The law firm representing the children, Kimber Bull, had stumbled into thalidomide litigation through its commercial work for one of the thalidomide parents. It was not a leader in the field of personal injuries. Legal aid funding for the claim was inadequate and it was doled out stingily, preventing the sort of major investigation necessary to produce convincing evidence of Distillers' negligence and incompetence. For example, no concerted effort was made to gather evidence that other drug companies tested drugs in pregnant animals, tests which Distillers failed to undertake. Such evidence existed but Kimber Bull did not find it. Kimber Bull's efforts to recruit appropriate experts to back the children's claim were also inadequate. It often seemed satisfied with merely sending polite letters to scientists and doctors seeking assistance, and all too willing to abandon the effort at the first sign of a witness's reluctance or non-responsiveness. And the wrong test case had been selected, a birth too early in the thalidomide era. Because Distillers' awareness of the risks associated with its drug grew over time, thus increasing its culpability, a better test case would have been a child exposed late in the period, ideally after Bill McBride's first warning to Distillers.

Not all of these failings can be laid at the lawyers' door. The inadequate legal aid funding was a real hindrance. Certainly many doctors and scientists were unwilling to get involved in a controversial legal case, and some feared the consequences of giving evidence against the pharmaceutical industry. But, as the *Sunday Times* journalists would later argue in private, a lack of urgency and a sense of defeatism seemed to pervade the trial preparation. For a very long time the children's lawyers and barristers appear to have been too readily convinced of the strength of Distillers' case. One of the surprising grounds for the lawyers' pessimism was their belief that Distillers could always argue that no matter what its failings had been, the drug had been on sale in Germany prior to its UK launch, and thus had effectively been tested on humans without malformations being discovered. This was a bizarre belief for the Distillers lawyers to hold—'a remarkable piece of idiocy', according to one *Sunday Times* journalist. Grünenthal's uncontrolled and irresponsible selling of thalidomide did not amount to any sort of test and provided no basis for comfort. In any event, by late 1967, with the test-case trial only a few months away, the lawyers and the families were in a deep hole.

At that point Distillers offered to settle the claims for forty per cent of their value. The children's lawyers leapt at the derisory offer, intent on salvaging something from the mess. A long analysis by the barristers engaged to act for the children, led by Desmond Ackner, set out the multiple weaknesses of the victims' claims and justified acceptance of the heavily discounted offer. Some of the pessimism in the memorandum was based on flawed reasoning, though perhaps some was understandable given the lack of a thorough investigation. But the conclusion was clear. 'We are firmly of the opinion that if the claim proceeds to trial its prospects of succeeding are substantially below forty per cent.'

Distillers had insisted that every single family had to agree or the deal was off, and the lawyers set about persuading their clients to sign. Most families were worn down by the pessimism about their prospects, or were in deep financial need, or were simply desperate for the whole thing to be over. Ultimately all sixty-two families accepted the miserly offer. Some felt they had been unreasonably pressured to do so. Announcing the settlement, Ackner, the children's barrister, said that had the case gone to trial the children might 'have failed to recover a penny piece'. The judge overseeing the case trumpeted his approval. It would have been 'folly' for the children to refuse such a 'fair and just' settlement, he declared.

Matters worsened for the families when their lawyers and Distillers could not agree on the full value of the claims, and hence what the forty per cent figures should have been. So to provide guidance for the negotiations a court hearing was held to assess two of the victims: David, born without limbs, and Richard, who had no arms. The hearing was a legalistic farce. John Prevett, the distinguished actuary who gave evidence for the boys, later said that he thought Justice Hinchcliffe had slept through parts of his evidence. Distillers' barrister John Wilmers pressed the judge to ignore the effect of inflation when calculating compensation, in part because the government had announced it would control inflation.

The insanity did not stop there. Distillers speculated that even had the boys been born undamaged they might have decided to abandon 'the chore of earning a living' and opted out of the workforce entirely. Prevett had cited averages in his calculations of the boys' life expectancies and this provoked Distillers' barrister. 'You would agree, would you not, that no one ever is the precise average?' Prevett replied that the reasoning behind the question was unhelpful. 'Never mind whether it's a helpful line of reasoning,' came the retort. 'I want the facts.'

The result of Justice Hinchcliffe's calculations was even more parsimonious than Distillers might have hoped, or the children may have feared. Hinchcliffe rejected the evidence offered by Prevett that David (born without limbs) needed £106,766 for a lifetime of care needs and lost earnings. Instead, the judge decided, £24,000 for future care was adequate plus £28,000 for the 'pain and suffering' of a life without limbs. Applying the forty per cent calculation, David was offered a total one-off payment of £20,800. Hinchcliffe assessed Richard (born without arms) as being due total compensation of £32,000, reduced to £12,800 under the forty per cent rule.

Shortly afterwards an eight-year-old girl named Heather, who like David was born without arms and legs, was also awarded £20,800. During the hearing her barrister, Ackner, compared her circumstances with David's, mounting an argument in step with the values of the era. 'It can always be said that a girl may be likely to earn less during her working life than a boy. But it can also be said that to be deprived of the pleasures of marriage and having a family is a greater deprivation for a girl than it necessarily is for a boy.'

Negotiations over the forty per cent sums dragged on for years, during which time almost another four hundred thalidomide-afflicted families joined the fight. During 1971 Distillers made a bulk offer to this further group of £3.25 million. On an individual basis the offer amounted to about half the scrooge-like sums to be paid to the first group of children. Nevertheless at a series of meetings all around the country, the families' lawyers urged the parents to accept. Many families were bitter and many resisted, yet all but six eventually signed up. At that point their own lawyers made an application to the High Court to remove the six dissenting sets of parents as their children's legal decision makers and instead allow a government solicitor to stand in their place. The application in March 1972 was successful, and the parents were sidelined. But an appeal heard the following month forcefully reversed the decision. 'Being in a minority,' one of the judges declared, 'is no evidence of unreasonableness.' Art gallery owner David Mason, the father who had led the minority, afterwards expressed disgust at the conduct of his own lawyers. 'I had to fight [his lawyers Kimber Bull] and prove I was acting in my daughter's best interests. It was an incredible situation.' Mason went on to play a crucial leadership role in the public brawl with Distillers and he remained a vociferous critic of Kimber Bull.

For the moment, though, the settlement was stalled: Distillers would not proceed without unanimous approval, and the hold-out parents would not agree.

Soon afterwards came the crucial intervention. The *Sunday Times* had been looking for a way to enter the thalidomide fray since 1968, when it had secretly bought caches of Distillers and Grünenthal documents. It had put an investigative team on the case, and had assembled vastly better material about the drug companies' negligence than had the children's lawyers. In fact the *Sunday Times* investigation became something of an inspiration for our own legal effort. I spent days in London studying the *Sunday Times* files of the period, and was astounded by the scale of the newspaper's ambition. Its journalists had travelled to Germany, the US and Australia in search of material, interviewing doctors, scientists, pharmaceutical company employees and thalidomide salesmen. Thousands of documents were collated and translated. The newspaper kept at it for years, never stinting on resources or expense. It was an expensive and deeply impressive forensic investigation, marked by the newspaper's refusal to accept glib assertion as fact and a profound scepticism that the UK legal process would ever achieve anything resembling justice for the children.

But the dynamite assembled by the *Sunday Times* could not be printed. English laws about contempt of court essentially banned any publication of material that might influence the ongoing legal cases. And the cases were dragging on much longer than any observers, including the *Sunday Times*, had expected. This had largely prevented the increasingly frustrated *Sunday Times* editor Harold Evans from printing anything but human-interest stories about victims, straight reportage of announcements and court hearings, and news about thalidomide developments overseas.

The turning point came in 1972. Outraged by a combination of the paltry assessments of the children's forty per cent entitlements, Distillers' apparent determination to pay the children as little as it could get away with, and a conviction that the children's lawyers were not likely to force a better deal, the *Sunday Times* could wait no longer. On 24 September 1972, the newspaper burst into campaigning mode under the banner 'Our Thalidomide Children: A Cause for National

Shame'. Claiming it was seeking 'moral justice' to provide cover against the charge that it was seeking to interfere in 'legal justice', the paper savaged the amounts being offered to the children, and called on Distillers to do more. The newspaper drew heavily on the assistance of John Prevett, the actuary whose evidence for the children had been rejected. Prevett's calculations demonstrated that the amounts allocated for the children's care were a fraction of what was required and in many cases would run out before the children reached the age of twenty. To the newspaper's frustration, it was still not able to print anything about Distillers' flawed behaviour in testing and selling the drug, and had to stick to moral arguments about the level of compensation.

The ongoing *Sunday Times* campaign kicked off a groundswell of public interest and support for the victims. With the veil of secrecy stripped away, Distillers, for the first time in the decade since thalidomide was pulled from the market, began to feel the force of public odium. Parliament debated the issue; a dogged (and deaf) Labour MP Jack Ashley, led the political fight for the children; a campaign began among Distillers shareholders to force the company to pay decent compensation; a supermarket chain announced a boycott of Distillers products; and the young American consumer activist Ralph Nader threatened to orchestrate another boycott in the United States. Some of the Distillers bosses began to hear mutterings when they went out in polite society. Meanwhile the *Sunday Times* and other media poured on the pressure, highlighting the plight of the families and their afflicted children, and the wholly inadequate nature of the Distillers offer.

There was also help from an unexpected quarter. Posters were suddenly plastered all over London one night, including over Distillers' St James Square head office. 'They said it was safe for pregnant women,' one read. 'Like hell it was.' There were variations on the theme—'Have a thalidomide old boy. Don't mind if I do.' Distillers was predictably enraged and the police hunted for the perpetrator. They never found him. Rupert Murdoch had been much too careful. Not yet the owner of *The Times*, Murdoch had bankrolled the exercise, appointed one of his tabloid editors to organise it and insisted on strict secrecy. Though the police tore the posters down, the incident caused a memorable fuss and the posters are collectors' items today.

While the *Sunday Times* was loudly and publicly orchestrating the campaign, in private it did even more. The children now had a new barrister in charge. Ackner, who had urged the acceptance of the forty per cent offer, had become a judge and was replaced by John Stocker. The *Sunday Times* had been trying to meet with the children's lawyers for months, determined to share the fruits of its investigation. The lawyers had maintained a frosty distance, and had urged the families to have nothing to do with the media. Finally, with Stocker in charge, a meeting was arranged. Bruce Page, one of the journalists leading the paper's investigation, met Stocker. 'I gave him detailed notes about drug-testing prior to the launch of thalidomide,' Page wrote in 1998. 'We could not say reproductive testing had been universal. But we could nail the old myth about its being unknown or ineffective, and show that it had been thought necessary by good companies with comparable products.' This information hardened the negotiating stance of the children's lawyers, who wrote to the parents advising that the *Sunday Times*' work had improved their prospects at trial.

The newspaper was generous with its information. When Distillers sued its insurer to force it to contribute to the compensation, the insurer made a smart decision. It sent its lawyers to meet with the *Sunday Times* journalists. Thanks to that meeting, the insurer was able to produce detailed information articulating Distillers' negligence (and incompetence) in the handling of thalidomide. The approach proved effective. Ultimately Distillers settled for a far smaller payment from its insurer than it had initially demanded.

• • •

Over the ten years between 1962 and 1972 the British children's lawyers had made little impact on Distillers: so little impact that the lawyers had been enthusiastic about settling for heavily discounted sums. Yet within weeks of the start of the campaign by the *Sunday Times* and its allies, Distillers began to yield to the pressure. Distillers, which had declared a profit of £62 million in 1971 and boasted £247 million worth of whisky maturing in oak barrels, first offered an ungenerous £5 million to its victims. That was met by a chorus of jeers, and a £12 million offer followed. Then in January 1973, Distillers offered to stump up what was effectively £16 million. Finally, in April 1973, Distillers scuttled up to £20 million, six times the £3.25 million that had been on the table only a year earlier. The children's families and even the *Sunday Times* pronounced themselves satisfied and the legal battle was over. It was sobering to realise that if the lawyers had had their way a year earlier, and had they been able to force the renegade parents into line, Distillers would have got away with its £3.25 million offer.

Even so, £20 million, when carved up, ultimately proved far too little to provide a decent life for the victims. In recent years Diageo, the company that now owns the Distillers group, has made large voluntary contributions to the UK trust which pays an annual pension to the official survivors. The UK Government has also contributed. The survivors now number about five hundred, though inevitably there are others who have never come forward, or whose evidence is deemed insufficient to prove their claim.

The *Sunday Times* kept fighting even after the thalidomide children settled. After a series of legal battles over the contempt law, in 1976 the paper published a six-page report trumpeting the result of its lengthy investigation into the development, sale and marketing of thalidomide. This exposé was later expanded into a book written by Phillip Knightley and other members of the newspaper's investigative team.

For Lyn's legal team there was much to learn from the UK events of the 1960s and '70s: the failure of the children's lawyers, the need for the *Sunday Times* intervention, the involvement of politicians and pressure groups. That battle underlined the fact that while the courtroom is the main forum in which legal fights play out, it's not the only venue. Far more so than forty years ago, companies today are sensitive to negative publicity and many place high value on their reputation. And few groups are more worthy of sympathy than people grossly damaged before even taking their first breath. This is not to say that we intended to engage the media to ratchet up the pressure on Diageo and on Grünenthal. We did not. But clearly the companies were aware of the reputational issues at stake. Before one of the early court hearings we heard that Diageo was holding briefings for Melbourne journalists and offering interviews with a London executive, putting its own spin on events. A multibillion-dollar drinks empire, Diageo was obviously going to be more sensitive to public perception than Grünenthal. More importantly, Diageo was a company that wanted to do the right thing, and to be seen doing the right thing, in relation to thalidomiders. Grünenthal was altogether different. As a private family-owned company, Grünenthal lacked the sensitivity that comes with having a large number of shareholders. It also appeared to possess a tin ear for criticism and a passionate determination to fight to the end.

• • •

Distillers' hardline approach to the early thalidomide claims meant that the surviving children were reaching their teens before they were compensated. For the devastated families, the shock and trauma of having severely injured babies had been compounded by the agony of the years-long legal imbroglio.

Distillers was consistent, though. It applied that same hard-hearted approach to its own employees with thalidomide-damaged children: there were at least six such families in the UK and another three Distillers men in New Zealand and one in Australia whose wives had given birth to damaged babies. All of them had to join the legal actions to receive any compensation from their employers. Distillers gave them no special treatment whatsoever.

John Gordon worked as a salesman for Distillers' New Zealand branch in 1961 and 1962. Eighty-two years old when he talked to us in 2011, he died not long afterwards. The passage of many years had not diminished Gordon's anger with his former employer. He told us that when he joined Distillers in New Zealand he was given the usual 'super-safe' sales pitch for thalidomide and explicitly told to promote the drug for use in pregnancy. He was not told about nerve damage. Gordon worked hard and he remembered the drug as a bestseller.

> In about early June 1961 my wife became pregnant with our second child. She had suffered from morning sickness while pregnant with [our first child] and suffered from morning sickness again during her second pregnancy. After she had been sick for a little while I gave her a few Distaval pills to take. I was confident there was no problem with Distaval because of its extreme safety.

Life went on as normal until late in 1961 when John Gordon received a terrifying phone call from his boss: there was a possible link between birth malformations and thalidomide. Sales were suspended. Gordon, of course, became increasingly concerned about his wife and unborn child. 'Initially we both felt reasonably confident that things would be OK. After all, Patsy had taken only a few of the pills, and the link between thalidomide and the birth injuries was only suspected, not proven.' But then Gordon started reading reports in medical journals and his optimism faded. 'Patsy and I were very worried. We were, and are, both devout Catholics and we prayed daily that our unborn baby would be healthy.'

During this period John Gordon's relationship with his employer deteriorated. He started requesting more information from his head office in Auckland and even wrote to Distillers in London. 'I wanted to know how they could have told us it was safe to use during pregnancy, when it turned out to have these terrible properties.'

On 15 March 1962 Patsy Gordon went into labour. As was the custom then, John Gordon did not attend the birth.

> Later that evening one of the doctors told me that Patsy had given birth to a baby boy, but that the boy had malformed arms and hands. I was devastated even though I had been preparing myself for this possibility for several months. Patsy had been sedated and I didn't get to see her until the next morning. When I went to see her all she had to do was look at my face to see that something had gone wrong.

The baby boy, Gerard, was in and out of hospital for several years and endured a long series of operations. 'He has had some very difficult times,' John Gordon said in 2011. 'But Gerard was, and is, a very determined person. He has made a success of his life and has a wife and a young son. Both Patsy and I are very proud of him.'

Shortly after Gerard's birth, Gordon's attitude to Distillers reached the point of no return. 'I took [Gerard's injuries] very badly and was furious with Distillers for having done this to us and other families… At some point I started talking about asking Distillers for compensation, or taking legal action to get some compensation for us and other families who had had babies injured by thalidomide.'

Towards the end of 1962 Gordon was sacked without explanation. He found a job in the medical supplies industry and threw himself into a legal action against Distillers, acting as the de-facto leader for a group of affected New Zealand families. The proceeding dragged on and on for years before, in the mid-1970s, Distillers offered to pay compensation. Gordon was cornered. He felt the money was nowhere near adequate. But the other families were anxious to settle and he wanted to make sure that Gerard had some compensation. He ended up agreeing to the deal, but his bitterness about Distillers never left him.

Distillers took a similarly combative approach to Australian claimants in the 1960s and '70s. The first writ in Australia was issued for Laura Thompson, a girl born without arms. Thompson sought damages from both the Distillers parent company in the UK and its Australian subsidiary. Distillers argued that its UK arm could not be sued in Australia because it had done nothing in Australia which could constitute negligence. Distillers fought on that legal issue for years, forcing Thompson's legal team all the way to London's Privy Council, where in January 1971 the Law Lords finally dismissed Distillers' argument and gave Thompson the go-ahead to sue the UK company in Australia. Not long afterwards, Distillers settled with the Australian children they accepted as having thalidomide injuries. As in the UK, the Australian settlements proved inadequate.

Grünenthal was every bit as recalcitrant when it came to

compensating its German victims. It dragged its heels until 1970 before offering, in the midst of the criminal trial of its executives, to make a contribution to a trust that would pay a pension to German victims. The pensions paid proved so insufficient that in 2013 the German Government (belatedly) stepped in and radically raised them, by up to five hundred per cent in some cases.

In dozens of the almost fifty countries where thalidomide was sold there has been no specific compensation scheme for thalidomiders. They have had to rely on their own endeavours, welfare or charity. Where there has been compensation, either through a dedicated scheme or through legal action, it was, as in the UK and Germany, slow in coming and far from adequate.

In Ireland, Grünenthal's products were sold by a local distributor. An early assessment found that eighty-seven damaged babies had been born in Ireland, though only thirty-four were accepted as thalidomide survivors by an Irish review board which applied 'typical' injury notions.

The official Irish thalidomide survivors had to negotiate with Grünenthal and accepted a pittance in compensation: a lump sum of between 1250 and 4200 Irish pounds and a tiny monthly allowance. The government subsequently added to the compensation, but Irish thalidomiders have long campaigned for further compensation from both Grünenthal and their government.

In Japan, where thalidomide sales were not halted until May 1962, six months after Lenz's warning, the Japanese company Dainippon and the government refused to offer compensation for a decade. In 1963 the Japanese families initiated legal action and eleven years later, in 1974, a settlement was announced, including a compensation fund, which like everywhere else eventually proved inadequate. But unlike elsewhere, the Japanese thalidomide manufacturer at least offered an appropriately grovelling apology for its appalling conduct, acknowledging the 'miserable calamity' inflicted on the children who had suffered 'unspeakable pain and humiliations'.

Dainippon's president made his regret even more explicit. 'We have not been able to extend a helping hand up to now,' he told a meeting of thalidomide survivors and their families. 'You probably hate me. That is only natural, and I apologise from the bottom of my heart.' He then bowed deeply to his audience, before working his way around the room, personally apologising to each of the children.

The Swedish victims of the drug found a legal team that pushed their claims with unusual aggression and confidence. Lawyer Henning Sjöström was a charismatic character who wrote novels and, during a long career, acted for high-profile clients including tennis star Björn Borg. Sjöström took on the Swedish thalidomide cases, and engaged an energetic scientific adviser, Robert Nilsson from the Royal University of Stockholm. In 1965 a writ was filed against Astra, Grünenthal's Swedish licence partner. The legal battle raged for several years, as much of the Swedish pharmaceutical and medical establishment lined up behind Astra, pushing the orthodox line about the whole thing being an unavoidable tragedy. Sjöström and Nilsson were having none of it. They researched widely and recruited the help of many leading specialists in birth malformations in Europe and the United States, including two of the greats of teratology, Walter Landauer and John Thiersch. The work of the Swedish legal team was well ahead of that of the English lawyers, and Sjöström and Nilsson always appeared confident and aggressive.

In 1969, faced with an increasingly strong case for the children, Astra agreed to a settlement in the form of an inflation-proof annual pension. The arrangement was soon extended to the Danish and Norwegian victims, a total of almost 150 children in the three countries. The pension was far from generous, but it did take in about twenty children in whose cases thalidomide consumption was a matter of apparent doubt.

The United States remains the only country where a thalidomide case has gone to a jury verdict. David Diamond was the first child in the US whose case reached the courtroom. He was born with shortened arms, a damaged spine and a host of other medical problems. David's mother Joanne had been given pills at a hospital where thalidomide was being used as part of Merrell's tricked-up clinical trial program. The drug had not been approved for sale by the US FDA, yet Merrell had supplied the Cleveland Clinic with 1500 pills. Merrell's 1969 defence of David Diamond's claim did not go well. The lowlights included evidence from Ray Nulsen about his ridiculous pregnancy trial for Merrell, and a former Merrell scientist's revelation that inconvenient test results for thalidomide had been withheld from the FDA. Reading the increasingly stark writing on the wall, Merrell settled with the Diamonds before the jury was given a chance to come up with a result and a figure.

Merrell then made a decision it later regretted: in 1971 it chose to fight Peggy McCarrick's thalidomide claim all the way to jury verdict. Peggy had been born with malformed legs and hips. Her right leg was amputated during infancy, and her left leg and hips required extensive surgery. Merrell had assembled what seemed a powerful case, even recruiting Widukind Lenz to give his opinion that Peggy's malformations were not caused by thalidomide. But if Lenz's opinion gave Merrell hope, the tide swiftly turned in favour of Peggy. Merrell was forced to admit it had done reproductive testing on other drugs but not for thalidomide. Then a leading expert in birth malformations giving evidence for Merrell admitted that Merrell was paying him an annual retainer and consultancy fees. Frances Kelsey gave important evidence for Peggy, but that was a just a prelude to the appearance of John Thiersch, the scientist who had procured abortions in women with aminopterin. Thiersch gave the court a compelling master class on Merrell's multiple failings, complete with slideshow.

All of this was orchestrated by Peggy McCarrick's lawyer James Butler, a charismatic former air force pilot, who told the jury that Merrell had 'greedy hearts' and urged them to ignore Merrell's medical experts and their technical arguments. Instead, he told the jury to remember that Merrell had spread a dangerous, inadequately tested drug around the United States 'like popcorn' and had to be held responsible for the consequences. 'I don't want sympathy for Peggy,' Butler told the jury, though of course that's exactly what he wanted. What he demanded instead was a 'cool and calculated judgment'. Butler asked the jury for $1.5 million in compensatory damages for Peggy and an extra award to punish the company. 'Stick it to them to the tune of another million dollars because I think that they deserve it,' he said in closing. 'I urge you to do it so that this corporation and other corporations will learn that they can't play with human life as they did in this case. They can't take a risk on generations to come. You can do it.'

The jury did as Butler asked. It found for the McCarricks, awarding Peggy a total of $2.5 million and her mother Shirley $250,000. The following month the judge reduced the damages award to $775,000. He told Shirley McCarrick she could accept the reduced amount or face a new trial. That sum was then further reduced in negotiations, to avoid an appeal by Merrell. But even the reduced figure ultimately arrived at was still more than the UK, Swedish and other victims received. Notwithstanding the judge's interference with the jury award, the case had a sobering effect on Merrell and it settled the remaining US cases. In Canada, after a bitter legal fight, Merrell paid many of its hundred-plus victims widely varying settlements of between $10,000 and $999,000. A million dollars may sound like a lot of money, but it had to last the lifetime of a person with escalating care needs and often without paid employment. Many of the Canadian survivors eventually found themselves in a desperate financial situation, reliant on welfare. In March 2015 the Canadian Government announced a one-off $125,000 payment to each survivor, plus a multi-million-dollar medical fund.

From the outset the thalidomide legal battle was everywhere a mismatch. It pitted wealthy and determined businesses backed by self-interested allies against struggling families anxious for a settlement. In the UK that imbalance almost led to a catastrophe for the children. But in the US, aggressive plaintiff lawyers were able to get the cases in front of a jury and either win a stunning verdict or force Merrell into settlements. Plaintiff lawyers in the United States are frequently denigrated. But it was the US system that delivered the best initial results for thalidomide victims.

The US cases were encouraging even forty years on. Certainly, thalidomide claims were legally difficult. Certainly, litigating fifty years after the event raised the degree of difficulty even further. But the only time a jury had passed judgment on a thalidomide claim, in 1971, it resulted in a US$2.75 million verdict. That was equivalent to about $15 million in 2012. Approached the right way, thalidomide cases were winnable.

CHAPTER 15

A Little Bit More Luxury

By the end of 2011 it looked as if Lyn and her parents would get what they wanted: a trial in 2012. On 21 December 2011 Victorian Supreme Court justice David Beach gave a clear preview of his intention. 'I don't think you're going to get any resistance to the notion that this case should move as expeditiously as reasonably possible to a trial date,' he told the assembled lawyers at a court hearing.

But soon we had to weather an attempt by both Grünenthal and Distillers to send us back to square one and start formulating Lyn Rowe's claim over again. At a hearing on 26 June 2012, our opponents tried to persuade the judge that Lyn's statement of claim should be struck out on the basis that it was confused and did not clearly set out the case that Lyn was making against the defendants. We had laboured over the statement of claim, a twenty-six-page document which accused Grünenthal and Distillers of negligently causing Lyn's birth injuries and laid out the legal basis for the fight ahead. Naturally we thought it was cogent and precise, but Grünenthal and Distillers (equally naturally) disagreed.

The Grünenthal barrister made a detailed argument to the judge for ditching the statement of claim and having us start again. We felt that the arguments were weak and that Grünenthal was overplaying its hand. But if Grünenthal was successful it would cause real delay and probably end the prospect of a trial in 2012.

So we were relieved when Justice Beach delivered a strongly worded decision on the spot, allowing Lyn's statement of claim to stand, and declaring that he was disinclined to be dragged into expensive and legalistic time-wasting. 'The resources of this court are too scarce to engage in what might prove to be lengthy and entirely sterile debates,' the judge ruled. 'The impression I have in this case is that the parties broadly know the cases each other seeks to bring…I suspect at trial many of the shadows that are currently being boxed at will disappear.'

Another dispute to be resolved was the trial date. The judge had floated October 2012 as a possibility, which had not pleased Grünenthal and Distillers. It was much too soon for them, a position viewed in our office as somewhat amusing. More than fifty years after their drug had wreaked havoc, Grünenthal and Distillers did not want to be rushed to trial. As Justice Beach himself remarked when Distillers' barrister suggested October 2012 was an unrealistic start date for the trial, 'This proceeding's been on foot for a couple of years. It relates to matters that occurred fifty-plus years ago.'

The proposal for an October 2012 trial delighted us. Wendy and Ian would soon be unable to care for Lyn, and the whole Rowe family wanted a result quickly. A win would secure her future. In the event of a loss, other plans would have to be made. And as Lyn's lawyers we had our own reasons for wanting a speedy trial. Nothing forces reason and sanity on lawyers and litigants like a looming trial date. We believed that the pressure of a trial might force the defendants (and us for that matter) to resolve some of the issues in dispute and hence limit the scope of the trial, making it a much less unwieldy beast.

Of course getting Lyn's case ready for a trial date a few months away was a tall order. There were tens of thousands of documents to be examined, expert witness statements to be prepared, medical evidence to be mastered. But a heavy burden would also fall on the defendants, who knew by now they were facing a strong claim, aggressively prosecuted.

At another hearing in June 2012, Grünenthal's barrister pushed again for a trial in 2013 rather than 2012, in part because of the difficulty caused by the fact that the men involved in thalidomide's development and sale are 'essentially all dead'.

Distillers' barrister agreed. The claim, he said, was forty years out of date.

> All lay witnesses are dead. Relevant experts are very hard to procure. Experts who would really know what evidence to give are dead. Discovery is enormous. If the defendants were to be successful…they're unlikely to have their costs paid by the plaintiff. How many cases present those kinds of features?

One major hurdle in the case was discovery, the process by which each side in a legal dispute gives the others their relevant documents. This exchange of documents often surprises non-lawyers. But litigation is not supposed to be an ambush, during which opponents try to spring new material on each other. Parties to litigation are supposed to lay their (documentary) cards on the table and conduct an open fight with access to the same material.

In Lyn's case the discovery problems arose largely because most of Grünenthal's relevant documents were in German and, being about fifty years old, reportedly in a somewhat fragile condition. Distillers' documents were similarly long in the tooth, but at least they were in English. By May 2012 Distillers had already discovered fourteen thousand documents to us, and its barrister told the court there were 'three hundred and fifty boxes of documents in the United Kingdom which have not yet been gone through'.

Grünenthal's discovery was even bigger. It said it would not complete analysing and handing over an estimated 620,000 German documents until March or April 2013. Distillers, which as well as defending Lyn's claim was (as a fallback position) trying to push any responsibility for compensating Lyn onto Grünenthal, had done some work on the problems posed by the German discovery. 'They're virtually all in a foreign language,' the Distillers barrister complained to the judge in June 2012. 'They're not very legible…if you just assume that only ten per cent of the documents discovered so far have to be translated from German to English, then that would require ten translators working more than ninety working days, that is eighteen working weeks to translate those documents.' That, the Distillers barrister argued, was a good reason for a later trial. He then turned to the Rowe family.

> Now one cannot but be moved, Your Honour, by the position of the plaintiff and the injuries she lives with. However, there isn't in truth the kind of urgency that demands a trial in October [2012] versus a trial in mid next year. Her parents have been looking after her for many years, but although they're ageing, there isn't a suggestion there's an immediate medical issue concerning her parents.

We had been dealing with the problems presented by the size of the discovery for months at that point. It was clearly a very unusual case, in that so much would turn on tens of thousands of old documents, many of them in German. Almost every single Distillers and Grünenthal manager and scientist from the thalidomide era was dead, so those documents were crucial.

The English-language Distillers documents were sent over in regular bundles by Distillers' lawyers. Our whole office—lawyers and non-lawyers—worked together on them as they arrived, keeping pace with the steady in-flow. Every single document was read and then coded as to subject matter, where it fitted into our case theory and for importance. Many were irrelevant, but our 'critical' category soon filled up. Reading the Distillers discovery was fascinating and horrifying, a chance to peer back into history and watch the developing catastrophe. An informal competition developed in the office over who could identify the 'document of the day'—the document best for Lyn's claim and most damaging for Distillers.

Grünenthal's documents were a different story. Using the criminal indictment drawn up by the German prosecution team in the 1960s—and thanks to the arduous work of Nina Stähle and our other consultants in Germany—we had already found many of the critical documents we needed. These were sent to our ever-growing team of German–English translators. Soon we became convinced of our ability to win a trial against Grünenthal on the basis of the damning documents we ourselves had obtained from the archive and other places. We were checking the Grünenthal discovery but it was yielding little of real importance given what we already knew. We already had most of what we needed.

Another strong argument for a speedy trial was that we had ageing witnesses, most crucially (but not only) Wendy Rowe. Wendy was in good health but there was no point taking any risks. If she were to become seriously ill or worse, then the loss of her evidence would be a severe blow. Self-evidently Wendy would be the most important witness in terms of establishing that Lyn had been exposed to thalidomide. In short we wanted a trial, and we wanted it quickly.

To our relief, and despite the opposition of Grünenthal and Distillers, Justice Beach listened to the various arguments and ruled that the trial would start, as proposed, in October 2012. 'As all sides have said on a number of occasions, many of the witnesses are, by virtue of the relevant facts having occurred long ago, old. They will not survive forever.'

The judge said that much of the defendants' objection to a 2012 trial focused on the size of the discovery and the difficulty in identifying relevant documents which had to be turned over to Lyn Rowe's legal team. 'It is difficult to believe that more than fifty years after the events that give rise to this proceeding, the defendants have not previously already identified the most relevant documents.'

The trial date was now set for less than four months away, and we redoubled our efforts.

• • •

By the middle of 2012 we felt we were in a strong position. For months we had worked to strengthen our weak points and to refine and test our case theory, including at a two-day retreat at which all members of the team presented papers on various aspects of the case, exposing themselves to rigorous cross-examination.

Some issues that had plagued previous thalidomide claims would not be an issue for us. In the 1960s the lawyers for the UK children worried that the fact that their clients were exposed to thalidomide as four-to-eight-week-old embryos might prove fatal to the claims. Did an embryo or foetus even have a legal personality? Could it be owed a duty of care? In a paper addressing these issues they predicted that the complex and somewhat undecided questions would ultimately be decided in the children's favour. More than forty years later these issues had been long settled and were of no concern to us: children now are clearly capable of suing over injuries received prior to birth.

Other issues would be hard fought. We were confident we could establish Grünenthal and Distillers had behaved negligently and should have foreseen a risk to Lyn. Their failure to test thalidomide in pregnant animals was just a part of our argument. More basically, both companies had pushed a drug they knew had a severe side effect (nerve damage) as extraordinarily safe and suitable for use in pregnancy, without ever trying to check its effect on the unborn baby. Both companies knew about the vulnerability of the foetus, and both knew that some drugs should not be given in pregnancy. In the US the FDA's Frances Kelsey, with a fraction of the information available to Distillers and particularly to Grünenthal, had worried about thalidomide's effect on the foetus. Neither Grünenthal nor Distillers ever even tried to follow up women who had taken the drug during early pregnancy to check whether their babies had been harmed.

More damaging for both Grünenthal and Distillers were the reports they had received of birth malformations. We knew Grünenthal had been asked by suspicious doctors and a pharmacist whether thalidomide might be responsible for birth malformations. But the German company's staff had appeared astonishingly uninterested in the issue—they denied any possible connection and made no investigation or inquiry. As for Distillers, its Australian office had been warned by Dr Bill McBride in June 1961 that he believed thalidomide had maimed and killed several babies. But the Distillers team had kept promoting the drug. Of course we'd face a fight from both defendants: there would be vigorous assertions that drug companies in the 1950s could not have been expected to test drugs in pregnant animals, and that even had such tests been conducted no problems would have been detected. The defendants would argue that the fact of nerve damage in adults implied nothing about any possible risk to the foetus. And Grünenthal and Distillers would also seek to minimise the legal relevance of birth malformations reported in Germany and Australia. We knew there would be lots of heat and noise around these issues, but we believed we had a much stronger hand than our opponents.

The other key issue we felt confident about was proving Wendy

Rowe had indeed taken thalidomide. We had a compelling, if circumstantial, case. Half a century later we did not have the bottle or the pills, but Wendy was very clear that she had taken Distaval, and her sister-in-law Margaret remembered Wendy taking the medication. Plus, there was the evidence of other family members, and Dr Ron Dickinson, who had delivered Lyn, had told us that free Distaval samples had been delivered to the medical practice where he and Dr Indian worked. Our team of medical experts would give evidence as to how thalidomide worked in the body and the way in which it caused Lyn's total absence of arms and legs. The doctors would also rule out a known competing genetic cause for Lyn's condition.

That left one major legal issue hanging. In some ways, it was the gateway issue. Had Lyn simply left it too long to bring a claim? A probable interpretation of the Victorian law was that her time to bring a claim had long expired. She had simply taken too long. This was Lyn's statute of limitations issue. But under the relevant law, the judge had the power to give Lyn an extension if he thought it 'just and reasonable to do so'. In making that decision, the judge could consider a range of factors. These included the length of, and reasons for, Lyn's delay in bringing her claim, the prejudice or difficulty the long delay would cause Grünenthal and Distillers at trial, whether a fair trial was possible so long after the relevant events, the extent of Lyn's injury, and the 'nature' of Grünenthal's and Distillers' past conduct.

So we had to mount a persuasive argument that it would be 'just and reasonable' to allow Lyn to bring her claim years late. Constructing the argument was, in the end, straightforward. The compelling facts of Lyn's case spoke for themselves. Lyn was terribly injured by the drug and she and her family had lived in difficult circumstances ever since her birth. The family was flat out coping with Lyn's care needs and finding the money to survive. Wendy had been told by her own doctor that it was a virus rather than thalidomide that had been to blame, an inexplicably misplaced piece of advice, but one that nevertheless ended any prospect that Lyn would bring a legal claim as a child. Grünenthal and Distillers would not suffer unreasonable prejudice if Lyn was allowed to bring her claim late. Both companies had defended thalidomide claims in the past and had vast archives of material recording the thoughts and positions and actions of their former thalidomide executives and scientists. They could rely on this material in court. A fair trial clearly was possible. Finally, the 'nature' of the companies' past conduct was a factor. Given that their drug had deprived Lyn of arms and legs, could Lyn really be penalised for not having brought her claim earlier?

Still, despite our confidence, the defendants knew that the long delay in bringing the claim was a potential weakness, and they homed in on it. Grünenthal's barrister told the court at one hearing that Lyn Rowe might not be entitled to a trial 'because of the operation of the limitation statutes'. By the end of June 2012 the companies were urging the judge to hold a separate hearing—quickly—to decide whether or not Lyn would be granted an extension. If there was to be no extension her claim was over. There would be no trial and no compensation. Lyn's future would remain clouded and uncertain.

• • •

As it turned out Lyn's claim never went to trial. On 18 July 2012, Peter Gordon told the Supreme Court that a settlement had been reached in which Distillers (Diageo) had agreed to pay Lyn a multimillion-dollar sum. Grünenthal was not contributing a cent. After leaving court we held a press conference and soon the settlement was making news around the world.

How had it happened? Only days earlier the parties had been frantically preparing and brawling in court over trial dates.

Much of what led to the settlement is subject to strict confidentiality agreements. And in any case there were some matters that we, as Lyn's lawyers, could only guess at. It is giving away no secrets, however, to say that at some point in 2012 informal talks began between Diageo and its lawyers and Lyn Rowe and her lawyers. The talks were conducted on a confidential basis. The talks progressed and ultimately a deal was reached. In early July 2012 Peter Gordon told Lyn, Wendy and Ian that the battle was over, and that Lyn would soon receive enough money to provide her with first-class care for the rest of her life. (The exact sum remains confidential, 'multimillion' being the agreed term.)

The news was given to the Rowes at Gordon's home and was followed by pizza, beer and wine. It was a happy evening. Lyn, Wendy and Ian were delighted by the result, but not surprised. They had been continuously consulted during negotiations and knew a conclusion was near. Still, the finality and certainty of the settlement drew tears from Wendy Rowe, a departure from her perennial calm. 'I never allowed myself to hope. There was too much at stake for optimism!' Wendy said later. Lyn had taken a similar stance throughout the litigation. 'Right from the start I was in a numb state really and I was very conscious not to think too far ahead.' On the other hand Ian, despite his family role as a pessimist and worrier, had felt increasingly optimistic. 'Every time one of the lawyers came out and spoke with us, or we went into the office, the news was positive and I felt a little bit better. I never did anticipate the amount, though. That was a shock.'

Grünenthal was never involved in the discussions and always appeared determined to fight to the bitter end. Why did Diageo take a different approach? In the aftermath Diageo said it was because of its ongoing commitment to properly compensate thalidomiders, and as a result of its genuine empathy for Lyn. It is true that over the years Diageo had demonstrated a willingness to front up to its responsibilities over thalidomide, a stark counterpoint to Grünenthal's unrelieved stinginess. Good citizenship was clearly part of the explanation for Diageo's decision to settle with Lyn.

But some of us suspected there was more to it. For one, Diageo is in the business of selling alcohol. It's an area fraught with legal issues, heightening the value of a good corporate reputation. And sensibly, for a company making its money from a potentially harmful product, Diageo zealously guards its reputation. Diageo's sustainability and responsibility report for 2013 featured a 'drink responsibly' warning on the cover alongside a photograph of its iconic brands, including Johnnie Walker whisky, Smirnoff vodka, Baileys Irish Cream and Guinness stout. The report talks about alcohol abuse, states that some people should not drink at all—including pregnant women—and commits the company to a program to 'reduce harmful drinking'. In a 2012 disclosure, Diageo said it was 'subject to litigation directed at the beverage alcohol industry and other litigation. Companies in the beverage alcohol industry are, from time to time, exposed to class action or other litigation relating to alcohol advertising, product liability, alcohol abuse problems or health consequences from the misuse of alcohol'.

Obviously alcohol contributes to and causes harm. Road injuries and deaths, alcoholism, family breakdown, violence, depression, obesity, cancer, diabetes. The list is long. And prominent on that list is foetal alcohol syndrome, where maternal drinking during pregnancy damages the foetus. For Diageo, having the spotlight focused on its history (or, more accurately, its subsidiary's history) with a notorious product that damaged foetuses could not have been a pleasing prospect.

It's also reasonable to speculate that PR-conscious Diageo was not thrilled by the thought of going through a very public three-month trial and having Lyn Rowe and her parents give heartbreaking evidence about the plight they'd endured for fifty years. Nor would Diageo have been attracted by the prospect of days of embarrassing evidence about the behaviour of former Distillers employees, or keen to have its relationship with Grünenthal cemented in the public mind. On top of all that, Diageo must have realised that Lyn had a strong claim, including persuasive evidence of Distillers' negligence. So if Diageo had opted to go through what promised to be an embarrassing, damaging and expensive trial, the likely reward was an order that it pay Lyn Rowe a huge chunk of compensation. And it might well have been even worse than that. We were also asking the court to order extra punitive damages to punish Grünenthal and Distillers for what we said was their unusually appalling past behaviour.

Taken together—the prospect of losing, the issue of reputation, Diageo's historic commitment to taking a decent approach to thalidomiders—it all made a strong argument for settling. By the eve of the trial the company decided there was little sense in going on.

There must also have been one further factor at play in the decision. Put simply, Diageo could afford it. In August 2012 it announced an operating profit of almost £3.2 billion. The multimillion-dollar sum it agreed to pay Lyn Rowe was not going to break the bank.

Which is not to demean the company's motives. Peter Gordon publicly described Diageo's conduct as 'compassionate and understanding' and offered deserved praise to the company at a press conference. On the other hand he described Grünenthal's refusal to consider compensating Lyn Rowe as miserable but unsurprising.

The star of the press conference, however, was Ian Rowe. 'You don't need arms and legs,' he said, 'to change the world.' Lyn, who had told us firmly that there was no way she was going to say anything in front of 'all those cameras', sat beside her parents during the press conference. 'Lyn was always prepared to go to trial to get the right result and Wendy and I are incredibly proud of her determination and persistence,' Ian said. 'Those pills that Wendy and thousands of other women took fifty years ago have caused so much heartache and suffering, but at least something positive is now being done to put some things right.' Best of all the compensation would allow Lyn some independence. 'Most children get away from their parents at some point but Lyn has been stuck with us for more than fifty years now!'

• • •

As part of the settlement, Diageo agreed not just to settle Lyn's claim but also to consider the claims of every other group member. That process turned into a year's work for Lyn's team, who moved from working on that one claim to gathering information and evidence on more than one hundred others.

Grace Wilson and Patrick Gordon had already done much of the work, preparing statements and affidavits for many of the clients and their mothers or fathers, but there were many more to do. We needed to assemble the evidence that each of the mothers had taken the drug—and in every single instance this was a difficult, time-consuming case of following very old, very cold leads. We also had to assemble medical records, X-rays, photographs and a pile of other documentation for each and every client. Ultimately, there were 107 cases strong enough to pursue. Many other injured people with whom we were dealing had to be told there was no possibility of bringing a claim, and naturally some of them were unhappy, even angry. People who had believed for fifty years that they were thalidomide survivors were understandably upset to be told either that they were not (if, for example, the drug had not been available at the time of their mother's pregnancy) or that there was simply no evidence to prove it.

To bolster our eligible clients' claims we had Professor Trent Stephens fly out from the United States for two tours of Australia, during which he examined about seventy clients and gave his expert opinion about the likely role thalidomide played in causing their malformations. Professor Ravi Savarirayan provided similar reports, and we ordered genetic testing to rule out competing causes in a handful of cases.

We took on extra staff to deal with the workload, including the administrative burden of chasing X-rays and medical records from multiple hospitals dating back to our clients' childhoods, and by the middle of 2013 the process was complete. Packages on just over one hundred claimants had been delivered to Diageo's lawyers, Herbert Smith Freehills.

Our clients' malformations and injuries ranged across a very wide spectrum. At one end were people with, for example, relatively minor hand and finger malformations, or partial deafness. At the other were those with severe injuries to two, three or all four limbs, sometimes in combination with internal injuries. The most severely affected of all of the claimants was Monica McGhie who, like Lyn Rowe, had been born without limbs. Monica's mother burned herself with hot gravy early in her pregnancy. Unable to sleep because of the pain, she tragically took some leftover sleeping pills that she had been given during an earlier pregnancy. Monica got to know Lyn as teenagers when they were both at the Royal Children's Hospital in Melbourne for the same operation: the insertion of a rod into their back to treat scoliosis. Monica says her reaction to first seeing Lyn was, 'Shit, no wonder I freak people out if that's what I look like.' She and Lyn became friends, a relationship that made a big difference to Monica's life many years later.

In 2011, as her own legal case progressed, Lyn and her parents told us about Monica. They knew she had never received any compensation and suggested we contact her to see if she was interested in bringing a claim. We did, but Monica was suspicious, and rightly so. She had looked out for herself for decades and was not about to be taken in by a bunch of lawyers swooping in from the other side of the country. Again, the Rowes played a decisive role. Lyn and Wendy vouched for us, and that eased Monica's concerns. She then worked closely with us for many months assembling material to help her claim.

• • •

As with Lyn's claim there was much confidential discussion between Peter Gordon (negotiating for our office) and Diageo and its lawyers over the 107 claims we had submitted. Finally, on 2 December 2013, we were able to tell the court, and subsequently a press conference, that the claims (ninety-five Australians and twelve New Zealanders) had been settled for a lump sum of $89 million. The result was a great relief to many of our clients, who greeted the news with tears and disbelief. The compensation was distributed among them according to a complex formula, guided by medical and legal experts, that factored in both the severity of the claimant's injury and the strength of their legal case. Some clients with less severe injuries received sums in the tens of thousands of dollars. There were others, with catastrophic injuries, who received a multimillion-dollar sum.

One client who received a large payment asked us to send him a cheque, rather than transfer the money electronically.

Two reasons why I prefer a cheque, he wrote to us. *1. I want to take a photo of it. 2. I want to go to the bank and see the look on the teller's face when I present the cheque—priceless.*

Another assured us by email that his money would be well spent. *Please thank all and sundry for winning the un-winnable. I plan on living my life the same as before but with just a little bit more luxury around me. Out go the 3 minute noodles and in comes seafood marinara. Thanks Guys xx.*

Monica McGhie flew to Melbourne from Perth for the announcement of the settlement. She told reporters that doctors had set her aside after her birth to allow her to die. 'Then Mum heard me cry, and said "That sounds like a healthy set of lungs there. I want my daughter".' Monica said the compensation would provide her with first-rate care and a future she could now face with greater confidence. And she planned a modest gift for her mother. 'I want to take my mum on a cruise before her time's up.'

In January 2014, only a few weeks after the settlement, I had lunch with Mary Henley-Collopy in one of Melbourne's laneway cafes. It was hot and Henley-Collopy was wearing a sleeveless dress. It was an emotional day for her: 'It's the first time I've ever exposed my shoulders and hands in public in Melbourne.'

I always enjoyed lunch or coffee with Mary, who is funny and interesting and good company. A recognised thalidomider, she had introduced us to the Rowe family in 2010. But on this day, just a few weeks after the $89-million settlement of the thalidomide class action, she was unhappy. Delighted, of course, by the compensation paid to more than one hundred people, some of whom she knew well, and generous with her praise of the legal effort. But she told me she had been feeling depressed and miserable ever since the settlement.

'I understand all the legal reasons for settling with Diageo,' she assured me. 'But part of me screams out that it's not fair. I want justice and that means getting Grünenthal.'

The sentiment was familiar. Our clients were mostly thrilled with the outcome of the litigation, but Grünenthal getting off scot-free had irritated some. And it had irritated Lyn's legal team as much as anyone. Our only real regret after more than three years of litigation was that we did not hold Grünenthal to account in Australia. The media picked up on it too. During the publicity surrounding the settlement, there were a number of journalists who seemed to become professionally irate over this, demanding we explain how Grünenthal had squirmed off the hook again.

But you can't eat revenge. And as much as we wanted to defeat Grünenthal and correct what we saw as a deep historic injustice, our first and deepest obligation was to our clients, almost all of whom had desperate material needs. So when Diageo stumped up an acceptable sum of money we had no sensible—or ethical—option but to accept it and end the proceeding. Our clients were properly compensated, and the case was over. Grünenthal was fortunate, in a sense, that its co-defendant was a company prepared to do the right thing. In this case, doing the right thing meant Diageo paid the whole compensation sum, allowing Grünenthal to pay nothing. After the settlement, Diageo had the option of pursuing its own action against Grünenthal to force it to contribute to the settlement, but that always seemed unlikely. Diageo wanted to put the litigation behind it, and if the cost of that was allowing Grünenthal to escape, then so be it.

Just a few days before the settlement was announced in late November 2013 there had been news reports that Grünenthal had been ordered by a Spanish court to compensate twenty-two local thalidomiders. We had given the Spanish lawyers some assistance and were delighted by the result. But the initial report was sketchy and it took a few weeks to get a copy of the court's decision and have it translated. When we read the comments by the Spanish judge, Gemma Díaz, we could not have been more pleased.

Distillers was not involved in the case, as it did not distribute thalidomide in Spain, so Grünenthal had to fight it out alone in front of a very decisive member of the Spanish judiciary. Judge Díaz gave Grünenthal's arguments short shrift, ruling that the German company's claim it acted with 'due care' was false. 'It is entirely obvious that if a drug which caused [malformations and nerve damage] was put on the market, this was because not all the preventative measures required in order to avoid them were adopted, or because those that were adopted proved manifestly inadequate and insufficient.'

The judge noted that thalidomide had been promoted in Spain as 'safe, bland and innocuous' and this resulted in false 'expectations of safety' and 'a situation of permanent risk'. Judge Díaz was also scathing of the decision by Grünenthal's Spanish agent not to properly inform doctors of the reason for halting sales of thalidomide in late 1961, which 'without doubt' played a part in worsening the scale of the disaster in Spain.

The amount of compensation Grünenthal was ordered to pay was not enormous, but it was still a terrific result. It was also an example of a judge cutting through all of Grünenthal's multiple excuses and justifications and going straight to the heart of the matter. Judge Díaz decided that Grünenthal had marketed an insufficiently tested and unsafe drug as perfectly safe, and had to accept the legal consequences. Grünenthal, naturally, announced an appeal. Sadly, Grünenthal succeeded. In late 2014 a superior Spanish court overturned Judge Díaz's decision for a series of technical legal reasons, including that too much time had passed since the events in question.

The ruling caused much grief among Spanish survivors—'a hard and low blow', one said—and relief at Grünenthal.

A growing concern for Grünenthal is litigation in the United States. The case, in which it is being sued by about fifty people, has spent most of the last few years bogged down in a fight about procedural issues. But Grünenthal would be well aware that the only thalidomide case that has ever gone to jury verdict was in the US in 1971. As we've seen, it resulted in a verdict of about $15 million in 2012 dollars. The worst-case US scenarios must be giving some Grünenthal executives nightmares.

• • •

Or perhaps not. The question of what exactly the Grünenthal elite say to each other around their boardroom table when the subject of thalidomide rears its head has always been imponderable. The executives and controlling family are all wealthy—in the case of the Wirtz family, incredibly wealthy. The family's net wealth has been estimated at between two and three billion euros. Being a little more generous towards thalidomide survivors would not cast Grünenthal's Wirtz family owners into poverty.

Thanks to the passage of time, the number of German thalidomiders is dwindling. All but a few are over fifty, with many closing in on sixty. In twenty years the number will have shrunk dramatically. In thirty there will be very few left. When there are no more than one hundred survivors will Grünenthal roll out the red carpet and pay each of them a generous pension? Or when there are only fifty? Ten? Or will even the last surviving German thalidomider have to rely on the German state to provide a pension carrying a measure of dignity?

One of the Wirtz family, Sebastian, the grandson of Hermann

Wirtz, who was charged with thalidomide crimes, is said some years ago to have raised privately the possibility of Grünenthal making a radical shift in its financial support of thalidomiders. The details of Wirtz's plan are not known. And who knows what prompted it. Genuine empathy, one assumes. Whispers found their way to German thalidomiders, whose hopes were raised. And then dashed. In 2009 Grünenthal made a one-off fifty-million-euro contribution to the German compensation fund—its first since the 1970s. That amounted to a grand average of about 18,000 euros for each beneficiary, every one of them a victim of the company's poorly tested and recklessly marketed drug.

Viewed another way, and putting aside Grünenthal's profit for a moment, the one-off fifty-million-euro contribution amounts to perhaps two per cent of the Wirtz family's wealth. In 2013 the German Government stepped in to markedly lift pensions—no contribution from Grünenthal or from the controlling Wirtz family.

And so there has been no dramatic shift on thalidomide from Grünenthal. Instead, the company remains huddled behind its ramparts, defences bristling, clutching hard at its self-serving view of history. When a noted German director made a television drama about the thalidomide scandal—called *A Single Tablet*—Grünenthal whipped into action, tying up the production in litigation. 'We resent the insinuation in the film that we behaved with infamy and without moral scruples,' thundered an insulted Grünenthal chief. Certainly the film had taken liberties with history in the name of storytelling. But while Grünenthal's heavy-handed attack forced the director into multiple changes before the screening in 2007, it won the company another round of bad publicity and increased the focus on its inglorious history.

Exactly why Grünenthal remains in such a defensive crouch is hard to fathom. Money? Pride? Inertia? Sheer bloody-mindedness?

Or more likely at the roof of Grünenthal's stance is its deluded belief that it never bore legal responsibility for the deaths and malformations. And as Grünenthal reminds everyone, it paid compensation in the 1970s and was given legal immunity in Germany by that country's government. Grünenthal's view of its past behaviour is nonsense. But even if it were not, what about a moral obligation? The indisputable fact is that Grünenthal's drug, massively promoted as ultra-safe, killed and maimed at least ten thousand babies, and probably vastly more.

The men who held the reins at Grünenthal circa 1958–62 and in the years immediately afterwards are long gone, almost all of them dead. They behaved appallingly within a corporate culture that tolerated—even encouraged—their dishonesty, obsession with profit and cavalier approach to safety. None of that disgraceful record need reflect on the Grünenthal of today, which is an entirely different beast. But the Grünenthal of today won't face up to a fair view of its history. Instead it serves up a battery of highly paid lawyers and a ruthless litigation policy. Not to mention such clueless initiatives as the 'apology' which took Grünenthal fifty years to deliver and then served to insult and enrage many thalidomiders.

How will Grünenthal respond to the account of the thalidomide saga in these pages? Perhaps with legal manoeuvres. Certainly it will be dismissed as a demented smear cooked up by a professed enemy. But for every document mentioned here detailing Grünenthal's poor behaviour in the years thalidomide was on sale, another twenty or thirty lurk in the German prosecutor's archive and at other sites around the world. For every survivor of Grünenthal's drug whose story has been told here, there are thousands more whose stories remain anonymous. What if raw material detailing Grünenthal's activities during the thalidomide era was put on a website for the world to see? Would Grünenthal face reality then? Who knows, but history gives little reason for optimism.

And the point is, it still matters. Grünenthal's culpability is not just a question of abstract historical justice. Even now it gnaws daily at many survivors, a piling of infuriating insult upon their grievous injuries. When, in 2014, Michael Wirtz, another of the Grünenthal Wirtzes, was granted an honour by the Catholic church for his long-time involvement in charitable works, it sent some thalidomide activists into a fury. There was talk of contacting the Pope. Aside from complaints about Grünenthal's treatment of thalidomiders, the activists also armed themselves with a 1980 Grünenthal letterhead on which members of the Wirtz family shared top billing with Otto Ambros, the chairman of Grünenthal's supervisory board. Ambros was, as we have seen, a notorious war criminal, convicted of mass murder and slavery at Auschwitz. Despite Ambros's shameful criminal background, the activists pointed out, the Wirtz family had afforded him a privileged and influential position at the family company. What might the Pope make of that, the activists wondered.

All these years later it is, it must be said, pathetic that Grünenthal is still so dogged by the actions of men long dead. But the responsibility for that lies solely with Grünenthal. There is nobody else to blame. Not the media, not bad luck, certainly not the survivors. So as long as Grünenthal won't face up to its past—and as long as it won't do more to support survivors—it's only fair that the spotlight shines brightly on its historically shameful conduct.

CHAPTER 16

Not Ready to Retire

As a child Lyn Rowe was insistent on trying for a swimming certificate. She tried repeatedly and eventually succeeded. 'I floated on my back and wriggled and made it to the end of the pool. They gave me a certificate for backstroke!' She brought the same upbeat mood and good humour to the litigation. 'You have to be nice to me because I'm the evidence,' she'd warn her parents and lawyers.

Lyn says she has 'never' felt sorry for herself. 'I don't believe in feeling miserable.' There's obviously some poetic licence in those declarations, but everyone who knows her attests that her low periods have been brief and relatively rare. In preparation for her trial we sent her to many doctors for examinations and reports, impositions she generally bore with good grace. 'It was all right,' she said. 'There were some odd ones though. Like that elderly doctor who told me to start exercising to lose weight. Exercising is not easy for me, but I'm trying.' Her relatively new exercise routine involves little sit-ups and trying to 'suck my tummy in while I'm sitting in my chair'.

By late 2012 Lyn had millions of dollars in the bank. Yet she was not prepared to quit work: for many months she kept fronting up to earn her thirty cents an hour. 'I'm not ready to retire,' she quipped. 'Also I want to give Mum and Dad some space. They can't have me spying on them all the time!'

It was not until March 2013, more than eight months after her legal win, that Lyn stopped work. The decision, she said, was 'devastating' after almost thirty-five years, but things had gone 'pear shaped'. Lyn got the impression that some of her colleagues believed she didn't need to work anymore and shouldn't be there. 'Also, I was supposed to be receiving people arriving at the workshop and showing them around, but really we had very few visitors and I was doing very little.' Lyn did not give up work completely though, and kept up a busy schedule of school talks.

• • •

Making light of her situation has helped Lyn cope. Years ago, one of her bosses at the workshop dubbed her 'sexy legs', a nickname Lyn embraced. 'Once I left my prosthetic legs at the podiatrist asking to have my nails done. I love making jokes about it. You have to laugh. What else is there?'

Fifty years of scrimping and saving, along with their inherently unfussed approach to life, left the Rowes well placed to deal with their new financial situation. Almost all of Lyn's money is tied up in trusts and long-term investments, with strategic decisions guided by an investment planner. Significant expenses require the consent of multiple family members. Not that Lyn was ever at risk of blowing the money. When I asked her whether she bought anything to celebrate her multimillion-dollar settlement, she had to think for a moment. 'Yes. I saw a denim jacket at the shop that I really liked. It was about $80. So I bought two—a blue one and a white one.' Lyn also treated her mother to high tea at the Windsor for her seventy-eighth birthday in 2012. Wendy had not been able to afford to return to the Windsor since her wedding night there in 1957.

Wendy and Ian initially found the post-litigation adjustment strange. 'It's hard to believe it all happened. It's as though a whirlwind swept into our lives, tipped everything over, put it all back together but much better, and then vanished,' Wendy said. The family is increasingly engaging professional carers for Lyn, lightening the load on Wendy and Ian, preparing for the day when Lyn's parents will provide little care, and then, someday, no care at all. And their finances are obviously in much better order. 'If there is something we need at the supermarket now, we buy it. We don't have to stop and figure out whether we can afford groceries.' The most extravagant purchase the family made was a small coffee machine. 'It seemed like such a massive indulgence. We would never have considered that before,' Ian said.

Wendy and Ian have also enjoyed a late-life window of freedom, leaving Lyn very occasionally for a weekend or low-key holiday. Each time, Lyn has paid one of her sisters to come and stay at the family home and act as her carer. 'I love it,' Lyn said. 'The fun starts as soon as Mum and Dad leave. I used to hate it when they went on holidays; now when they go, it's like a holiday for me too.'

Wendy might have embraced the change a little more hesitantly. 'We've been very closely connected for a long time, so it takes a little while. Letting go after fifty years takes some doing. But it's been liberating, for Lyn and also for me and Ian.'

In the years after Lyn's claim finished, Wendy often found herself wondering about the meaning of it all. Lyn's birth, the fifty years of struggle, thalidomide, the legal win. *Why Lyn? Why me? Why us?*

There are no answers, she's decided. But still, Wendy is certain about some things. 'A lot of good has come of Lyn's birth. Was there a greater purpose? Did God have anything to do with it? Absolutely not. I just don't believe that. It was the drug that damaged Lyn, pure and simple,' Wendy said. 'But once it happened, it was up to us to turn it into a positive or a negative. Lyn has showed us all what grace and courage and determination are and we're better people for it. She changed our direction in life. You'd never wish what happened to Lyn on anyone. But there was no changing it. We had to dig down and find the good in it.'

ACKNOWLEDGMENTS

My thanks first to the Rowe family. Lyn, Wendy and Ian were not just the perfect clients, but patient and supportive when it came to the writing of this book (by which time they might justifiably have had their fill of lawyers, questions and intrusion). My respect and gratitude to them, and a large measure of heartfelt thanks to all the other members of that remarkable family.

Mary Henley-Collopy, Monika Eisenberg, Monica McGhie, Barbara-Ann Hewson and the Gordon family in New Zealand all took it on faith that their stories would be fairly told. Many other survivors and and family members spoke with me over the years. I am grateful to all of them.

Woody Woodhouse and Phil Lacaze worked for Distillers during the early 1960s and then, fifty years later, helped us win compensation for survivors. They were willing and brave and always a complete pleasure to speak with. I am indebted to each.

There were many others who assisted in the litigation and/or in the research for this book. A few without whom this account would be substantially lesser: Ron and Aylsa Dickinson, Leslie Florence, Lance Fletcher, Phillip Knightley and the venerable, inestimable and indefatigable Ken Youdale, a great man whose life warrants its own published history.

The modern Australian legal story is told in unavoidably short compass in these pages. Peter Gordon conceived of the thalidomide claim, an audacious and ambitious venture, and, by force of personality, breathed life into it. I'm thankful for the invitation to join the team. The legal effort was, of course, a group effort, progress made fraction by fraction. The full team was Peter Gordon, Kerri O'Toole, Dael Pressnell, Sarah Roache, Patrick Gordon, Brett Spiegel, Grace Wilson, Lucy Kirwan, Julie Clayton, Paul Henderson, Andrew Baker, Caitlyn Baker, Amanda Barron, Kelly Hart, Jane Tarasewicz, Mariano Rossetto and Sasha Molinaro. Our barristers were Jack Rush, Julian Burnside, John Gordon and Andrew Higgins. Dr Sally Cockburn and Nina Stähle were also integral to the effort. Tosca Looby, Simon Millman and Andrew Taylor helped out in the crunch.

Peter Rielly, Campbell Rose and Jeff Kennett all played important roles in the charitable effort to build a new home for the Rowe family when the result of the litigation still hung in the balance.

At Slater & Gordon, managing director Andrew Grech backed the litigation and then this book.

While writing I relied on family and friends for advice, encouragement and, from many, a careful and wise reading. Thanks to Rob Lewis, Marcus Godinho, Lucy Kirwan, Jacinta Dwyer, Grace Wilson, Kay Reeves, Jeremy Blumenthal, David Blumenthal, Samantha Gee, Craig Pasch, Shaan Beccarelli, Di Sarfati, Nina Stähle, the extended Joseph clan (especially Rachel for the informal focus group) and the following Magasaniks: Simon, Lorraine, Ery and Laura. Neil Vargesson, Trent Stephens, Ravi Savarirayan and Sally Cockburn offered insightful comments on parts of the book. Thanks to Chris Prast for litigation wisdom and to Ingrid Dewar and Tom Raabe for last-minute translations.

My appreciation to the team at Text, especially my editor Mandy

Brett for grace under pressure and precise, brilliant work; and to publisher Michael Heyward for backing the project.

To all I have overlooked in this last-minute rush, my apologies.

Which leaves two final votes of thanks and love. My parents Ariel and Daniel, for reading, editing and commenting on every word of a rough first draft of every chapter; and for their (sometimes) optimistic faith in me and for much, much else besides over many years. And finally (and inadequately) to Nicole, partner, lawyer and non-fiction adviser: for unstinting love, encouragement and patient counsel, even as the four years of litigating over—and writing about—thalidomide coincided precisely with the arrival of our children: Asher, Jonah and Zara. My deepest thanks and love.

NOTES AND SOURCES

Silent Shock, inevitably, draws heavily on research and interviews conducted in support of Lyn Rowe's legal claim between 2010 and 2012. Once this book got off the drawing board, much further research and many more interviews (including follow-up interviews) were conducted. Many people, as is clear in the text, were exceedingly generous with their time. The documents referred to and quoted from in the text come from many sources, and these sources are often made explicit.

The legal team was able to inspect documents held by the *Sunday Times*, the Nordrhein-Westfalen state archive (then in Düsseldorf, now in Duisburg), the National Archives and National Library in Canberra, the National Archives in New Zealand, the United States Food and Drug Administration, and various libraries in Australia, the United States and the United Kingdom.

Lyn Rowe's legal team also received (gratefully) valuable documents from thalidomiders (or their family members) in several countries. One such early document was a highly-prized complete copy of the German prosecutor's 1000-page indictment. Other important documents related to the litigation in the United Kingdom and Australia in the 1960s and 1970s, plus a number of newspaper clippings collections kept by affected families.

After the conclusion of the litigation I was very fortunate to access one further, and especially valuable, store of documents. Elinor Kamath, an American woman, was working as a medical correspondent in Germany in 1961 when the thalidomide disaster became public. Multilingual, curious and extraordinarily bright, Kamath embarked on a twenty-five-year study of the medical aspects of the disaster. Later, while working at Stanford University, she won funding to turn her investigation into a book. During the 1980s Kamath interviewed Leslie Florence, the Scottish doctor who migrated to New Zealand and who had published on thalidomide's neurotoxic effect in 1960. In 2012 Florence told me of Kamath and her work, but after inquiries I found Kamath had died in 1992. Then in 2014, by chance, I found on a book-sales website some proposed chapters Kamath had prepared for a potential publisher. Somehow thirty years later they had ended up for sale. I bought them, and, following clues, eventually found Kamath's nephew Chris Kahn. He was first curious and then enormously helpful. In June 2014 I flew to the US to spend a week looking through the thalidomide treasures Kamath had assiduously assembled over a quarter of a century: contemporary documents, interviews with key players, trial transcripts. My only disappointment was for Elinor Kamath—despite all her effort she had never seen the publication of the book she had provisionally entitled *Echo of Silence*. In some key areas *Silent Shock* draws on Elinor Kamath's work, and tribute is paid to her here.

Some other sources of material included the FDA's oral history project—many interview transcripts are accessible via the agency's website, including with some of the participants in the thalidomide affair and its legislative aftermath. A number of the important actors in thalidomide, principally Frances Kelsey, Widukind Lenz and Bill McBride, have left voluminous records, all of which were useful in recounting their roles.

Some other matters of note. In a very few places full names have been omitted. This has been done to protect the identity of thalidomide survivors who have not been prominent publicly and who may not have wished to be identified. In several places that meant using an initial only for a parent: i.e. Dr K, Mrs H etc.

'Malformation' is one of the most-used words in this text. Fifty years ago the chosen term was 'deformed' or 'deformity'—words still used today but certainly not embraced by thalidomide survivors or by the disability community more broadly. The word 'deformed' and its variations have only been used when quoting, or because of context.

In accordance with Australian usage, the spelling 'foetus' has been used throughout—again, except when quoting documents in which the medical (and American) spelling 'fetus' was used.

And finally, German documents have been translated by qualified translators, sometimes by more than one. Where translations varied slightly, the more fluent English rendering has been preferred.

SELECT BIBLIOGRAPHY

Henning Sjöström and Robert Nilsson. *Thalidomide and the Power of the Drug Companies.* 1972.

Ralph Adam Fine. *The Great Drug Deception: the Shocking Story of MER/29 and the Folks Who Gave You Thalidomide.* 1972.

The Sunday Times. *The Thalidomide Children and the Law.* 1973.

Harvey Teff and Colin Munro. *Thalidomide: the Legal Aftermath.* 1976.

David Mason. *Thalidomide: My Fight.* 1976.

The *Sunday Times* Insight Team. *Suffer the Children: the Story of Thalidomide.* 1979.

Bill Nicol. *McBride: Behind the Myth.* 1989.

William McBride. *Killing the Messenger.* 1994.

Rock Brynner and Trent Stephens. *Dark Remedy: the Impact of Thalidomide and its Revival as a Vital Medicine.* 2001.

Louise Medus. *No Hands To Hold and No Legs To Dance On—A Thalidomide Survivor's Story.* 2009.

T. V. N. Persaud (ed.). *Problems of Birth Defects: from Hippocrates to Thalidomide and After.* 1977.

Diarmuid Jeffreys. *Hell's Cartel: IG Farben and the Making of Hitler's War Machine.* 2008.

Arthur Allen. *The Fantastic Laboratory of Dr Weigl: How Two Brave Scientists Battled Typhus and Sabotaged the Nazis.* 2014.

INDEX